Homolytic and Heterolytic Reactions: Problems and Solutions

Homolytic and Heterolytic Reactions: Problems and Solutions

Gennady E. Zaikov
Yuri B. Monakov
Alfonso Jiménez
Editors

Nova Science Publishers, Inc.
New York

Library of Congress Cataloging-in-Publication Data
Available upon request

ISBN 1-59033-980-0

400 Oser Ave, Suite 1600
Hauppauge, New York 11788-3619
Tele. 631-231-7269 Fax 631-231-8175
e-mail: Novascience@earthlink.net
Web Site: http://www.novapublishers.com

Printed in the United States of America

CONTENTS

PREFACE

To understand poetry means to understand life.
Ancient Greeks

There are people on the Earth (including the editors and the authors of this volume) who suggest that investigation of the mechanisms of homolytic and heterolytic processes is poetry. Though such investigations have been successfully implemented for more than 150 years, there are still a lot of blind-spots in this branch of science. Moreover, step by step we come to "higher floors" of our knowledge. In the 1980s, there was a discussion in the Institute of Chemical Physics (Moscow), which reactions should be considered elementary and which non-elementary (a superposition of several elementary reactions). After long discussion, the leader of Soviet chemistry of those years, Nikolai M. Emanuel, suggested the following definition of elementary reactions: "An elementary reaction is a reaction, which is considered to be elementary at the present moment". Assuming the humoristic essence of this definition, it displays an essential element of truth. While we are moving from science towards knowledge, we perceive deeper the facts, which seemed "absolutely clear" to us before.

In this situation perfect investigatory methods and more high-quality equipment are important, which are developed in science, but no less important is "Its Majesty Chance" which sometimes helps (and sometimes cramps) us in investigations.

Let us give an example in the Preface, when change has deteriorated the "Progress of Humankind". It is known that some eagles like to eat tortoise meat, but they cannot break the tortoiseshell to get it. However, the eagles have solved the problem: they seize a tortoise, fly high in the sky and drop it on stones. The shell is broken, and the eagles can enjoy the delicious meat. Once an eagle has by mistake dropped a tortoise on the bald head of Aeschylus, the famous ancient Greek author of the "Acheron" – the shadowland. Thus, there was a chance for Aeschylus to go to the Land of Shadows – he was killed by this tortoise. This is the case of "poor" chance. You will find in this book examples of "good" chance in the studies of homolytic and heterolytic reactions.

Professor Gennady E. Zaikov *Institute of Biochemical Physics, Moscow, Russia*
Professor Yuri B. Monakov *Institute of Organic Chemistry, Ufa, Bashkortostan, Russia*
Professor Alfonso Jiménez *University of Alicante, Alicante, Spain*

In: Homolytic and Heterolytic Reactions: Problems and Solutions ISBN 1-59033-980-0
Editors: G.E. Zaikov, et al., pp. 1-15

Chapter 1

THERMAL DEGRADATION OF BIODEGRADABLE POLYMERIC MATERIALS

Roxana A. Ruseckaite[1,2] and Alfonso Jiménez[3]

[1.] Research Institute of Material Science and Technology (INTEMA), University of Mar del Plata, Juan B. Justo 4302, 7600- Mar del Plata, Argentina. e-mail: roxana@fi.mdp.edu.ar

[2.] Chemistry Department, Sciences Faculty, Funes 3350, 7600-Mar del Plata, Argentina

[3.] University of Alicante. Department of Analytical Chemistry. PO Box 99, 03080, Alicante, Spain. e-mail: alfjimenez@ua.es

ABSTRACT

The search of new strategies for manufacturing of products based on plastic materials with high performance properties and real possibilities of biodegradation leads to consider biopolymers and biodegradable synthetic polymers as promising raw materials for some processing operations. However, some problems, such as their high costs and the incomplete information on some of their properties, are associated to their current use. Among all advantages in the use of biodegradable polymers, the most important is the possibility of biodegradation, which raises considerable interest form the environmental and industrial point of view. Some researchers have recently studied the thermal degradation of these polymers but there are still a lot of efforts to perform for a complete thermal characterization of such materials. Some thermogravimetric and calorimetric studies have been recently presented in communications and papers in many international publications. Other current research efforts are focused on the determination of products of pyrolysis. The main goal of this paper is a complete review of the more recent literature in this field as well as proposals for future work.

Keywords: Biopolymers; Biodegradable synthetic polymers; Thermal Degradation; Thermogravimetry; Pyrolysis

INTRODUCTION

Few scientific developments in recent years have captured the attention of people like the subject of "biodegradable" plastics. There are many reasons for this and some of them lie in the human imagination. Biodegradation can be seen as an ecologically acceptable solution to the problem of plastic packaging waste.

Most synthetic carbon-based polymers are inert toward microorganisms in the form they are initially produced. In order that the carbon nutrients that they contain could be made available to the biological cell, they must be first transformed by a variety of chemical reactions to low molecular weight metabolites that can be absorbed by the cell. These reactions can be based on many different mechanisms, among them the thermal degradation is one of the most important.

Polymeric biomaterials can be divided in two main classes, natural and synthetic biopolymers. While natural biopolymers were well known from centuries, e.g. starch and cellulose, synthetic biomaterials were developed in the last decades. The first biodegradable synthetic polymer was poly (glycolic acid) (PLA) in 1954 [1]. When first developed, it was discarded because of its poor thermal stability. Two decades later, after the use of thermal stabilizers was common, PLA became the first commercial synthetic biopolymer. This is an indication of the importance of the knowledge of the thermal degradation and stabilization of biopolymers.

Most of the biodegradable polymers discovered during the last twenty years contain hydrolysable linkages, such as amide, ester and urea along the polymer chains. These chemical groups usually show a lower thermal stability than aliphatic chains. This is another reason of the importance of the study of thermal degradation in such polymers.

NATURAL BIOPOLYMERS

Starch and cellulose are abundant, inexpensive and natural raw materials that permit the development of products recyclable to CO_2 when biodegraded or incinerated. These characteristics have promoted a renewed interest in starch and cellulose based plastics, as testified by the impressive increase in literature in recent years [2]. Starch is probably the most abundant and economical natural polymer available and its use in plastics production would greatly reduce the demand for petrochemicals and the negative impact on the environment caused by discarding plastics that do not biodegrade. Starch alone is not usually employed in plastic production as it forms a brittle product once hydrated with water. It has to be combined with other materials in order to produce a satisfactory blend. For instance, blending of starch with synthetic thermoplastic polymers can produce a huge variety of products [3]. Another important application of starch in polymer technology is the use as plasticizer, with the obvious advantages of using a natural compound. During the modification process, the heterogeneous structure of native starch, brought about the poor interpenetration of its macromolecules, is eliminated, so as to convert it to an essentially homogeneous material useful for thermoplastics processing [4]. Kind of native starch, moisture content, pressure, and temperature are significant factors influencing the thermal degradation of thermoplastic-starch blends.

As a reflection of the interest in the development of new formulations based on natural biopolymers, many studies on the thermal degradation of the raw materials as well as blends were recently carried out. While most of them were focused on the characterization and determination of thermal properties of new formulations, some of them studied the thermal degradation of natural biopolymers, mainly starch and cellulose. Thermogravimetric analysis (TGA) was employed to determine temperatures and rates of pyrolysis as well as kinetic parameters, mainly apparent activation energies. The thermal behavior of starch and oxidized starch was then studied and parameters were determined by simple observation of TGA curves [5]. As expected, the degradation temperatures decreased with the addition of oxidants from 305 to 285°C and therefore, the process was slightly favored by the presence of oxygen-forming agents.

In 1998 Dollimore et al developed a very interesting application of thermal methods to the study of starch properties [6]. It is known that raw starch granules are used as substrates for the hydrolysis to glucose. Two enzymes usually control this process: glucoamylase and α-amylase. The importance of the control of enzymatic saccharification has been recognized from the viewpoints of energy saving and effective biomass utilization. But this process causes an undesirable degradation of some amounts of starch, which do not occur uniformly. Moreover, the transition from starch to glucose entails a loss of structural order. Deterioration of texture in starch macromolecules is also a common subject of study in terms of molecular mechanisms, so that it should be minimized or inhibited. Thermal analysis techniques provide powerful methods to probe all those transitions. Thus, characterization of starch products by thermal analysis is an important approach to the understanding of the functionality of starch on a molecular and structural level.

It was also observed that, when heated, an aqueous suspension of starch in excess water undergoes an endothermic transition known as gelatinization [7]. This process can be characterized by using DSC techniques with determination of the onset and the peak temperatures. In general, an increase in the initial gelatinization temperature was observed for partially hydrolyzed starch.

Thermal treatment of starch studied by TGA usually leads exclusively to its depolymerization with the formation of β-(1,6) anhydro D-glucopyranose (levoglucosan) and 2-furaldehyde (furfural), unless the temperature applied exceeds 300°C. The starch undergoes a series of irreversible changes in its structure. A carbonaceous residue remains after all the volatile products have evolved. A typical TG thermogram for the degradation of corn starch in nitrogen is shown in Figure 1. The main peak at 300-310°C appears to involve elimination of the polyhydroxyl groups, accompanied by depolymerization and decomposition.

Another important fact of the thermal degradation of starch is the formation of products known as dextrins that are commercially used as industrial gums. In spite of no significant differences in the thermograms between starches from different origins, some studies were carried out to develop a general TGA technique for the comparative analysis of starches [8]. They used a method based on differences between degrees of conversion at different regions of the TGA curve. It was observed that while all starches degrade to carbon in an atmosphere of flowing nitrogen, the kinetic mechanisms were different. In general, the reactivity of rice and potato starch in the solid state was found to be higher than wheat and corn starch.

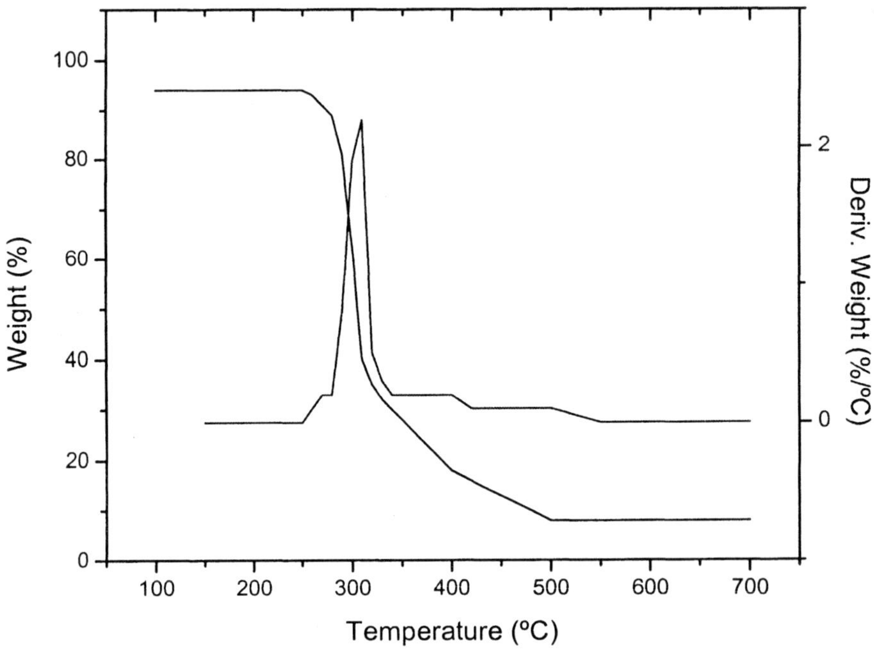

Figure 1. Typical TGA-DTG curve of starch

DSC has been extensively applied for many studies on the behavior of starch at high temperatures, including gelatinization [9], glass transition temperature [10] and crystallization [11]. However, the reported results sometimes are not consistent because of the complexity of thermal behavior of starches at different measurement conditions. The main reasons of this complexity are the numerous physicochemical changes that occur while the sample is heated. Many of these processes are water dependent as they depend upon the moisture content. Furthermore, the thermal conductivity of starch is very poor, especially for starch granules, since their bulk density is low, causing unstable results. In addition some experimental conditions of measurement, such as sample preparation, type of pan and amount of sample are important for the final result. These studies concluded that DSC was a valid technique for application to the study of the behavior of starch at high temperatures, despite some difficulties caused by: (i) a peak missing because of a large mass pan; (ii) the appearance of false peaks due to poor conductivity of starch; (iii) confusion for peaks assignation caused by water evaporation.

Studies on blends of starch with thermoplastic polymers were carried out along the last decades [12-16]. The inclusion of starch, a readily biodegradable biopolymer, into the synthetic polymer is believed to result in rapid enzymatic hydrolysis of the starch under biotic exposure conditions. But some problems must be overcome in order to get good results to explain behavior at high temperatures of these blends. First of all blending of two dissimilar polymers brings out an interesting processing problem due to the difficulty in achieving a good dispersion of one polymer in another. Therefore, good mixing is necessary to obtain products with uniform properties. Sometimes the presence of compatibilizers or interfacial adhesion promoters is at least advisable.

On the other hand, combustion of these organic materials leads to strong exothermic effects and complete gasification. This might be deleterious to the possible use of TGA as an analytical device. Sometimes it is necessary to confine the study to thermal analysis of binary mixtures of both polymers with no further additions.

One example of TGA studies on the thermal degradation of starch blends was proposed by Aggarwal [16] for polyacrylonitrile (PAN). Figure 2 shows the TGA curve for such blend. A very distinct weight loss is observed in the temperature interval of 250-340°C. This is characterized as two peaks on the DTG plot, with temperatures of 295°C and 330°C. PAN undergoes an exothermic reaction followed by a loss in weight at a higher temperature. There is so much heat given off that the system becomes hotter than the programmed heating rate. The products evolved include volatile gases, such as HCN, and less volatile materials, such as monomers and dimers. The exothermic reaction is caused by the uncontrolled polymerization of nitrile groups with destruction of the polymer chain. In spite of all these problems, TGA has shown as a useful tool for the analysis of starch-based blends at high temperatures.

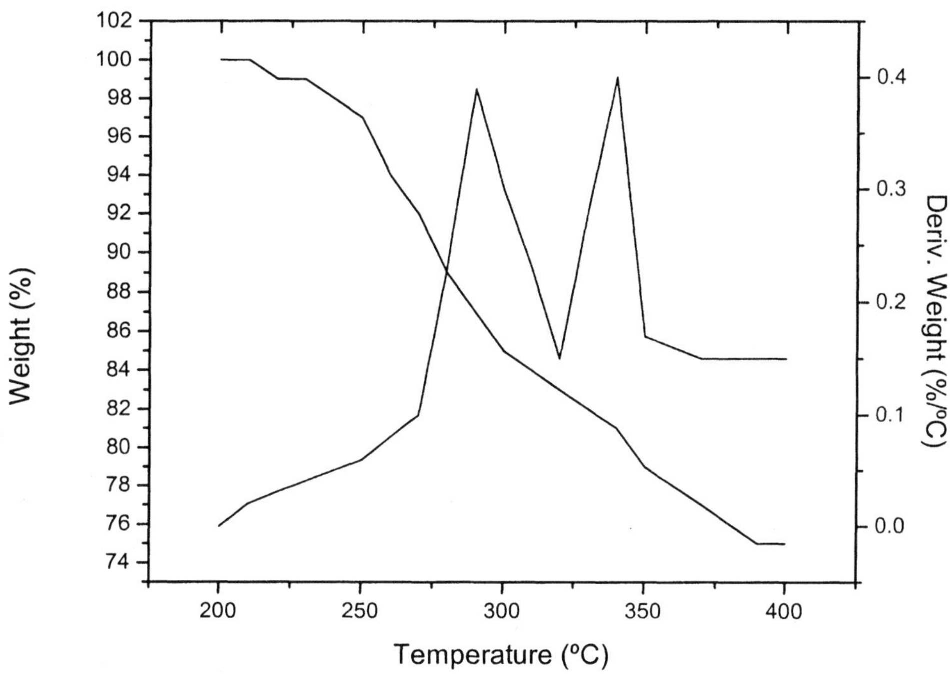

Figure 2. TG-DTG plot of a starch-PAN blend in nitrogen atmosphere

Cellulose is a partially crystalline material with cellulose chains organized in crystallites, surrounded by non-organized cellulose chains. Thus, inhomogeneities in the bulk structure give rise to accessible and inaccessible regions when cellulose fibers are esterified in heterogeneous conditions and the substitution of cellulose hydroxyls first occurs in more accessible amorphous regions and on the surface of the elementary crystallites. Thermal decomposition of cellulose fibers shown in Figure 3 followed a single step reaction with a maximum decomposition temperature between 325 and 350ºC depending on the heating rate of the TGA experiment.

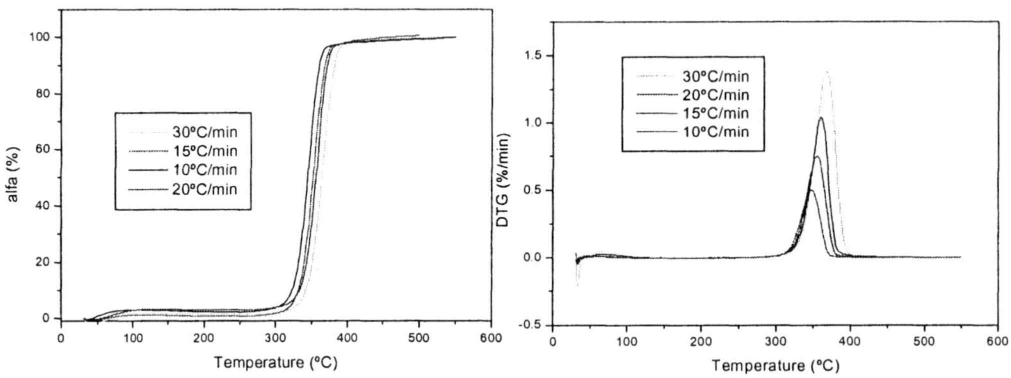

Figure 3. Thermogravimetric analysis of microcrystalline cellulose [28]

It is well known that during pyrolysis of cellulose and lignin some gases and vapors are formed. Lignin is more thermally stable and forms more char than cellulose and hemicelluloses [17]. The rate of pyrolysis can be determined from TGA measurements with this information being very useful in assessing the chemistry of the thermal decomposition of different products. A high number of papers have been published on the topic of thermal degradation of cellulose and the process is well known yet [18-20].

One point where many researchers have focused their interest is the use of cellulose esters and the mechanism of its thermal degradation. It was found that, in the case of cellulose acetates prepared by homogeneous esterification reaction, the thermal stability of esters is proportional to their molecular weights and increases with higher degree of substitution [21]. Thermal analysis of a series of cellulose esters with linear aliphatic substituents ranging in size from C_{12} to C_{20} with high degree of substitution (around 2.9) prepared in homogeneous solution was also investigated [22]. It was found that these esters exhibit a series of transitions that represent motion by both ester substituents and cellulosic main chain. Some recent papers were devoted to the study of the thermal degradation behavior of heterogeneously esterified cellulose fibers with unsaturated or saturated long chain organic acids.

BIODEGRADABLE POLYMERS AND BIOCOMPOSITES

Biodegradable polymers have recently attracted much public and industrial interest because of the increasing waste disposal problem [23]. Besides solutions such as incineration, recycling or re-use, biodegradable polymers can be entirely converted by microbial activity in a biologically active environment to biomass and biological by-products. This process which is also called mineralization can be considered as a biologically mediated recycling of plastic articles.

Nowadays, the use of biodegradable polymers as replacement of the commodities for massive applications is quite reduced, as their cost is still no competitive [24]. One economically and ecologically attractive approach to overcome these limitations is to incorporate natural fibers into biodegradable polymers to obtain environmentally friendly composite materials called *biocomposites* which are quite similar to the already known synthetic fiber - reinforced plastics with the advantage of being completely biodegradable. Biocomposites are called to render a contribution in the 21st century to the serious environmental problem [25].

Among all the biodegradable polymers which are nowadays on the market, polycaprolactone (PCL), poly(lactic acid) (PLA), polyvinylalcohol (PVOH) and poly(3-hydroxybutyrate) (PHB) and its copolymers, are the most attractive since their combine biodegradability, compostability and compatibility with different forms of waste disposal with remarkable physico-mechanical performances [26,27]. The understanding of their thermal stability and thermal degradation is of great importance, not only from the recycling but the processing point of view. Thermal degradation of such polymers was recently analyzed: PCL [28-31], PLA [30,33-37], PHB and its copolymers with hydroxyvalerate (HV) [30,38-42], PVOH and its copolymers with ethylene [43-46].

On the other hand, thermal degradation of biocomposites is less reported in the literature. At the best of our knowledge, a few studies are recently reported even in international meetings or in the literature [24,28,47,48].

THERMAL DEGRADATION OF BIODEGRADABLE POLYMERS

Characteristic temperatures such as melting temperature (Tm) and glass transition temperature (Tg) are commonly determined by differential scanning calorimetry (DSC). The melting point is the most important parameter in thermal degradation as processing temperatures are usually about 20 to 100ºC higher. This range depends on the presence of additives that can prevent thermal degradation and deterioration during processing [48].

PCL is used in many applications such as pharmacy, agriculture and packaging. This polymer shows good mechanical properties, is relatively cheap compared to other biodegradable polymers and is easily compatible with other polymers [49]. New commercial blends based on PCL and starch are nowadays on the market [50,51]. These new materials are cost-competitive with commodity plastics and can be used in massive applications, such as compost bags, trash bags or mulching films. PCL and its blends are also reinforced with cellulose fibers in order to obtain biocomposites, which have similar properties to the traditional fiber-reinforced thermoplastics with the additional advantage of the complete biodegradability.

Many researchers [28-31] have studied thermal degradation of PCL under different conditions. We have analyzed the thermal degradation of pure PCL and mixtures with cellulose derivatives [28]. Figure 4 represents the TG/DTG curves for PCL obtained at different heating rates under nitrogen atmosphere. As expected, the shape of curves does not change with variations in heating rate, but temperature for the maximum mass loss suffers a slight increase at higher heating rates.

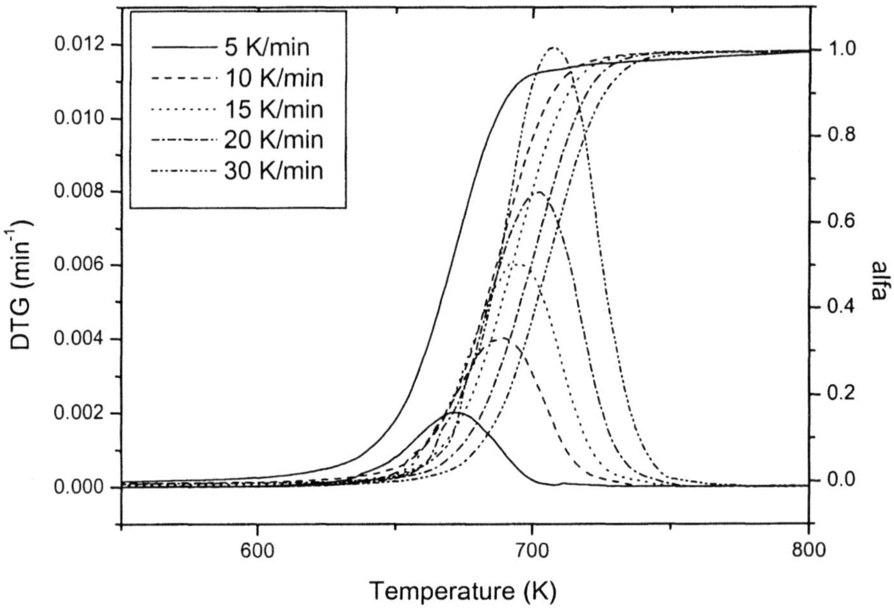

Figure 4. TG/DTG thermograms for PCL at different heating rates and under nitrogen atmosphere [28]

Two different approaches are proposed for the thermal decomposition of PCL. Persenaire et al [29], proposed a two-step degradation mechanism, based on the results obtained from TGA coupled to FTIR. DTG showed two well resolved degradation peaks and, based on the gases evolved, they concluded that PCL degradation proceeds via a first step, concerning *cis*-elimination which produces CO_2, CO and 5-hexenoic acid, and a second step, via unzipping depolymerization, to form ε-caprolactone (Scheme 1). These results were confirmed by High-Resolution TGA [31].

On the other hand, Aoyagi et al [30], analyzed PCL, PHB and PLA thermal degradation under dynamic and isothermal conditions. In the case of PCL, TG/DTG curves suggest only one-single step. The constant value of apparent activation energy (Ea) during all the degradation process suggests also a simple degradation mechanism, but this last result does not exclude the possibility of a two-step mechanism. Draye et al [31] used High-Resolution TGA and TGA coupled to FTIR/MS techniques as tool for determining the structure of policaprolactam-co-polycaprolactone (PCLA-co-PCLO) copolymers, which are considered as a new class of synthetic biodegradable polymers [32]. Both techniques confirmed a block structure for the copolymer with 4 degradation steps at 340, 379, 395 and 420°C respectively. The two main peaks were those at 340 and 420°C, corresponding to PCLO and PCLA blocks, respectively. The intermediate peaks could be attributed to the degradation of heterosequences of CLA/CLO. Results showed the efficiency of TGA coupled to FTIR/MS and High-Resolution TGA in determining the structure of copolymers, even though a quantitative analysis was not performed due to exchange reactions taking place at high temperatures.

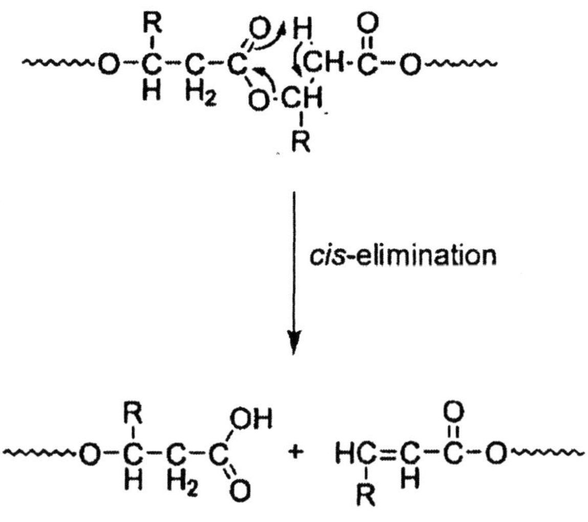

Scheme 1.

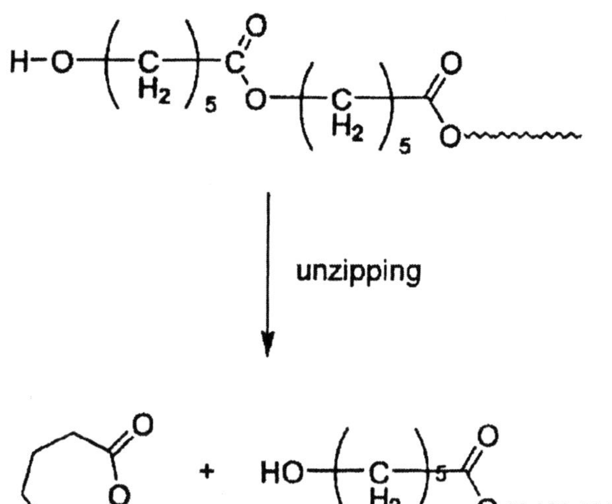

Poly(lactic acid) (PLA) is one of the most promising synthetic biodegradable polymers. The first commercial applications of PLA were in the biomedical field, biodegradable sutures, prosthetic devices, and controlled drug release applications. Lactic acid has a chiral center and can exist in two stereoisomeric forms, (S) l-lactic acid, and d-lactic acid. The repeated units are either added as dimer (lactide units) or as lactic monomer units. Both involve acyl cleavage of the ester bond with retention of chirality. The dilactide monomer has two chiral centers and can exist in three stereisomeric forms (SS) l-lactide, (RR) d-lactide, and (RS) meso-lactide. The molecular architecture of PLA is determined by the stereochemical makeup, and depending upon the isomer composition, the polylactides can either be semi-crystalline or amorphous. Interestingly, the properties of PLA prepared by the direct process are similar to those of the lactide process, the exception being the melting point. Poly(l-lactic acid) (163 °C) shows a lower value than poly(l-lactide) (178 °C). If the starting lactic acid feedstock is a racemic mixture, then one obtains an amorphous poly(d,l-lactic acid/lactide).The presence of a few percent meso-isomer in the predominantly poly(l-lactide) polymer will render the polymer amorphous. Essentially all the PLA literature involves l and d,l-lactide copolymers [51].

PLA thermal degradation was extensively studied and many workers [30,33-37] reported a complex mechanism. PLA thermal stability is influenced by many factors, such as moisture, residual monomer and residual metals [35-37]. Kopinke et al [35] suggested that degradation above 200°C includes internal trasesterification leading to *cis*-elimination of lactide and cyclic oligomers as well as to fragmentation of acrylic acid and oligomers, resulting in CO_2 and acetaldehyde. Aoyagi et al [30] showed that the presence of residual metal (from aluminum catalyst) produces a metal-catalyzed degradation at lower temperatures, which are the origin of the changes in apparent activation energy values during the thermal degradation (variation between 80-160 kJ mol^{-1} with the weight loss). The same authors performed PLA thermal degradation under isothermal conditions in order to clarify the degradation mechanism. PLA showed a higher thermal stability at a given temperature than PCL or PHB. The chemical structure of the monomeric units determines the degradation mechanism. The chemical structure of the monomeric unit in PHB is characterized by an activated C–H bond neighbor to a carbonyl group, which can participate in the cis-elimination reaction. Although the PCL unit also possesses an activated C–H bond, it does not participate in a six-member cyclic transition state. PLA possesses a tertiary C-H bond, which is influenced by the two neighbor ester groups. However, only the non-activated C–H bond of the methyl group can form a six-member cyclic transition state. The authors concluded that availability of the *cis*-elimination (see scheme 1) in thermal degradation would determine the thermal stability of the polyesters.

Poly(3-hydroxybutyrate) (PHB) is a genuine biodegradable material which degrades in biotic environment to carbon dioxide and water and exhibits mechanical properties comparable to those of the traditional thermoplastics [24].Copolymers with hidroxyvalerate (PHB-co-HV) are in commercial use for blow molded shampoo bottles in the U.S., Japan, and Germany. It is also being used in razor handles in Japan [51]. Thermal degradation of PHB occurs quite rapidly at temperatures above the melting point of the polymer (171°C). The significant benefit of the (PHB-co-HV) copolymers is their lower melting points that enable them to be melt processed at lower temperatures than PHB, generally in the range of around 140-180 °C, reducing significantly the thermal degradation [53].

The thermal degradation mechanism of PHB is considered to be primarily a random chain scission process by a cis-elimination reaction via a six member cyclic transition state [30,38-40]. Chemical structure of the monomeric unit in PHB is characterized by an activated C–H bond neighbor to a carbonyl group, which can participate in the cis-elimination reaction [30]. Apparent activation energies between 109 kJ mol^{-1} for PHB and 126 kJ mol^{-1} for (PHB-co-HV) copolymers have been reported [41]. The major pyrolysis product of PHB is crotonic acid produced by the *cis*-elimination reaction. Secondary products such as propylene, ketene, CO_2, acetaldehyde, etc., are also formed by further decomposition of the primary products [30,38]. The thermal degradation mechanism of PHB-co-HV copolymers was reported to be analogous to that for PHB [38]. Shah et al [42], found that an increase in the hydroxyl termination in PHB leads to an increase in the thermal stability, most likely by prolonging the condensation and delaying the degradation reaction.

The good processability and the well-known biodegradability of poly(vinylalcohol) (PVOH) have been the guidelines for the formulation of PVOH-water soluble items [52]. Most of these PVOH-based systems, i.e. laundry bags, packaging, and mulching, are designed to be environmentally disposable [53].

The thermal degradation of poly(vinyl alcohol) (PVOH) is extensively reported in the literature [43-45]. Below 300°C the major degradation product reported is water, produced by elimination of the hydroxyl side-group [43]. Recently, Holland and Hay [44] reported that thermal degradation mechanism of PVOH in the molten state consists of water elimination and chain scission, via a six-member transition state, leading to the formation of volatile products, such as saturated and unsaturated aldehydes and ketones [45]. However, even though the well known improvement in PVOH thermal stability due to the presence of ethylene co-component (EVOH), there is a lack of information concerning the kinetic parameters involved in the thermal degradation process of such copolymers. Ethylene-vinyl alcohol copolymers (EVOH) are worldwide used in practical applications due to their excellent oxygen barrier properties, easy processability and thermal stability. Alvarez et al [46] studied the thermal degradation of EVOH with different ethylene content. TG and DTG curves obtained for EVOH-32 at different heating rates are presented in Figure 5 a) and b). Thermal decomposition seems to be a gradual process. DTG curves show two peaks, corresponding to temperature at maximum degradation rate (Tmax): the first one, at temperatures in the range 387-407 °C at 10 °C/min, which corresponds to the major component, PVOH. The second one is observed at higher temperatures and it is attributed to the ethylene co-component by comparing with the pure component. For a given heating rate, the temperature at the maximum degradation rate of PVOH is shifted to higher values as the content in ethylene increases; whereas Tmax values for the ethylene co-component are almost unmodified (by comparing with those of the pure component, Tmax = 480°C). It should be noted that an increment in Tmax is associated to an improvement in the thermal stability, therefore polyethylene acts as a thermal stabilizer of PVOH. It is important to note that decomposition curves of both components are partially overlapped (Figure 5a), thus, some kind of interaction should be expected. Therefore, EVOH thermal degradation may be viewed as a superposition of the degradation processes of the two different co-components. The first step, associated to PVOH decomposition was in the range $0.1<\alpha<0.80$; whereas the second one for polyethylene is found in the range $0.89<\alpha<0.96$. Apparent activation energy values for the first step are between 123.3 and 161.4 kJ mol^{-1} for EVOH-32; 134.6 and 146.2 kJmol^{-1} for EVOH-38 and 156.4 kJ mol^{-1} and 161.4 kJ mol^{-1} for EVOH-44; while for the second stage (associated to polyethylene) the values were: 158.2 and 171.1 kJ mol^{-1} for EVOH-32, 159.4 and 174.9 kJ mol^{-1} for EVOH-38 and 161.3 and 171.7 kJ mol^{-1} for EVOH-44. It was also observed that apparent activation energies do not change drastically with conversion. This result indicates that the degradation mechanism of PVOH remains unchanged throughout the whole process and could be attributed to the cleavage of linkages with similar energy bonds. The activation energy values ($0.1<\alpha<0.80$), agreed with the fact than polyethylene increases the thermal stability of PVOH.

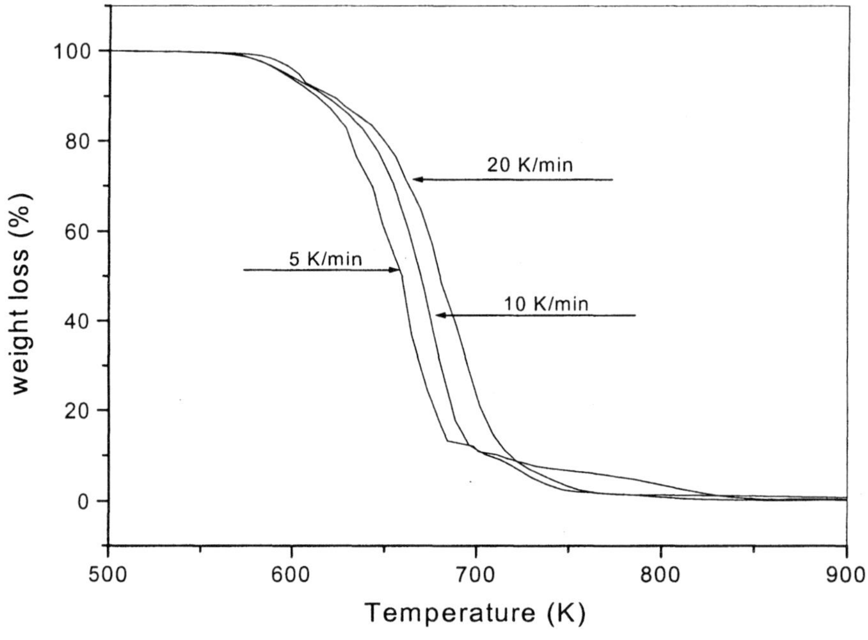

a)

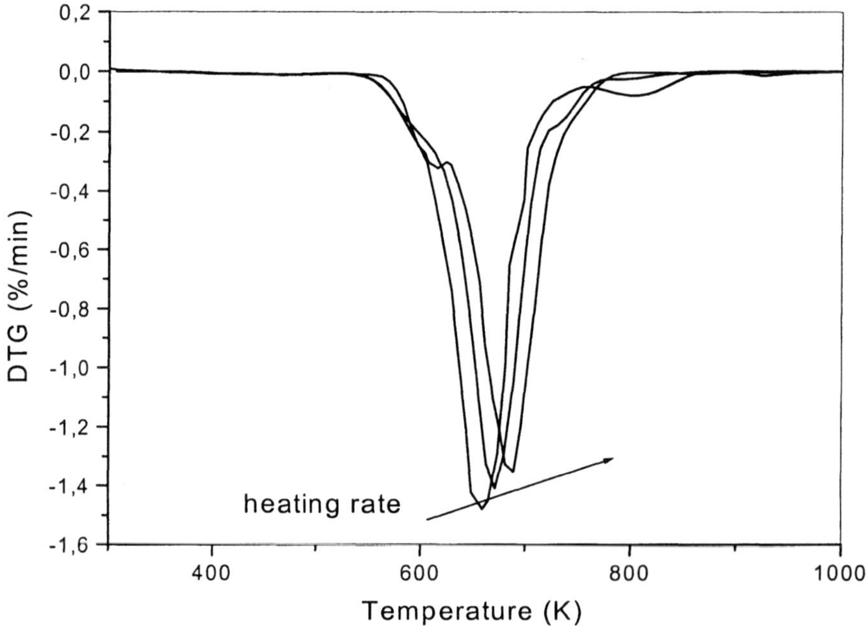

b)

Figure 5: TGA thermograms (a) and the corresponding DTGA (b) curves for the thermal decomposition of EVOH32 obtained at different heating rates in nitrogen atmosphere [46]

THERMAL DEGRADATION OF BIOCOMPOSITES

Synthetic biodegradable polymers and their blends are being introduced with the aim of fulfilling new environmental requirements regarding the effective management of post-consumer waste. However, the high price of such materials limits their use to a few exclusive applications. One economically and ecologically attractive approach to overcome these limitations is to incorporate natural fibers into biodegradable polymers to obtain environmentally friendly composite materials called *biocomposites,* which are quite similar to the already known synthetic fiber reinforced plastics.

On the other hand, Aoyagi et al [30], analyzed PCL, PHB and PLA thermal degradation under dynamic and isothermal conditions. In the case of PCL, TG/DTG curves suggest only one-single step. The constant value of apparent activation energy (Ea) during all the degradation process suggests also a simple degradation mechanism, but this last result does not exclude the possibility of a two-step mechanism. Draye et al [31] used High-Resolution TGA and TGA coupled to FTIR/MS techniques as tool for determining the structure of policaprolactam-co-polycaprolactone (PCLA-co-PCLO) copolymers, which are considered as a new class of synthetic biodegradable polymers [32]. Both techniques confirmed a block structure for the copolymer with 4 degradation steps at 340, 379, 395 and 420°C respectively. The two main peaks were those at 340 and 420°C, corresponding to PCLO and PCLA blocks, respectively. The intermediate peaks could be attributed to the degradation of heterosequences of CLA/CLO. Results showed the efficiency of TGA coupled to FTIR/MS and High-Resolution TGA in determining the structure of copolymers, even though a quantitative analysis was not performed due to exchange reactions taking place at high temperatures.

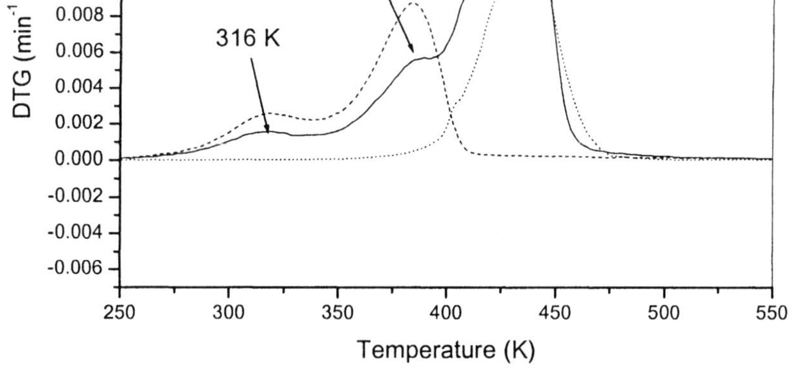

Figure 6: DTG of a PCL:SF mixture 2:1 (w:w) performed at 30 °C/min [28]

Tomassucci et al [47] recently analyzed the thermal behavior of biocomposites obtained from flax cellulose pulp and Mater-Bi, a commercial thermoplastic based on starch and biodegradable synthetic polymers, as a matrix. The authors observed that, even if fibers have a low thermal stability, the thermodegradative behavior of this composite material confirms a good chemical interaction between the fiber and the matrix; in fact, the matrix degrades at a higher temperature when combined with the flax cellulose reinforcement

REFERENCES

[1] E.H. Charles, "Preparation of high molecular weight polyhydroxyacetic ester" *US Patent, 2668162* (1954).

[2] C. Bastioli in "*Degradable Polymers. Principles and Applications*", G. Scott & D. Gilead (Eds.), Chapman & Hall, Cambridge (UK), 1995.

[3] C. Bastioli, *Polym. Degrad. & Stabil.*, 59, 263, (1998)

[4] J. Lorks, *Polym. Degrad. & Stabil.*, 59, 245, (1998)

[5] A.A. Soliman, N.A. El-Shinnawy, F. Mobarak, *Thermochimica Acta*, 296, 149 (1997)

[6] P. Aggarwal, D. Dollimore, *Thermochimica Acta*, 319, 17 (1998)

[7] N.I. Davidora, S.P. Leontev, Y.V. Genin, A.Y. Sasov, *Carbohydr. Polym.*, 27, 109 (1995)

[8] P. Aggarwal, D. Dollimore, *Talanta*, 43, 1527 (1996)

[9] R.L. Shogren, *Carbohydr. Polym.,* 19, 83 (1992)

[10] P. Chinachoti, *J. Therm. Anal.,* 47, 195 (1996)

[11] L. Yu, G. Christie, *Carbohydr. Polym.*, 46, 179 (2001)

[12] E.B. Bagley, G.R. Fanta, R.C. Burr, W.R. Doane, C.R. Russell, *Polym. Eng. Sci.*, 17, 311 (1977)

[13] D. Rankumar, U.R. Vaidya, M. Bhattacharya, M. Hakkarainen, A.C. Albertsson, S. Karlsson, *Eur. Polym. J.,* 32, 999 (1996)

[14] R. Mani, M. Bhattacharya, *Eur. Polym. J.*, 34, 1477 (1998)

[15] S. Lerdkanchanaporn, *Thermochimica Acta*, 340-341, 131 (1998)

[16] P. Aggarwal, *Thermochimica Acta*, 340-341, 195 (1998)

[17] A.M. Nada, M.L. Hassan, *Polym. Degrad. & Stabil.* 67, 111 (2000)

[18] M.J. Antal Jr., G. Varhegyi, *J. Indust. Chem.*, 34, 703 (1995)

[19] R.S. Miller, J. Bellam, *Combust. Sci. Tech.,* 119, 331 (1996)

[20] B. Azambre, O. Heintz, A. Krzton, J. Zawadzki, J.W. Weber, *J. Anal. & Appl. Pyrolysis,* 55, 105 (2000)

[21] B.N. Tosh, C.N. Saika, *J. Polym. Mater.*, 15, 185 (1998)

[22] J.E. Sealey, G. Samanarayake, J.G. Todd, W.G. Glasser, *J. Polym. Sci., Part B, Polym. Phys,* 34, 1613 (1996)

[23] E. Chellini, "Environmentally Degradable Plastics: An Overview" in *International Workshop On Environmentally Degradable And Recyclable Polymers In Latin America,* November 1998, Campinas (Brazil).

[24] P. Gatenholm, J. Kubat, A. Mathiasson, *J. Appl. Polym. Sci.*, 42, 1667 (1992)

[25] K. Van de Velde and P. Kiekens, *Polymer Testing*, 21, 433 (2002)

[26] M. Vert, J. Feijen, A-C. Albertsson, G. Scott, E. Chiellin, Editors, "Biodegradable Polymers and Plastics"; *Royal Society Chemistry*, Melksham, Wiltshire: Redwood Press, 1992
[27] D. Rutot, E. Duquesne, I. Ydens, Ph. Degée, Ph. Dubois, *Polym. Deg. & Stabil.*, 73, 561 (2001)
[28] R.A. Ruseckaite, A. Jiménez, *Polym. Deg. & Stabil,* 81, 353 (2003).
[29] O. Persenaire, M. Alexandre M, P. Degée, Ph. Dubois, *Biomacromolecules*, 2, 288 (2001)
[30] Y. Aoyagi, K. Yamashita, Y. Doi, *Polym. Degrad. & Stabil*, 76, 53 (2002)
[31] A. Draye, O. Persenaire, O. Brozek, J. Roda, T. Kosek, Ph. Dubois, *Polymer*, 42, 8325 (2001)
[32] X. Chen, K. Gonsalves, JA. Cameron, *J. Appl. Polym. Sci.*, 50, 1999 (1993)
[33] F-D. Kopinke, K. Mackenzie, *J Anal. & Appl Pyrolysis*, 41, 43 (1997)
[34] C. Migliaresi, D. Cohn, A. De Lollis, L. Fambri, *J Appl Polym Sci,* 43, 83 (1991)
[35] F-D. Kopinke, M. Remmler, K. Mackenzie, O. Mo der M Wachsen,. *Polym. Degrad. & Stab.*, 53, 329 (1996)
[36] D. Cam, M. Marucci, *Polymer*, 38, 1879 (1997)
[37] K. Jamshidi, SH. Hyon, Y. Ikada, *Polymer*, 29, 2229 (1988)
[38] M. Kunioka, Y. Doi. *Macromolecules,* 23, 1933 (1999)
[39] N. Grassie, EJ. Murray, PA. Holmes, *Polym. Degrad. & Stab.*, 6, 95 (1984)
[40] N. Grassie, EJ. Murria EJ, PA. Holmes, *Polym. Degrad. & Stab.*, 6, 127 (1984)
[41] H. Mitomo, E. Ota, *Sen-I Gakkaishi*, 47, 89 (1991)
[42] A. Ballistreri, S. Foti, G. Montaudo, E. Scamporrino *J. Polym. Sci, Polym. Chem.*, 18, 1147 (1980)
[43] B.J. Holland, JN. Hay, *Polymer*, 42, 6775 (2001)
[44] Y. Tsuchiya, K. Sumi, *J. Polym. Sci., Polym. Chem.*, 7, 3151 (1969)
[45] V.A. Alvarez, R.A. Ruseckaite, A.Vázquez, *J. Appl. Polym. Sci.* submmited
[46] A. Tomassucci, D. Puglia, J.M. Kenny, Processing And Thermal Characterization Of Biodegradable Composites Based On Mater-Bi® And Flax Cellulose Pulp" in *2nd International Conference on Polymer Modification, Degradation and Stabilization* (MODEST 2002), July 2002, Budapest (Hungary)
[47] K. Van de Velde, P. Kiekens, *Polymer Testing*, 21, 433 (2002)
[48] U.S. Ishiaku, K.W. Pang, W.S. Lee, Z.A. Mohd-Ishak, *Eur. Polym. J,* 38, 393 (2002)
[49] C. Bastioli, V. Bellotti, A. Montino, G. Tredici, R. Lombi, R. Ponti, *United States Patent 5,412,005*, (1995).
[50] R. Narayan "Overview and Case Studies of Biodegradable Plastic Technologies" in *Workshop on Environmentally Bio/Degradable polymers in Latin America* (WEDPLA '98) Campinas (Brazil), November 1998
[51] T. Suzuki, *J. Appl. Polym. Sci.: Appl. Polym. Symp.*, 35, 431 (1979)
[52] A. Corti, R. Solaro, E. Chiellini, *Polym. Degrad. & Stabil.*, 75, 447 (2002)
[53] E. Jakab, G. Varhegyi, O. Faix, J. *Anal. Appl Pyrolysis*, 56, 273 (2000)

In: Homolytic and Heterolytic Reactions: Problems and Solutions ISBN 1-59033-980-0
Editors: G.E. Zaikov, et al., pp. 17-90

Chapter 2

FRACTAL ANALYSIS OF STRUCTURE AND PROPERTIES OF THE FILLED POLYMER

G. V. Kozlov, V. U. Novikov and G. E. Zaikov*
The Moscow State Open University. Korchagin st., 22, body 2, 107996, Moscow, Russia.
* Institute of Biochemical Physics, Russian Academy of Sciences. Kosygin st., 4, 117334,Moscow, Russia.

ABSTRACT

With utilization of the fractal analysis and multifractal formalism the filled polymers are considered as heterogeneous systems. The influence of filler particles aggregation on the structure and properties of polymer composites is discussed. The greatest attention is given to physical treatment of interaction between filled polymer components and correlation relationships between their properties. The possibility of the fractal parameters experimental determination is shown.

Keywords: Polymer, filler, fractal, multifractal, interphase layer, aggregation, particle.

INTRODUCTION

A growing interest to the filled polymers causes all extending their application [1–7]. The incorporation to a polymer of a solid filling material yields polymers with a number of desirable properties: increases rigidity, reduces thermal expansion coefficient, increases creep resistance and fracture toughness etc. The difficulties in research of structure-properties relationships for filled polymers are connected with so much that they are heterogeneous systems of a composite structure and are thermodynamically non-equilibrium solids. So, on the value of a elasticity modulus some interactions between separate components of phases – polymeric matrix, filler and interphase layer are influenced. So far indicated, researches within the framework of a mechanics of continua [5] and thermodynamic concepts are made [4]. However, these concepts application yet does not allow satisfactorily describing properties of such materials. In essence, a set of experimental data dictates the selection of the physical model of structure for the description of macroscopic properties. As it is noted in [5], the various models in a mechanics of continua were designed for the description of the obtained set of experimental data. In this connection the new approach allowing new physical consideration of structure and description of filled polymers properties is required.

One of such possible approaches can be the utilization of the fractal analysis methods and principles of a multifractal formalism receive recently widespreading application [8 – 19]. The reasons of these applications are obvious. As experimental studies have shown, the fractal properties are generic to the main components of filled polymers (matrix [13, 20], to particles and aggregates of filler particles [21, 22]), i.e., they are fractal objects. This requires the application of the fractal analysis methods for their description [23]. As Euclidean objects having a translational symmetry, enable usage only of one order parameter (dimension of Euclidean space d), the fractal objects having a dilatational symmetry, require the application of not less than three order parameters: Euclidean d, fractal (Hausdorff) d_f and spectral (fracton) d_s dimensions. This requirement will be in agreement with the well-known Prigogin rule in non-equilibrium thermodynamics [24] for the description of thermodynamically non-equilibrium solid polymers. Thus, it is necessary, as a minimum, two order parameters. This is the reason for the application of the concepts of equilibrium thermodynamics and mechanics of continua operating representations of a Euclidean geometry, They can only approximately characterize the structure of considered materials and require the application of empirical factors.

The successful application of the fractal analysis methods to polymers [25–27] and the use of recent concepts of a multifractal formalism [28] allow to hope the successful propagation of this approach for parameterization of structure and estimation of filled polymers properties. In this review the analysis and description of filled polymers structure and physical characteristics with usage of such approach for the first time is offered.

MULTIFRACTAL FORMALISM

The polymer structures, especially of filled polymers and the processes of their formation were traditionally studied with the application of parameters describing its various elements: roughness, porosity, size of the structural particle, which are simulated by geometrical images with integer dimension. Moreover, the dimension of an inner structure does not receive often much attention.

For the quantitative description of such structures a fractal dimension was offered [8, 13], having not the whole, but fractional value, which allows the determination of the topology features of a subtle inner structure of objects. The fractional metric dimension of fractal an object not only characterizes a geometrical image but also describes internal processes at their formation and evolution.

However, it is not enough for the exact description of the natural, many synthesized and modeled structures to know just the value of the fractal dimension. The wide possibilities are represented by a multifractal formalism, basically described in papers [29–31], and that are used in many different applications [32–45].

The attraction of multifractal formalism principles, based on the utilization of concepts of a measure concerning to the general structure of a material, allows to quantitatively characterizing its parts as a whole structure that essentially supplements the data received by the fractal analysis methods. Thus, the transition from fractal analysis to the utilization of a multifractal formalism means not only the study of geometrical properties, but also research to determine sizes.

The basis of multifractal formalism consists of generation by a determined way of a measure dividing space encompassing a studied object, called the measure support. Let us imagine some strange object with non-regular, non-ordering, loosely packing, porous structure placed in a Euclidean space. Let us divide this space into cells by the size l_1 (i = 1/N), so that the selected size satisfies the condition $l_i \le l$, where l is the selected size. The given procedure allows assigning to each cell a measure ("weight", p_i) dependent on the nature of the studied object. For a fractal object of total weight M, "weight" can be the relative part of mass in a cell, $p_i = m_i/M$, where m_i is weight of the ith cell [33, 38]. In the space of separate phases for a measurement of a cell it is possible to calculate the number of transits in a dynamic system pathway through each cell M_i for enough large period of time [29, 30], supposing

$$p_i = M_i \Big/ \sum_{i=1}^{N} M_i \qquad (1)$$

In a similar way it is necessary to analyze a solid structure or discontinuities in its sections [31], an energy distribution which is based on the fracture of structural elements [46] under a condition, that they are divided into cells of encompassing space together with object generates on a measure p_i ($\Sigma p_i = 1$), as the distribution of some value, not changing the sign. Moreover the selected measurement has a definite physical sense.

The simple canonical interpretation of a multifractal formalism, in the one-dimension case considering Cantor set can be received [47]. As we know, the abstract triadic Cantor set can be calculated and, dividing it at each iteration on three equal parts, removing thus a mean element (Fig. 1a). The fractal dimension of such object is equal to D = ln 2/ln 3 ≅ 0,6309.

Here Cantor set is distinct from the abstract Cantor set. Consider that seed is not a unit cut, but a rod from any of the materials, for example, from a filled polymer with density ρ_0 = 1, length l_0 = 1 and weight m_0 = 1. The procedure, connected with application of a generating element, consists of two halves of equal weight $\mu_1 = \mu_2 = 0,5$, as a result of hypothetical compression are shortened up t_0 length l_1 = 1/3 (identical for both halves). As a result of such procedure, density is raised to $\rho_1 = \mu_2/l_1 = 3/2$. Repeating $N = 2^n$ of small rods, each of them has length $l_i = 3^{-n}$ and weight $\mu_1 = 2^{-n}$ at i =1, ..., N. We have to note, that the weight during this procedure is preserved, therefore μ_i = 1. Consequently, the weight of a cut of length l_i is determined by the expression $\mu_i = l_i^{\alpha}$, where α is the scaling exponent equal to ln 2/ln 3. Density of each of small sections of a rod is determined by a relationship $\rho_i = \mu_i / l_i = \rho_0 l_i^{\alpha-1}$ and deviated at $l_i \to 0$.

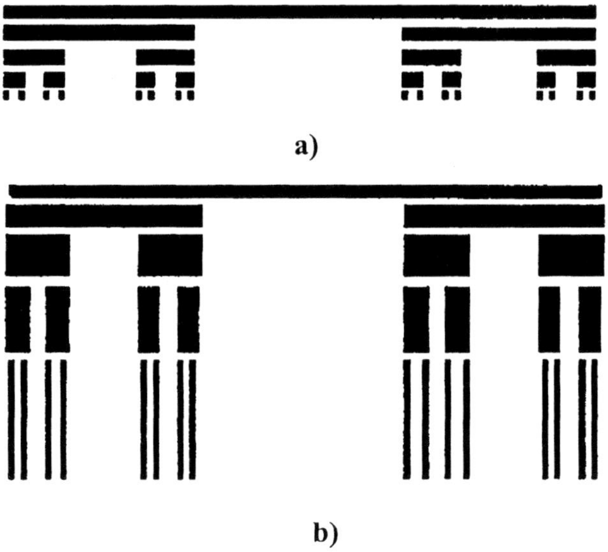

Figure 1. The triadic Cantor set. a) Abstract triadic Cantor set with $D = \ln 2/\ln 3 \approx 0,6309$. b) Triadic Cantor rod: the height of rod in n-th generation is proportional to its density ρ_i, an exponent of Lipschitz-Helder $\alpha = \ln 2/\ln 3 \approx 0,6309$, fractal dimension of the mass carrier $f = D = \ln 2/\ln 3 \approx 0,6309$.

In Fig. 1,b the described version of Cantor set is shown. The height of each piece is determined by its density ρ_i. This modification of Cantor's construction requires a scaling exponent α for the description of rod pieces height increase at decreasing their width. It is possible that the singularities with an exponent α are supported with fractal dimension $f = D \cong 0,6309$. Generally a carrier of the geometrical set μ_1 can be measured at any value.

Let us consider N links of a macromolecule [0, 1] at $N \to \infty$, where N is calculated from the basic distribution (at finite N). If the piece of macromolecule [0, 1] is divided on links of length $\delta = 2^{-n}$ then the number of cells should be $N = 2^n$, where n is the number of generations at binary divisions. Let us designate cells by an index $i = 0, 1, 2, \ldots, N - 1$. The distribution of links on a piece at solvability δ will be determined by a set of number N_i, demonstrating, how many links are in the ith cell. The convenient measurement contained in the ith cell can be calculated by a fraction $\mu_i = N_i/N$ of the number of links fallen in the ith cell from total of links N. The set of fractions $H = \{\mu_i\}_{i=0}^{N-1}$ gives the full description of links distribution at the solvability δ. A value for H(Z) of a subregion Z (for example, segment) piece [0, 1] is determined by the sum $H(Z) = \sum_{i=Z} \mu_i$.

In order to describe links distribution by a piece on one place, it is necessary to task H at a good enough solvability, i.e., at small δ, that sometimes is inaccessible. But when H has scaling property, there is no need to describe the position of each link.

It is possible to show that H has singularities with an exponent α on fractal sets X_α with fractal dimensions $f(\alpha) = f(\xi(\alpha))$. Thus, the studied set is modeled by a set of interpenetrating iso-singularities α, each of which has the corresponding dimension $f(\alpha)$ [29]. The typical graph $f(\alpha)$ is shown in Fig. 2a.

The following general statement is true: the maximal value of fractal dimension of subsets X_α is equal to fractal dimension of the carrier of a measurement [13]. In the case of Cantor set this fractal dimension is equal t_0 1, as the measurement is determined on all a unit cut. For measurements defined on fractals with fractal dimension D, we receive $f_{max}(\alpha) = D$.

Another relevant characteristic of multifractal measurements is the sequence of weight exponents. Let us consider a set X, consisting on N points, each one has N_i points in i[th] cell. These points can be considered as reflecting distribution of a measurement (probability) $\mu_i = N_i/N$, corresponding to a ith cell, and we shall construct a measurement, which can be written as follows [13]:

$$H_\alpha(q,\delta) = \sum_{i=1}^{N} \mu_i^q \delta^d = N(q,\delta)\delta^d \xrightarrow[\delta \to 0]{} \begin{cases} 0, d > \tau(q), \\ \infty, d < \tau(q), \end{cases} \tag{2}$$

where q and τ are arbitrary real numbers. This measurement has an exponent of weight $d = \tau(q)$, where it will not vanish and in infinity, when $\delta \to 0$. The measurement is characterized by all the sequence of weight exponents $\tau(q)$, determining, by which power law change depending on probability of δ $\{\mu_1\}$ From (1) it follows, that the weighted number of cells N(q, d) is represented by:

$$N(q,d) = \sum \mu_i^q \sim \delta^{-\tau(q)} \tag{3}$$

and the weight exponent is determined by the expression:

$$\tau(q) = -\lim_{\delta \to 0} \frac{\ln N(q,d)}{\ln \delta} \tag{4}$$

By choosing q = 0 (in this case q is the order of the moment), we calculate $\mu_i^{q=0} = 1$. Therefore $N(q = 0, d) = N(d)$ is simply the number of cells which are formed and $\tau(0) = D$. The probabilities are normalized: $\Sigma\mu_i = 1$, and from (2), $\tau(1) = 0$.

The sequence of weight exponents is connected to a curve $f(\alpha)$ by general relationship [13]:

$$\tau(q) = f(\alpha(q)) - q\alpha(q) \tag{5}$$

Thus, the exponent of the weight can be expressed through an exponent $\alpha(q)$ for weight and fractal dimension $f(\alpha(q))$ of carrier set of this exponent.

At the same time, when the weight exponents $\tau(q)$ are known, it is possible to determine α and f, using the equations (4) and (5) and then we have:

$$\alpha(q) = \frac{d}{dq}\tau(q),$$
$$f(\alpha(q)) = q\alpha(q) + \tau(q). \qquad (6)$$

These two equation are parameter representations of a curve f(α), which characterizes the measurement describing distribution of links and is equivalent to the sequence of weight exponents τ(q). The pair of equations (6) task transformation of Legendre from independent variables τ and q to independent variables f and α.

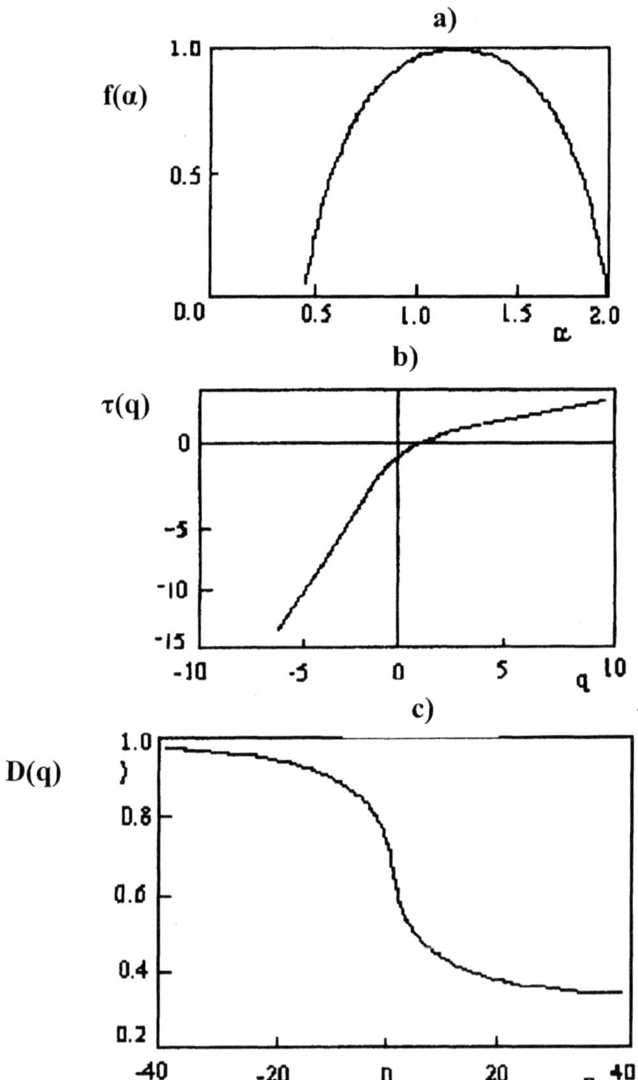

Figure 2. The typical plots of dependences describing fractal subsets, generated by binomial multiplicative process: a) $f(\alpha)$; b) $\tau(q)$; c) $D(q)$.

Halsey [30] analyzed a measurement set by relationship (2), having connected it with dimension D_q, as Grassberger [34] and Hentschel and Procaccia [28] and defined by dimension of Renju:

$$D_q = \tau(q)/(1-q) \tag{7},$$

where the numerical factor (1–q) will modify a weight exponent, so that for sets of constant density in E-dimensional space the equality D_q = E is in force. The spectrum of fractal dimensions D_q was set by a limiting relationship:

$$D_q = \frac{1}{q-1}\lim_{\delta\to 0}\frac{\ln N(q,\delta)}{\ln \delta} \tag{8}$$

The moment order q can be any number in the range from $-\infty$ up to $+\infty$, and the function $D_q(q)$ is a spectrum of fractal dimensions for a fractal measurement on set X. If we choose value q = 0 for moment order q, we would receive $\mu_1^{q=0} = 1$. Therefore, N(q=0, d) = N(d) there is simply the number of cells necessary to cover the set, and the value $D_{q=0}$ = D is equal to the fractal dimension of set. In a limit $q \to \infty$ we calculate that $D_\infty = \alpha_{min}$, while $D_{-\infty} = \alpha_{max}$. The typical dependences τ(q) and D(q) are shown in Fig. 1 by the way of two curves, which one formally correspond with studied structure. As they have a characteristic form and are mathematically described by two equations, identical to any structure, this approach was called a multifractal formalism. The parameters of these curves are rather precisely calculated even at a coarse treatment of studied structures that allows them to be used in quantitative parameterization. So, at q = 0, 1, 2 we calculate generally accepted definitions fractal D_0, information D_1 and correlation D_2 dimensions. A criteria of multifractality is the nonequality $D_0 > D_1 > D_2$. The equalites $D_0 = D_1 = D_2 = \alpha_{max} = \alpha_{min} = f(\alpha)$ and $\tau(q) = (q-1)D_1$ indicate the absence of multifractality. Such fractals are called homogeneous, that means the existence in the structure of one characteristic ratio of scales at transition from one scale level to another. The value α always has finite magnitude, and difference $M_x = \alpha_{max} - \alpha_{min} = D_{-\infty} - D_\infty$ can be used as a chaos measure [16, 19].

On the basis of a theoretical-informational interpretation of a multifractal formalism the authors [23–25] have offered a determination technique of characteristic of two-dimensional (planar) depictions of structures. They offered their uniformity by a parameter $f(q = 40) = f_{40}$, and latent ordering (periodicity) – by parameter $D_1(q = 1) - D_4(q = 40) = \Delta_{40}$. This approves [19] with reference to metals, that the higher f_{40} and D_{40}, then the structure is more uniform and more ordered. As with reference to polymers, this statement is not always true [48].

The possibilities of a multifractal formalism are considered in the review [49], where two approaches are discussed: a) geometrical, when the initial piece is divided on some blocks, and the number and mutual positions of them are changed, thus the process multiply repeats, and b) a method of convolution, when the process of block construction represents their compression (convolution). In correspondence to these approaches two methods of the multifractal sets description are reviewed: geometrical (study of spacing intervals between points of set) and thermodynamic (distribution of a measurement on points of a set). In this connection all individual interpretations of a multifractal formalism can conditionally be divided into geometrical, thermodynamical and informational groups [17].

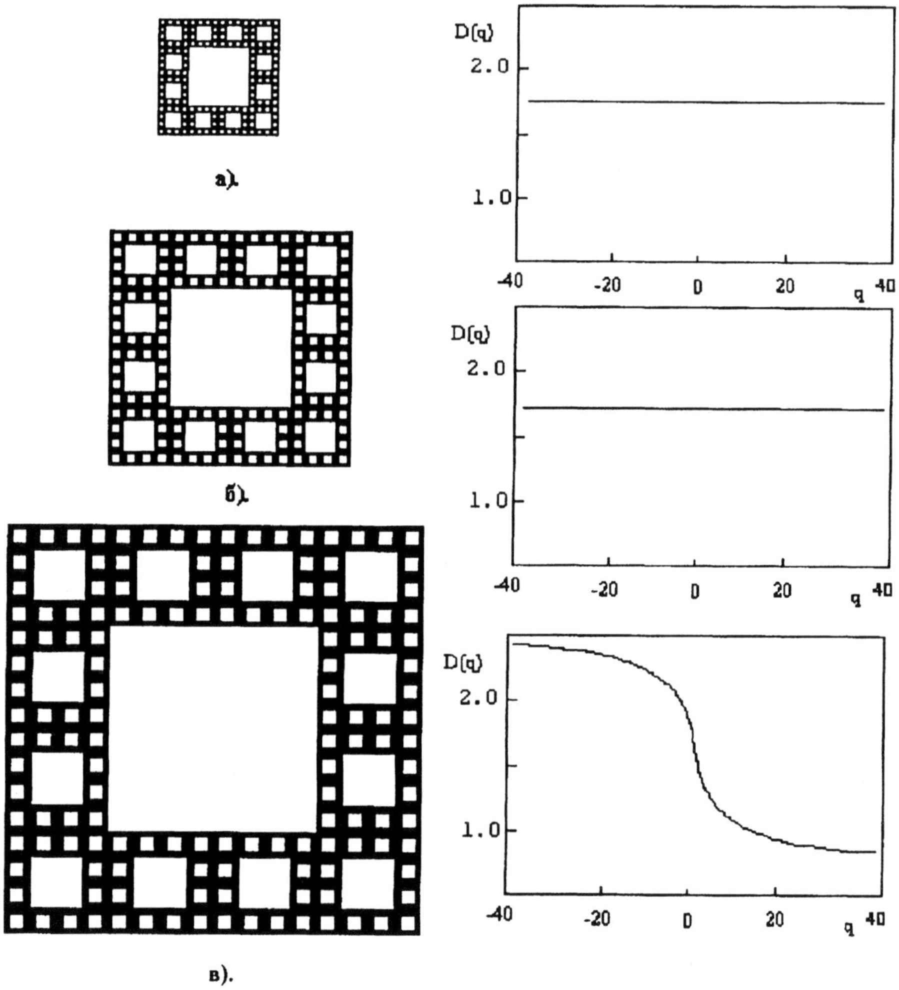

Figure 3. Sierpinski gaskets with the corresponding multifractal spectra: 128 × 128 of pixels (a), 256 × 256 of pixels (b), 480 × 480 of pixels (c).

As an example of the visual interpretation of the object description by set of interpenetrating isosingularities, we can consider a Sierpinski carpet [28], for which one multifractal spectrum of dimensions D(q) and spectrum f(α) are shown in a Fig. 3.

As well as it was necessary to expect for homogeneous geometrical fractal, the spectrum D(q) has degenerated in a horizontal straight line $D(q) = D_{teor} = 1{,}7925$, and spectrum f(α) – in point $f\,(1{,}7925) \cong 1{,}7925$. It indicates the absence of subsets with singularities which are distinct from a singularity of the measurement geometrical support, equal to fractal dimension $D_{theor} = \ln(12)/\ln(4) \cong 1{,}7925$. After transformation of the Sierpinski carpet image to the graphic file and its increase up to 256 × 256 pixels, the similar multifractal spectrum (Fig. 3b) is obtained due to the same changes of image sizes in vertical and horizontal directions do not cause of a symmetry breakage. These two examples indicate, on absence of multifractal properties for geometrically exact regular fractal, Sierpinski carpet, i.e., the fractal dimension D_0 of model structures can be treated as the degenerated information dimension. When the image is increased up to 480 × 480 pixels the ratio 480 to 128 is not an integer and the geometrical periodicity of an image pattern is distorted. As the consequence, there has taken place "spreading" of the straight line D(q) and point f(α) in curves (Fig. 3c). The obtained spectrums indicate appearance of subsets with fractal dimension of distinct from fractal dimension of the geometrical support, i.e., appearance of multifractal measures.

FILLED POLYMERS AS HETEROGENEOUS SYSTEMS WITH POLYFRACTAL STRUCTURE

Filled polymer represents a heterogeneous system with intrinsic features of structure and properties, including fractal. It allows to consider such system structure as a set (spectrum) of fractals, i.e., as polyfractal structure [48,50], which can be described by the multifractal formalism. Now there are two main concepts of their description. Its application to study structure and properties of filled polymers will be shown below.

The multifractal formalism describing normalized distributions (measurements), based upon fractal sets, is presented in [30], where the main attention is concentrated on scaling properties of such measurements. The consideration of their singularities was characterized by two parameters: α, determining concentration of singularities (their power), and f, describing density of their distribution. The spectrum of singularities is described by a tack of a probable interval of values α and function f(α). Williford [46] has applied this formalism in the some simplified variant to the description of multiphase materials fracture. In papers [51,52], a technique [46] was used to describe properties of polyhydroxyether (PHE) filled by disperse graphite with non-treated (PHE-Gr-I) and treated (PHE-Gr-II) surface. The authors suppose that the main fault of large number of studies, investigating fracture of materials within the framework of the fractal analysis [53-55], was the attempts to connect the mechanical properties of materials to fractal dimension of their fracture surface d_r, instead of the structure of fractal dimension, d_f. In [52] Balankin used the equation for calculation of fractal dimension of a fracture surface for quasi-brittle ($d_{r,br}$) and quasi-ductile ($d_{r,duc}$) fractures on the basis of Poisson's ratio ν:

$$d_{r,br} = \frac{10(1+\nu)}{7-3\nu} \qquad (7)$$

$$d_{r,duc} = \frac{2(1+4\nu)}{1+2\nu} \qquad (8)$$

whereas the fractal (Hausdorff) dimension d_f of a polymer structure is determined [57]:

$$d_f = (d-1)(1+\nu) \qquad (9)$$

where s is the dimension of Euclidean space, in which one the fractal is considered (in the studied case d = 3).

It is noted [52], that for studied graphite-reinforced PHE the value of critical strain energy release rate G_{Ic} (describing plasticity of materials) decreases with the increase of fractal dimension of a fracture surface d_r, irrespective of equations (7) or (8). As such behavior is indicative of a "ductile" branch of the multifractal diagram [46], the value $d_{r,duc}$ is used. In Fig. 4 the dependences ($d_{r,duc}$ – 2) on ln G_{Ic} are shown, similar to those obtained by Willifford [46], from which we see, that these dependences are similar to a "ductile" branch of the multifractal diagram for metals fracture [46]. This has given the basis (at least, formal) for the description of the behavior for graphite-reinforced PHE fracture by using a multifractal formalism.

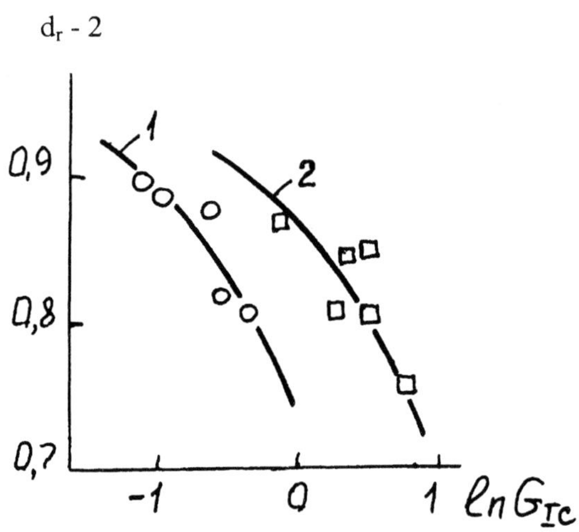

Figure 4. The dependences of a fractional part of fractal dimension (d_r – 2) of a fracture surface on critical strain energy release rate G_{Ic} for PHE–Gr-I (1) and PHE–Gr-II (2).

The Cantor set ("dust") was used as mathematical model [47]. It was supposed that the piece with length l_1 and probability measure p_1 characterizes the filler, and l_2 and p_2, accordingly, the polymer matrix. Such reference is due to that the piece characterized by an index 1, falls into branches of brittle fracture according to [46] and an increase of the filler content leads to fragility of the studied composites. An estimation of values l_1, p_1, l_2 and p_2 can be made by investigating the electron micrographs of the specimen fracture surfaces. The details of the multifractal characteristics by the indicated method are described in section IX.

The results of computer calculations in the form of multifractal diagrams have allowed receiving a number of characteristic points. So, at q=∞, D_∞ = lnp_2/lnl_1 and at q = –∞, $D_{-\infty}$ = lnp_2/lnl_2, which characterizes only "brittle" and only "ductile" types of fracture. At q = 0, D_0 = (f + 1), where D_0 is Hausdorff dimension, i.e., it is necessary to expect, that D_0 = d_f. Besides in [46] it is supposed that D_0 is the dimension of all fractal, i.e., this dimension can be considered as the dimension of the filled polymer structure. The second on magnitude dimension D_1 < D_0 (information dimension) characterizes the greatest subfractal, which can be the border of all fractal fracture surfaces under the condition α = f D_1 [30]. In Fig. 5 the generalized diagrams for two composites PHE-Gr-I and PHE-Gr-II are shown. From the analysis of these diagrams can be seen that they are asymmetrical. More flat branch of the diagram α-f for filled PHE with volume content of filler φ_f = 0,088 means a predominantly ductile fracture, and for PHE-Gr-I with φ_f = 0,176 these types of fracture are equiprobable. The second qualitative feature are the essential distinctions of a difference $\Delta = D_{-\infty} - D_{\infty}$ as shown on Fig. 5. As it was indicated earlier [58], the value Δ can represent the parameter of a randomness of fracture processes.

The quantitative characteristics of the multifractal diagrams are much more interesting. The comparison of values D_0 (Hausdorff dimension) and d_f (dimension of structure, equation (9)), for four composites PHE-Gr, demonstrates a close correspondence of both parameters. Simultaneously these data allow to define D_0 as the fractal dimension of composites structure, and following dimension D_1, determined from the condition α = f (see Fig. 5a), as a fracture surface dimension, i.e, $D_1 = d_r$. The comparison of values D_1 and d_r ($d_{r,br}$ and $d_{r,duc}$) demonstrates that for composites with non-treated filler, a quasi-brittle fracture ($D_1 = d_{r,br}$) is observed, and with treated a quasi-ductile ($D_1 = d_{r,duc}$) is observed [15].

The analysis according to model [46] demonstrates, that the dimension f does not depend on probability measurements (p_1 or p_2) and, therefore, does not depend on the adhesion strength (at least, a first approximation), but depends on the size of filler particles (l_1). On an insert of a Fig. 5 the dependences f and $(d_2 - 2)$ on l_1 are shown. Both of them are rather close on absolute values, and on a form of relationship. The value α, which characterizes energetic parameters of system, can be expressed [46]:

$$\ln G_{Ic} = (\alpha - 2)\ln L_{av}, \tag{10}$$

where L_{av} is the average size of a specimen.

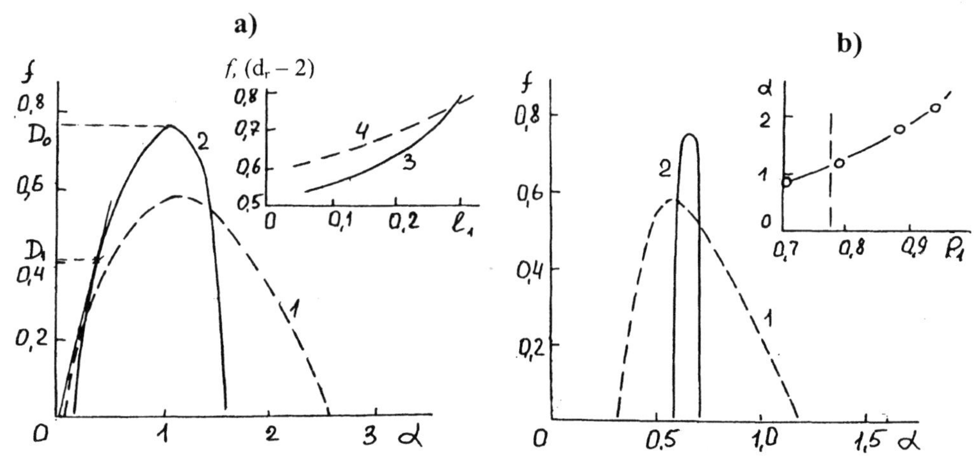

Figure 5. The multifractal diagrams $f - \alpha$ for PHE–Gr-I (a) and PHE–Gr-II (b) with volumetric contents of filler φ_f = 0,0088 (1) and φ_f = 0,176 (2). On the insert of a Fig. (a) dependences f on l_1 (3) and $(d_2 - 2)$ on l_1 (4), and on an insert of a Fig (b) dependence α on p_1.

The comparison of values G_{Ic}, obtained experimentally [59] and calculated on the equation (9) demonstrates their satisfactory correspondence (for PHE-Gr-I was accepted p_1 =

0,70). On Fig. 5b the dependence α (and, therefore, G_{Ic}) from p_l (i.e., on decrease of adhesion degree) is shown. From the dependence α (p_l), it can be seen that by the corresponding adjustment p_l (on Fig. 5a this corresponds to a shaped line at p_l = 0,77) it is possible to achieve the exact conformity of experimental and calculated by equation (10) values G_{Ic} [52].

Having choose a three-dimensional Sierpinski carpet as the basic mathematical set and using main principles [30] for multifractal parameterization of polyfractal objects structure, authors [60] offered the computer technique. By using it, authors [49] have studied carbonic fibres structure and have established that it represents a polymeric carbon (micromatrix), in which the microfibrils (microfiller) are distributed.

There are also other methods of the multifractal characteristics applications for an estimation of structural parameters and properties of materials [15, 61–63].

The filled polymers structure can be considered as a set of fractals, as filled polymers are heterogeneous systems with polyfractal structure in the sense that the parts of this structure have static self-similarity in restricted interval of linear scales. Under this consideration, the filled polymers structure can be represented by a set of different weights of fractal objects [8,74]. So, in filled polymers, fractals are a backbone of filler particles (at least, near a percolation threshold [65]), a polymer matrix [20,27], a surface of filler particles [66], aggregates of filler particles [67–72], etc. Therefore, there is a problem of determination of dimensions of the indicated fractals in filled polymer, and their interaction in common structures of filled polymer is reviewed [46]. The filled polymer in [73] is considered as a combination of two fractals representing a backbone ("skeleton") of filler particles (or aggregates of particles) with dimension D_b and a polymer matrix with dimension d_f. In this case, two values f for each of the mentioned above fractals will correspond to each α. The correspondence of dimensions D_0 and D_b for two considered multifractal models is assumed [31]. As stated above, f (and, therefore D_0) is determined only by contents of filler and does not depend on other factors, for example testing temperature T. The same is possible to say about dimension D_b (see section IX). Both indicated dimensions are defined by the structure of filler particles backbone in a polymer matrix [73]. From a comparison of values D_0 and D_b for filled PHE a good enough conformity follows (correlation coefficient 0,93) [73]. In the treatment of filled polymer as the combination of two fractals, all changes of external factors not concerning D_b (or D_0), will influence the structure of the polymer matrix, which can be described by its fractal dimension d_f (equation (9)) [74].

In Fig. 6a the relationship between dimensions $D_k(D_0)$ and d_f for composites PHE-Gr-II is shown. This relationship is approximated by a straight line and magnitudes d_f at limiting values $D_b(D_0)$ have the expected character. So, at D_b = 2, i.e., for an absence of any influence of filler, d_f = 2,5, that corresponds to a quasi-equilibrium state of the polymer structure [25,26]. At D_b = 3, i.e., at the greatest possible influence of filler, the value d_f = 2,88 corresponds to the greatest possible value d_f for glassy polymer [57].

According to the Mandelbrot rule [8], the fractal dimension of a set consisting of two independent fractal sets p_1 and p_2, is equal to half of sum of fractal dimensions of sets p_1 and p_2. In [75] it is supposed, that the fractal dimension of a fracture surface is equal to the half-sum of fractal dimensions of this surface profiles in two orthogonal directions. The similarly of the fractal dimension of filled polymer structure d_k can be represented as follows [73]:

$$d_k = \frac{D_b + d_f}{2} \tag{11}$$

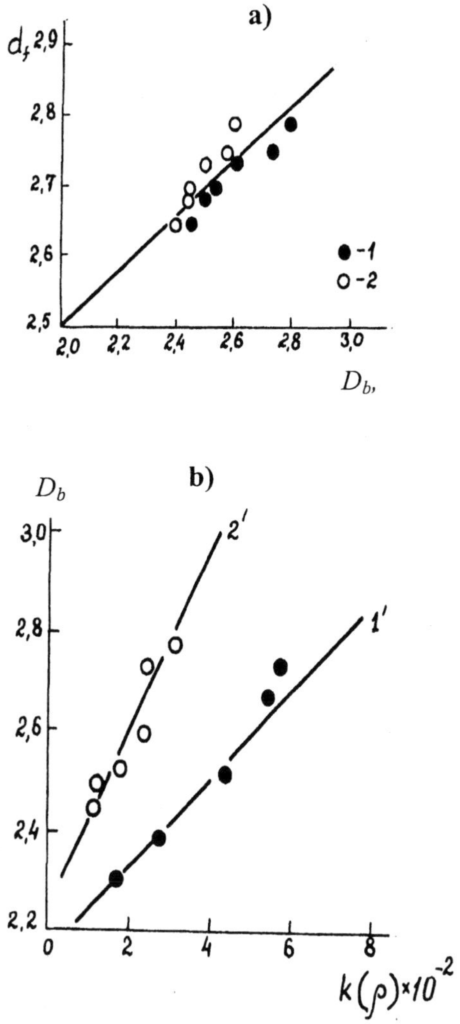

Figure 6. The dependences of fractal dimension of filler particles frame D_b (1) and Hausdorff dimension of structure D_0 (2) on fractal (Hausdorff) dimension of a polymer matrix d_f for PHE–Gr-II (a), and D_b on aggregation parameter $k(\rho)$ for PHE–Gr-I (1′) and PHE-Gr-II (2′).

The comparison of experimentally obtained and calculated according to the equation (11) fractal dimensions demonstrates the systematic excess for calculated d_k and the equality is reached only at enough large φ_f, i.e. where the possibilities of modifying the initial polymer structure practically are depleted. Apparently, the default of the mentioned above Mandelbrot rule is due to that the considered fractals (multifractals) are not independent.

The aggregation degree of filler particles can be described within the framework of a dispersion fracture theory [76], where shearing yield stress of filled polymer τ_{FP} is determined:

$$\tau_{FP} = \tau_m + \frac{Gb}{k(\rho)\lambda}, \quad (12)$$

where τ_m is the shearing yield stress of a polymer matrix, G is shear modulus, *b* is vector of Burgers, k(ρ) is parameter of aggregation and λ is spacing interval between filler particles.

In Fig. 6b the dependences D_b on the values k(ρ), calculated by the equation (12), for both series of filled PHE specimens are shown. The tendency of increasing D_b in process of rising k(ρ) is observed. This demonstrates the process of a filler aggregation at increasing φ_f. However, distinct dependences $D_b(k(\rho))$ for PHE-Gr-I and PHE-Gr-II indicate that parameters D_b and k(ρ) characterize different properties of an aggregation process. The value of k(ρ) gives an average parameter of the rise of the filler particle sizes, and D_b characterizes the distribution of these sizes. Therefore, intervals of the filler particles sizes 20-80 μm and 40-60 μm will give the identical mean size of particles 50 μm and same k(ρ), but the distribution of particles (or aggregates of particles) at the same φ_f will be different and it is demonstrated by value D_b. From Fig. 6b it can be seen, that at identical distribution (i.e., equal D_b) the average size of particles aggregates will be lower for composites PHE-Gr-II with the treated filler surface, i.e., D_b characterizes the space filling density of a polymer matrix by filler particles. Using a Menges sponge [65,66], as mathematical model of filled polymer means an increase of approximation number K at rising D_b and vice-versa.

We shall indicate a number of possible research directions of filled polymers within the framework of the offered approach, which demonstrate its advantages as contrasted to a multifractal formalism, incorporated in papers [30, 46].

At first, the value of information dimension D_1 (at q=1) characterizes a multifractal surface [46]. Apparently, for a filler particles backbone it will be the dimension of particles surface (which is a function of their aggregation degree [77]) and for a polymer matrix formed in the process of its structure changes. It is possible to suppose that the misfit of values D_1 of a filler and polymer matrix will lead to the deterioration of an interphase adhesion.

Secondly, values D_b and d_f of a filled polymer are corresponded by the same value α. In turn, α is connected with G_{Ic} according to equation (10). As at q = 1, $D_1 = 2 + f$ or $D_1 = 2 + \alpha$, we can express α through fractal dimension of a filler surface. Besides having estimated value G_{Ic} within the framework of networks model [78], we can connect the characteristics of a filler and polymer matrix to calculate analytical relationships determining the influence of a filler particles backbone on a polymer matrix structure.

In third, the equation (10) assumes that (at L_{av} = const) the plasticity of a filled polymer will be decreased with α increases as well as fractal dimension of a filler particles surface.

In fourth, known condition $D_1 \leq D_0$ [30] assumes that D_b will depend on fractal dimension of a filler particles surface. Presumably, the higher this dimension, the higher D_b and this expressed the brittleness of filled polymer.

AGGREGATION OF FILLER PARTICLES

The process of filler particles aggregation has strong effect on filled polymers structure. For the description and prediction of this process the models of an irreversible aggregation will be used [79].

In papers [21,72] the aggregation of nickelous dust particles (non-treated and treated by stearic acid) to an epoxy matrix was studied. The calculation of fractal dimension D of these aggregated is based on a relationship [21]:

$$R \sim N_{\mathrm{p}}^{1/D} \tag{13}$$

where R is the radius of the aggregate and N_{p} is the number of particles in it.

The obtained values of D for the treated and non-treated nickelous dust differ among themselves, as well as by value of fractal dimension of aggregates, obtained at a numerical simulation by a method of diffusion-limited aggregation. Simultaneously they are lower than $D = 2{,}10$, corresponding to a kinetically limited aggregation process.

The weak increase of D with the increase of curing temperature was also observed. Higher values of an aggregation temperature correspond to the larger sizes of initial particles aggregates. The increase of the aggregates size is connected to a viscosity decreasing of epoxy at heating. The viscosity decreasing promotes larger mobility of particles in the polymer matrix and a faster completion of the aggregation process. There is an assumption of some seal of aggregates at heating, by which it can be explained the larger values of fractal dimension of these aggregates [21,22].

The cited results have allowed the authors [77] to use them for the description of processes of graphite particles aggregation in PHE with the following relationship of model of an irreversible aggregation a cluster–cluster [80]:

$$R_{\mathrm{a}}^{T} \sim \left(\frac{4c_0 kT}{3\eta m_0} \right)^{1/D} t^{1/D} \tag{14}$$

where R_{a}^{T} is the theoretical value of radius of particles aggregate, c_0 is the initial concentration of particles, k is the Boltzmann constant, T is temperature, η is viscosity of medium, m_0 is particle mass, t is the duration of an aggregation.

The maximal experimental values of radius of particles aggregates $R_{\mathrm{a}}^{\max}$ were estimated by electron microscopy [77]. From comparison of values R_{a}^{T} and $R_{\mathrm{a}}^{\max}$ (Fig. 7) their ratio is well approximated by a linear correlation passing through an origin. This circumstance allows postulating a simple empirical relationship [77]:

$$R_{\mathrm{a}}^{\max} = 2{,}74 \times 10^{5}\, R_{\mathrm{a}}^{T},\ \mu\mathrm{m} \tag{15}$$

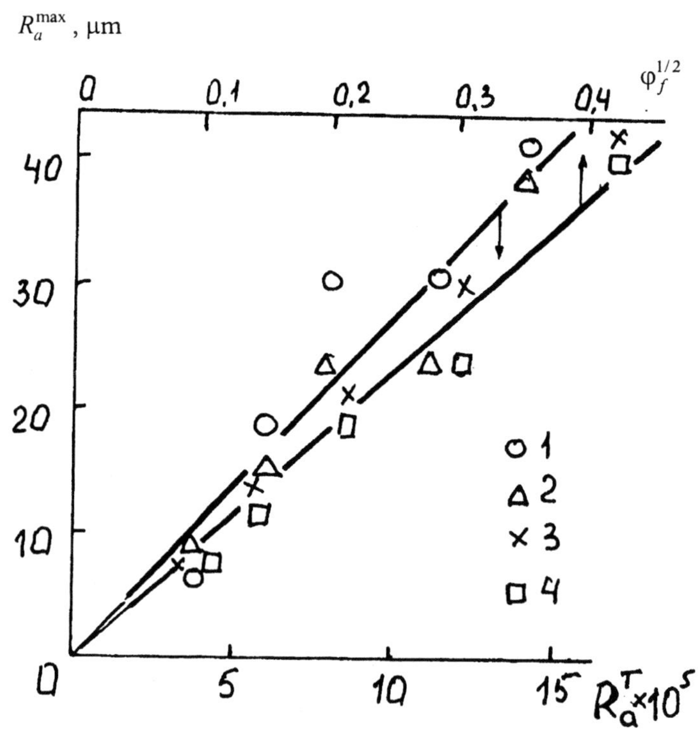

Figure 7. Relationship between radiuses of filler particles aggregates (1,2) and influencing on them of the volumetric contents of filler $\varphi_f^{1/2}$ (3, 4) for PHE–Gr-I (1, 3) and PHE–Gr-II (2, 4). The values R_a^{max} are experimentally determined, values R_a^T are calculated according to (10).

Let us note that in relationship (14) are only two variables ($\varphi_f = c_0$ and η), and the remaining parameters are assumed to be constant. The variation intervals of φ_f and η essentially differ: by changing φ_f 20 times the value η changes only in 1.5 times. Therefore it is possible to assume, that for filled PHE the value R_a^T (or R_a^{max}) depends mainly on φ_f and at $D = 2$ this dependence will look like $R_a^T \sim \varphi_f^{1/2}$. In Fig. 7 the dependence R_a^{max} on $\varphi_f^{1/2}$ is shown, which has the expected linear form and can be approximated as follows: $R_a^{max} = 97\ \varphi_f^{1/2}$, μm [77].

The fractal dimension of a surface of filler particle aggregates d_{sur} is a function of particles aggregation degree, being raised at increase of φ_f. Therefore, $d_{sur}(R_a^{max})$ is possible to get from the following considerations. The simplest variant is [77]:

$$d_{sur} = 2 + c \ln R_a^{max} \quad (16)$$

where c is constant, because the increase of an aggregation degree expressed by increasing R_a^{max} results with d_{sur}.

However, equation (15) has as a minimum two obvious lacks. At first, at minimal values R_a^{max} = 5 μm, we shall obtain identical values d_{sur} for systems PHE–Gr-I and PHE–Gr-II. It does not agree with experimental data, as the processing of graphitic fillers by mixture of acids results in a decrease of fractal dimension of a surface for initial filler particles d_0. This distinction can be taken into account in equation (16) by changing constant 2 in its right part by d_0. Secondly, at minimal value R_a^{max} = 5 μm, $d_{sur} = d_0$. For elimination of the indicated lacks the equation (16) is then transformed [77]:

$$d_{sur} = d_0 + \left(1 - \frac{\ln 5}{\ln R_a^{max}}\right) \tag{17}$$

where R_a^{max} is expressed in μm.

In Fig. 8 it is shown the comparison of values d_{sur}, calculated by equation (17) (full curves) and obtained experimentally [36]. The good correspondence of experimental and calculated values is observed.'

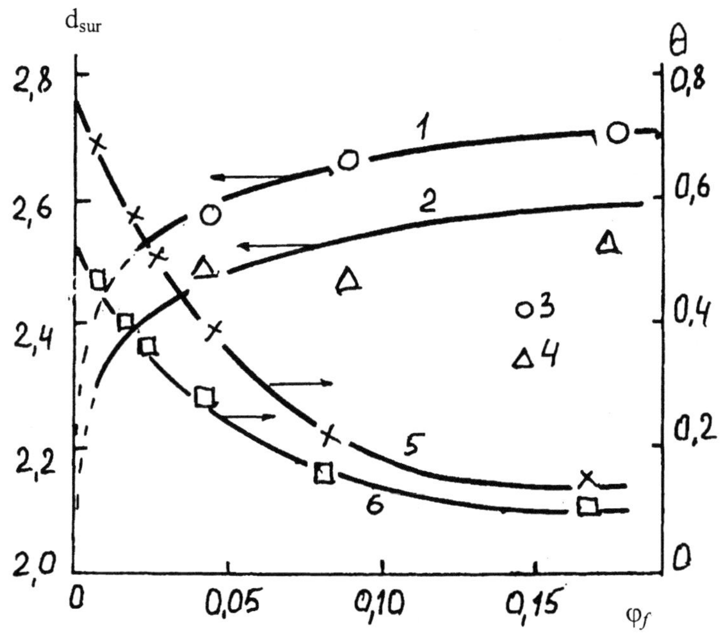

Figure 8. Dependences of fractal dimension of filler particles aggregates surface d_{sur} (1-4) and parameter θ (5, 6) on filler contents φ_f for PHE–Gr-I (1, 3, 5) and PHE–Gr-II (2, 4, 6). 1, 2 calculated according to equation (14), 3, 4 – experimental data [84].

Let us consider the possible influence of the different factors, described by the parameters of relationship (14), on the value of R_a^{max} and, therefore, on filled polymer structures. R_a^{max} will be raised due to the increasing of $c_0 = \varphi_f$ and also by the rising of processing temperature and decreasing of the size of particles (m_0). The increase of the initial filler density at its invariable size will raise m_0 and, therefore, will decrease R_a^{max}. The rising of melt viscosity weakens filler particles aggregation. Obviously, this factor is very important at different polymeric matrix usage. So, the melt viscosities of high density polyethylenes (HDPE), having different molecular weight, can differ 5 times [81]. According to relationship (14), with other parameters being equal, replacement of low-molecular HDPE on high-molecular suppresses the process of filler particles aggregation practically at any increase of φ_f.

The rising of the processing time will lead to an increase of R_a^{max}. But it is necessary to make the following remark about parameter *D*. In [82] it is shown, that during processing of a cluster-cluster aggregation of particles, the aggregation of particles to cluster and disaggregation of particles from a cluster are observed in parallel. $D = 2$ assumes a high level of particles disaggregation and formation of their aggregate [83]. The increase of *D*, due to disaggregation, results in decreasing of exponents in (14) and, therefore, to a reduction of R_a^{max}. In [77] D was adopted equal to 2 for both series of filled PHE. However, as it was above indicated, a small distinction in D for the treated and non-treated filler is observed. The same distinction is not expected for the treated and non-treated graphite. From the data of Fig. 7 we shall drawn the conclusion that R_a^{max} for PHE-Gr-II is lower than the corresponding value for PHE–Gr-I. It assumes higher values *D* for the first system and, therefore, a higher level of filler particles disaggregation [77].

As a model for the description of the formation process of filler particles backbone the generalized model of a diffusion-limited aggregation (DLA) [85] was selected, the authors have created the following equation for fractal (Hausdorff) dimension determination (in our case meant as D_b):

$$D_b = \frac{d^2 + \theta(d_w - 1)}{d + \theta(d_w - 1)} \quad (18)$$

where θ is a parameter whose physical sense will be discussed below, d_W is the dimension of particles trajectories (in our case filler particles) forming the aggregate.

Aharony and Stauffer obtained the following equation for an estimation of d_W [86]:

$$d_W = D_b + 1 \quad (19)$$

As was shown in [86], equation (19) has a high precise approximation for processes of diffusion-limited aggregation, that gives the basis to use it for an estimation of d_W in case of a generalized DLA.

Matsushita. [85] interpreted parameter θ as the n/m ratio (n and m are positive numbers), describing the "chemical" reaction between n random-walked particles with m sites of the aggregate perimeter. Apparently in the considered case, n characterizes the number of filler particles (or their intermediate aggregates), and m the number of perimeter sites of the particles aggregate accessible to "reaction" (not screened) of the subsequent particles, determined by n. It is understandable that the process of aggregation should result in the increase of the number of intermediate aggregates from filler particles, i.e., to decrease of n. In turn, the sites number, accessible to the aggregation of large aggregates perimeter m. This can be described by a following fractal relationship [87]:

$$m \sim R_a^{d_u} \tag{20}$$

where d_u is the fractal dimension of unscreened perimeter [87]:

$$d_u = (D-1) + (d-D)/d_W \tag{21}$$

The small reduction of d_u at a filler volume contents φ_f increases at rising D_b and, therefore, d_W (equation (19)) in equation (21) will be compensated by the strong increase of R_a in the filler particles aggregation at increasing φ_f [77]. Thus, the process of filler particles aggregation results in a simultaneous decrease of *n* and increase of *m* that determines a of reduction θ. This circumstance allows using θ as a measure of filler particles aggregation degree in filled polymers. In Fig. 9 the dependence of θ, calculated according to equation (18), on φ_f for filled PHE is presented. As it was expected, there is a reduction of θ at increasing φ_f, i.e., a growth of filler particles aggregation degree at rise of its contents is observed. Let us note that at $\varphi_f \approx 0{,}17$ the achievement of θ of an asymptotic branch is observed. The marked values of φ_f correspond to the formation of a continuous percolation backbone of filler particles [65].

In [85] is shown that the reduction of θ defines an increase of fractal dimension for the formed aggregates. In Fig. 9 the dependence $D_b(\theta)$ for filled PHE is shown. The expected results are obtained. An increase of filler particles aggregation degree characterized by the parameter θ reduction, results in a raise of fractal dimension, D_b of the filler particles backbone. In the same figure, the dependences of the polymer matrix fractal dimension d_f, determined according to equation (9), on θ are shown. The comparison of a relationship $D_b(\theta)$ and $d_f(\theta)$ allows to obtain some interesting conclusions. At first, the greatest possible degree of a filler particles aggregation (θ = 0) will be realized under condition $D_b = d_f$. At second, as follows from equation (18) and condition θ = (*n*/*m*) > 0, the value D_b can not exceed d_f, i.e., $D_b \le d_f$. These two circumstances visually demonstrates that in filled polymers are observed not only a filler influence on the polymer matrix structure [1], but also the opposite effect, i.e., a polymer matrix structure changed during filling [73], is influenced, as a minimum, by the filler particles aggregation degree. And, in third, from the equation (18) at θ = 0 the mentioned above condition follows:

$$D_b = d_f = d \tag{22}$$

which one entails very important consequences. This condition assumes, that the formation of a filler particles backbone should proceed not in Euclidean, but in fractal space, whose dimension is defined by d_f ($d_f \leq 2,88$ [78]). Let us note that equation (18) is correct for $d > 1$ including for non-integer values d [85]. Or else, the formation of a filler particles backbone is considered as proceeding on a fractal substratum [88] or as formation of fractal on a fractal lattice at computer simulation [89, 90].

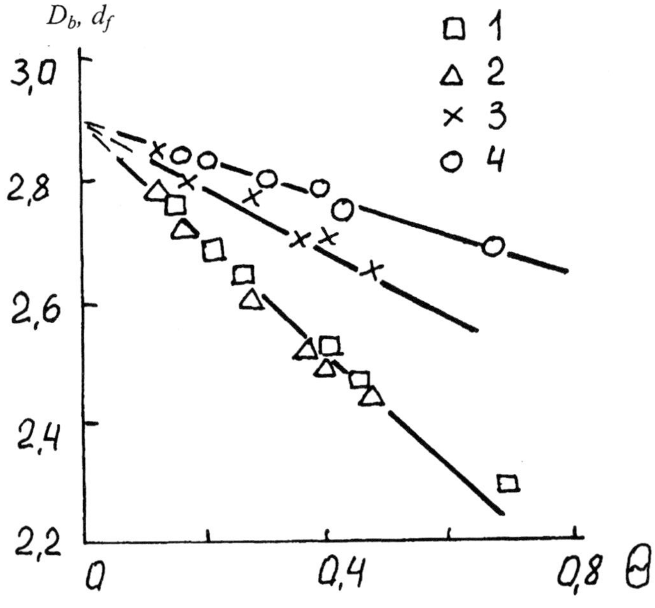

Figure 9. Dependences of fractal dimensions of filler particles frame D_b (1,2) and polymer matrix d_f (3,4) on the value of parameter θ for PHE–Gr-I (1,3) and PHE–Gr-II (2,4).

At last, we should consider the practical consequences which follow from the above results. One of the possible ways for the control of a θ value, as indicated in equation (18), is the variation of particle trajectories dimension, d_W. So, at fixed values, $D_b = 2.7$ and $d = 3$ the change d_W from 4 to 1.2 results to increase θ from 0.18 to 2.65. In practice the condition of fixation D_b is impracticable and the decrease of d_W, i.e. the transition from trajectories of random walks of particles to quasi-linear results in growth d_f [91]. In turn, this defines a reduction of θ, i.e. raising of filler particles aggregation (Fig. 9). In laboratory, the selection of conditions to influence d_W is possible by changing of the processing method of the filled polymer. So, molding under pressure in essence arises predominantly trajectories of random walk of particles, and at extrusion, predominantly trajectories approach to linear ($d_W \rightarrow 1$). The last effect results in increase of d_f for extruded polymers [92], assuming also data of computer simulation [91]. Therefore, for extruded polymers it is necessary to expect a decrease of θ.

DISTRIBUTION OF THE FILLER PARTICLES AGGREGATION SIZES

The filler aggregation can be quantitatively connected to distribution of particle aggregates [93]. Within the framework of the model of an irreversible aggregation, the cluster-cluster is obtained from some theoretical treatments of such distribution [82,94,95], which can be utilized for the description of a filler particle aggregation process. So, the treatment of an aggregation of a cluster-cluster takes into account the existence of real processes of an aggregation with connection of a particle to a cluster [82,95]. In a system "polymer melt–filler particles" the particle aggregates are in random environment influencing the processes of aggregation and disaggregation and this circumstance can be expressed by the stochastic equation [82]:

$$\dot{N} = \lambda N^{a} - N^{b} + \xi_t N^{a} \tag{23}$$

where N is the number of particles in an aggregate, $\dot{N}$ is the aggregation rate ($\dot{N} = dN/dt$), a and b are the indexes describing the processes of aggregation and disaggregation, respectively ($a < b$), $\xi_t = C_t/m$, where C_t is the stochastic contribution to the intensity of the aggregation process due to the influence of the environment, $\langle C \rangle$ is its average value, and m is the coefficient describing the disaggregation process. The quantity λ is defined as follows [95]:

$$\lambda = \langle c \rangle / m \tag{24}$$

The authors [96] have assumed that the characteristic times of random actions on the process of fractal aggregation of particles are much lower than the characteristic times of these particles aggregation and, therefore, ξ_t can be represented as a white noise of intensity. $\langle \xi_t \rangle^2 = \sigma^2$.

The index a, in the case of a cluster-cluster aggregation, is connected with the fractal dimension D of a filler particle aggregate by the following equation [95]:

$$a = \frac{2D - d}{D} \tag{25}$$

Equation (22) allows to obtain an expression for the probability density $P_s(N)$, whose stationary solution is [95]:

$$P_s(N) = AN^{-a} \exp\left\{ 2\lambda N^{1-a} \left[1 - (1-a) N^{b-a} / \lambda (b + 1 - 2a) \right] / (1-a)\sigma^2 \right\} \tag{26}$$

for $a \neq 1$, where A is a normalizing constant.

As the initial assumption, the authors [96] have accepted $D = 2$, taking into account the arbitrariness of the choice of A. Therefore, the probability density $P_s(N)$ can be replaced by $P_s(D_p)$, where D_p is the diameter of an aggregate of filler particles.

Since, in equation (25), the value λ does not affect the distribution $P_s(N)$ or $P_s(D_p)$, it assumes three main parameters which influence the shape of the distribution $P_s(D_p)$: a, b and σ^2. Each of these parameters reflects a particular feature of an aggregation process. The value of a is actually determined by the structure of particle aggregates or, more precisely, by the spatial distribution of particles in the aggregates, which directly follows from equation (25) at $d = 3$. The value of b characterizes the type and intensity of the processes of disaggregation (a possible separation of a particle from a cluster during its formation). The parameter σ^2 characterizes the stochastic contribution connected with the degree of aggregates mobility and we can assume, with a sufficient high degree of probability, that it depends on some characteristics of the system, namely the filler content, viscosity of the polymer melt, sizes of the initial filler particles, and others. The experimental curves $P_s(D_p)$ have a monotonically descending shape, which assumes high (above unity) values of σ^2, i.e., a large mobility caused by the forced high speed of displacement of the composite melt in the screw extruder [96].

Let us consider general aspects of three indicated factors influence on aggregation processes. The analysis of a relationship $P_s(D_p)$ with alternative variation only one out of three parameters, leaving the remaining two fixed has shown, that are in practice the decrease of a filler particle aggregation degree, i.e., decreasing of number and sizes of particles aggregates. The analysis of relationships $P_s(D_p)$ at variable fractal dimension D, variable σ^2 and for a variation b has shown:

(a) at small sizes of aggregates the value of D does not affect their distribution, but with their growth, an increase in D raises the fraction of large aggregates. Since, in particle, a growth in D increases the aggregates compactness, it is obvious that the formation of "looser" particles aggregates is preferable;
(b) an increase in σ^2, i.e., in the stochastic contribution to the aggregation intensity leads to widening of the particle distribution and raises the fraction of large aggregates;
(c) the factor b exerts the strongest influence on the particle aggregation processes. For $b = 1$ (which corresponds to the existence of a channel of decay for each cluster bond), a rather wide distribution is obtained. For $b = 0{,}6$ (which means fixation of large aggregates) is especially great. If the number of decay channels exceeds unity, the distribution is almost monodisperse.

By comparison of the experimental and calculated by equation (26) curves, the authors [95] have estimated the most probable values of D, σ^2 and b for each of the six examined composites. Based on these parameters, the probability distributions for the aggregate sizes were calculated according to equation (26) and then compared with the experimental data (Fig. 10). The comparison shows that the model of irreversible aggregation, within the framework of which equation (26) was obtained, exactly describes the size distribution of the filler particle aggregates formed in real composites.

Returning to the data of table 3, it should be noted that the value of D for the studied composites varies insignificantly. At small values of φ_f, the stochastic contribution to the intensity of the process for the PHE–Gr-II is somewhat lower than for similar PHE–Gr-I composites, but as the value of φ_f approaches 0,176, this difference fades away. The greatest distinction between the PHE–Gr composites with treated and non-treated fillers is observed for the index *b*. At small values of φ_f, the treated filler shows a much greater degree of disaggregation than the non-treated one; whereas at $\varphi_f \approx 0,176$, the values of *b* for both series of PHE–Gr composites are practically equal. This is reflected in the macroscopic properties of the composites [96].

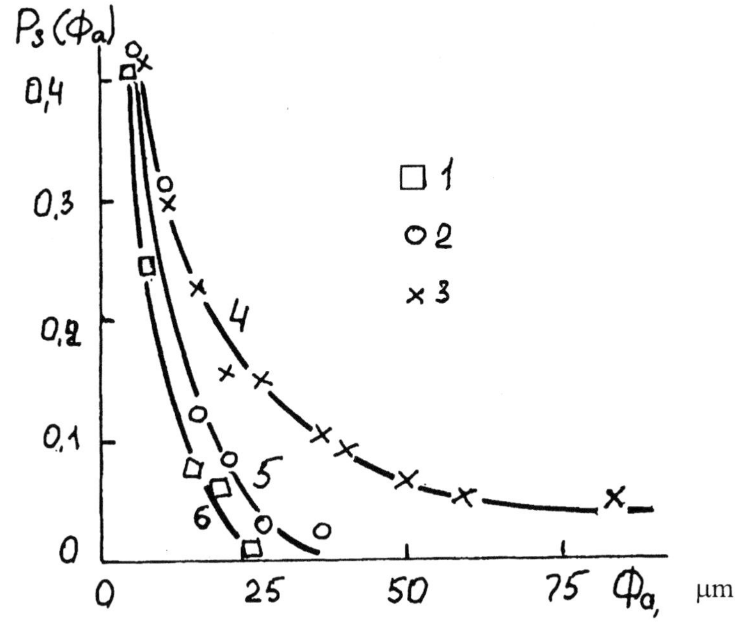

Figure 10. Comparison of theoretical (1-3) and experimental (4-6) distribution curves $P_s(\Phi_a)$ for PHE–Gr-II with $\varphi_f = 0,044$ (1,4), 0,088 (2,5) and 0,176 (3,6) [96].

The value of $D \approx 2$ obtained in this study for particle aggregates indicates that they have a rather loose structure. As is known [13], the density ρ of a fractal aggregate is determined as

$$\rho \sim R_a^{D-d} \tag{27}$$

where radius of the aggregate, R_a is connected with the number of its particles, *N*, by the fractal relationship (13).

The relationships (13) and (27) allow the following estimation. If an aggregate of filler particles consists of $N = 100$ particles, its density will be an order of magnitude smaller than that of a compact aggregate with the same number of particles, since their dimensions are $D = 2$ and $d = 3$, respectively. Therefore, the breakdown of the large aggregates of filler particles described in [97] was to be expected.

Therefore, the application of the fractal analysis and models of an irreversible aggregation allows obtaining in essence new and physically correct representations about filled polymers structure.

Dimension of a Filler Aggregates Surface

There is a number of methods for the estimation of fractal dimension of a filler particle aggregates surface characterized by value of d_{sur}. The experimental method for the estimation $d_{sur}\left(d^{e}_{sur}\right)$ is considered below. Besides the values $d_{sur}\left(d^{M}_{sur}\right)$ can be calculated on the equation (10) under condition $\alpha = f$ and then $d^{M}_{sur} = 2 + f$, and also according to (16), which will be named later as d^{a}_{sur}.

In [98] one more method of an estimation of $d_{sur}(d^{k}_{sur}) = D_1$ is presented within the framework of a multifractal formalism. According to this method, the dimension of multifractal with an arbitrary index q (q is an integer) D_q is connected to its Hausdorff dimension D_0 (at $q = 0$) so:

$$D_q = D_0 - 9q\varepsilon^2/64 \tag{28}$$

Where ε is determined as follows [98]:

$$\varepsilon = 4 - d \tag{29}$$

Equation (27) is obtained for a case of self-avoiding random walks which correspond to a walk of filler particles at their aggregation in a polymer melt during processing of filled polymers specimens [99].

In Fig. 11 the dependences D_b and d^{M}_{sur} on the contents of a filler φ_f for a system PHE–Gr-I are shown. As it is possible to see, the dependences $D_b(\varphi_f)$ and $d^{M}_{sur}(\varphi_f)$ with an approximately constant difference between these dimensions, equal to ~ 0.11, is observed. Such change, shown in Fig. 11 and according to equation (28), the indicated difference is equal to 0.141. It confirms that d_{sur} is information dimension of a multifractal structure of filler particles (aggregates of particles) backbone [99].

The indicated treatment assumes that the raising of filler particles aggregation results to increase D_b [73] and should result also to increase d_{sur}. In Fig. 12 the dependence d_{sur}, determined by the four above-mentioned methods, on an aggregation parameter θ^{-1} is shown. As demonstrate data on Fig. 12, the value d_{sur} increases at raising of filler particles aggregation, i.e., increase θ^{-1} [99].

Influence of a Filler on Polymer Matrix Structure

The changes at formation of the structure of filler located in the polymer matrix are above described. In turn, the incorporation of filler to a polymer results in change of its structure. The analysis of this influence with the use of fractal analysis methods and cluster model of polymers amorphous state structure is described below.

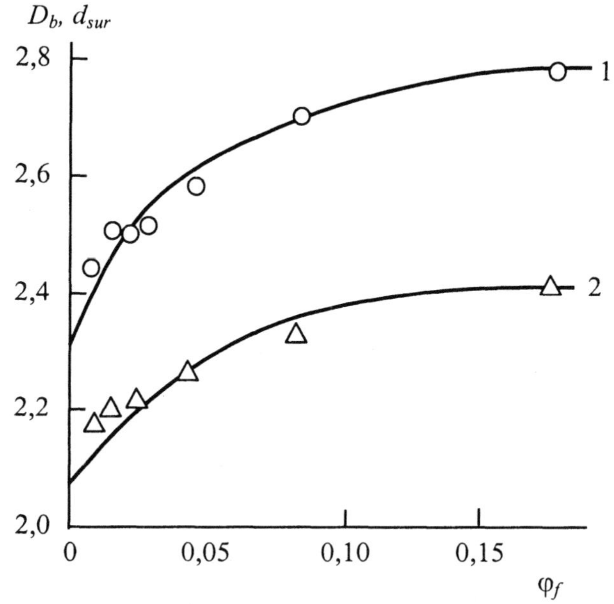

Figure 11. Dependence of the fractal dimensions of a filler particles frame D_b (1) and a filler particle aggregates surface d_{sur} (2) on volumetric contents of filler φ_f for PHE–Gr-II [99].

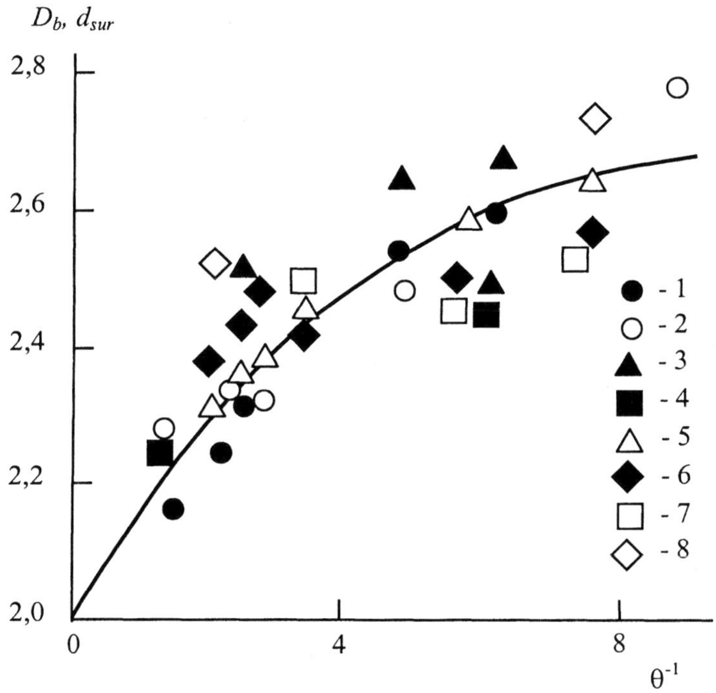

Figure 12. Dependence of fractal dimensions of a filler particles aggregate surface d_{sur}^{k} (1, 5), d_{sur}^{M} (2, 6), d_{sur}^{e} (3, 7) and D_l (4, 8) on aggregation parameter θ^{-1} for PHE–Gr-I (1-4) and PHE–Gr-II (5-8) [99].

DESCRIPTION OF POLYMER MATRIX STRUCTURE MODIFICATION

The structure of a polymer matrix can be characterized by its fractal dimension d_f. A relation between dimension D_b and d_f for filled PHE is approximated well enough by a straight line (Fig. 6a). Let us consider physical sense of change ("disturbance") of a polymer matrix structure, which is not necessarily connected to the incorporation of filler. Quantitatively and qualitatively (physically), such "disturbance" is described within the framework of a cluster model of polymers amorphous state structure [100,101]. In this model the structure is considered as a set of the local order domains (clusters), submersed in a loose-packed matrix. In turn, the cluster represents a set of several collinear highly-packed segments of different macromolecules (amorphous analog of a crystallite with the extended chains). A relative fraction of clusters φ_{cl} is an order parameter of structure in strict physical sense of this term [74,102]. The values d_f and φ_{cl} are connected by a following relationship [74]:

$$d_f = 3 - 5{,}98 \times 10^{-10} \left(\frac{\varphi_{cl}}{C_\infty S} \right)^{1/2} \tag{30}$$

where C_∞ is the characteristic ratio, which is a parameter of a chain statistical flexibility [103], S is cross-sectional area of a macromolecule, m^2.

Equation (29) assumes that the increase of d_f at rising of the filler volume content φ_f means a reduction of a relative fraction of clusters φ_{cl}, i.e., decreasing of the degree of the local order of a polymer matrix structure [73,104]. Besides a raising d_f means an increase of the spacing interval between clusters or, otherwise, increase of a structure automodelity factor Λ_i, which is equal [25]:

$$\Lambda_i = D_f = \frac{2(1-\nu)}{(1-2\nu)} \tag{31}$$

where D_f is the dimension of regions of extra energy localization.

By virtue of that $D_f \approx C_\infty$ [25], raise D_f means change of the chain statistical flexibility. Besides D_f characterizes the distribution of sizes of a fluctuation free volume microholes [25], which also changes at filler incorporation [105]. Therefore, the term "disturbance" of structures describes a wide spectrum of changes at molecular, topological and supramolecular levels of structure. In Fig. 13 the dependences $\varphi_{cl}(\varphi_f)$ are shown, from which the above mentioned decrease of φ_{cl} follows at increase φ_f. The greatest effect is reached at rather small values of φ_f (up to ~ 0.10) with the subsequent asymptotic change of the function $\varphi_{cl}(\varphi_f)$ [73].

As shown earlier, the interaction degree of two main components of a filled polymer can be expressed by the parameter Δd_k. In turn, the relative degree of "disturbance" of a polymer matrix structure $\Delta\varphi_{cl}$ can be estimated by a decrease of φ_{cl} of filled polymer in comparison with previous [73]:

$$\Delta\varphi_{cl} = \varphi_{cli} - \varphi_{cli+1} \quad (32)$$

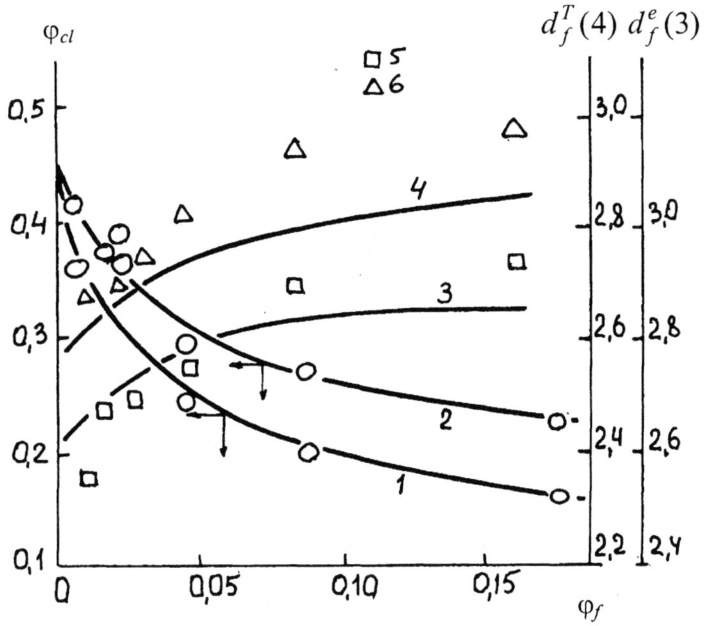

Figure 13. The influence of a filler contents φ_f on the relative fraction of clusters φ_{cl} (1, 2) and fractal dimension of a polymer matrix d_f (3-6) for PHE–Gr-I (1, 3, 5) and PHE–Gr-II (2, 4, 6). 3, 4 – experimental data, 5, 6 – calculation according to equation (32) [109].

The dependence $\Delta\varphi_{cl}(\Delta d_k)$ for filled PHE has appeared linear and is extrapolated to $\Delta\varphi_{cl} = 0$ at $\Delta d_k = 0$ [73]. This confirms a postulate that two fractals (multifractals) in structure of filled polymer are affected against each other and that the invariance of the polymer matrix structure can be reached only in case of absence of an interaction between filler and polymer, i.e., independence of the two indicated fractals [73].

As it is known [88], the fractal dimension of an object is a function of the space dimensions in which it is formed. In computer simulation this situation is considered as the behavior of fractals in fractal (instead of Euclidean) lattices [89,90]. The elementary model of polymeric macromolecular coil in the good solvent is the self-avoiding random walk, for which it is possible to note [89]:

$$R_g \sim N^{\nu_F} \quad (33)$$

where R_g is a gyration radius of coil, N is a polymerization degree, ν_F is a Flory exponent.

In a fractal lattice with dimension D_{lat} the value of ν_F can be estimated from the simple formula [89]:

$$\nu_F = \frac{3}{2 + D_{lat}} \tag{34}$$

Assuming $D_{lat} = D_b$ (as it was mentioned above, we consider that the polymer matrix structure is formed not in an Euclidean three-dimensional space, but in a fractal space with dimension D_b [84]), it is possible to calculate ν_F for the studies filled PHE and then the fractal dimension of a macromolecular coil D_{MC} from the following relationship [106]:

$$D_{MC} = \nu_F^{-1} \tag{35}$$

The fractal dimension of the polymer in the condensed state, i.e., d_f, for a linear polymer with spectral dimension of a chain $d_s = 1$ [107] is possible to obtain from the equation [108]:

$$D_f = 1{,}5\ D_{MC} \tag{36}$$

The comparison of the experimental and calculated with equations (34) and (36) values of the fractal dimension of structure for a polymer matrix of filled PHE have shown, that the full qualitative identity of the dependences $d_f(\varphi_f)$ is observed. However, quantitative correspondence is much worse (the divergence exceeds 15 %). It is possible to improve this correspondence empirically, by replacing the factor 3 in equation (34) by 2.5. In this case the excellent correspondence between above-mentioned values of d_f is obtained (the divergence is less than 1 %). Nevertheless, the applicability of a factor 2.5 in equation (34) requires a theoretical proof.

The simplest proof can be the incorporation of 2.5 factor to equation (34) from the following boundary condition. The values D_b and d_f in three-dimensional Euclidean space ($d = 3$) can not be more than d by definition [57]. While substituting these limiting values $D_b = 3$ and $d_f = 3$ with account for relationship (36) to the equation (34), we shall use 2.5 instead of 3 in a denominator of the right member of the indicated equation.

For an estimation of ν_F on fractal lattices we utilized the following and more precise [89, 90] formula:

$$\nu_F = \frac{1}{D_{lat}} \frac{4d_e - d_s}{2 + 2d_e - d_s}, \tag{37}$$

where d_e is a chemical dimension or a dimension of "spreading", which characterizes the distance between two points of a fractal object not as geometrical spacing interval (straight line connecting these two points), but as a "chemical distance", i.e., the shortest particles of an object between these two points [89].

To estimate d_e we can use the simplest variant based on the approximation of Flory and presented in [110]. For dimension $4/3 < d < 4$, it is possible to calculate the value of parameter Z:

$$Z = \frac{4 + 3D_b}{8} \tag{38}$$

and then to determine d_e as follows [110]:

$$d_e = \frac{D_b}{Z} \tag{39}$$

The spectral dimension d_s is determined from the Alexander – Orbach equation [107]:

$$D_s = 2D_b/d_W \tag{40}$$

where the dimension d_W, in turn, is calculated according to an approximation of Aharony – Stauffer (equation (19)).

In Fig. 13 the comparison of experimental d_f^e and theoretical d_f^T values, where the theoretical magnitudes d_f are calculated by the above-indicated way with the use of equation (37), is shown. In that case there is not only a good qualitative, but also a good quantitative correspondence (maximal divergence of values d_f^e and d_f^T is lower than 6 %). Let us note that equation (37) is an approximation and its check on Sierpinski gaskets has shown that the values ν_F, obtained according to this equation, diverged with the exact values of this parameter ~ 3,5-7,5 % [89]. This error corresponds with the results presented in [109].

The relevant check of calculation of ν_F under any scheme is the constancy of product $D_{lat}\nu_F = D_b\nu_F$. As shown in [111], the mass of fractal M within the limits of mean square spacing interval $\left\langle R_g^2 \right\rangle^{1/2}$ can be recorded as:

$$M \sim \left\langle R_g^2 \right\rangle^{D_b/2} \sim N^{D_b\nu_F}. \tag{41}$$

At distortion (change of dimension) of lattice, $\left\langle R_g^2 \right\rangle$ changes, but M and N remain invariable, since they are only a set of sites. The constancy of M and N gives the condition obtained from (40):

$$D_b\nu_F = \text{const}. \tag{42}$$

In [109] the dependence ($D_b\nu_F$) (φ_f), to check correctness of calculations of ν_F is estimated according to equation (37), is obtained. It was shown that the condition $D_b\nu_F$ = const is fulfilled with good exactness, though some (lower than 3 %) increase of this product is observed when φ_f is raised. Taking into account the above approximations at calculations, it is necessary to admit such an error to be acceptable.

A POLYMER MATRIX STRUCTURE AS A THERMAL CLUSTER

It was earlier shown [74,102], that the structure of amorphous polymers can be considered a percolation system with critical temperature T_{cr}, which is the glass transition temperature T_g. The value φ_{cl} in this case is connected to T_g by a relationship [74]:

$$\varphi_{cl} \approx 0{,}03\ (T_g - T)^{0{,}55} \tag{43}$$

where T is the testing temperature.

It is to note that critical indexes of the order parameter β are rather close to classic percolation indexes (equal to 0.3-0.4) [74,102], but all differ from them on an absolute value. The reason of the indicated difference is that the percolation cluster represents only a geometrical arrangement, which is a too simplified model for real amorphous polymers having a thermodynamically non-equilibrium structure. Therefore the structure of the indicated polymers is under the influence of thermal interactions considered as molecular mobility of segments, forming a percolation system. Let us remind that the cluster structure is postulated as a thermofluctuation system [100]. Therefore, it is correct to simulate amorphous polymers structure by a thermal cluster, i.e., cluster, whose equilibrium configuration is determined by both geometrical and thermal interactions [113]. Besides the formation of a cluster is studied not as a scale of relative concentration, but on a scale of relative temperatures. In this case the order of the polymer structure φ_{cl} is described by a relationship [113]:

$$\varphi_{cl} = \left(\frac{T_g - T}{T_\beta} \right)^{\beta_T} \tag{44}$$

where an order parameter index β_T is not necessarily equal to the corresponding critical index β in geometrical percolation models.

The cited reasons give the basis for the study of a polymer matrix structure of filled polymers within the framework of a thermal cluster model [27]. In [65] was shown that the critical indexes universality of a percolation system is directly connected to fractal dimension of this system. The self-similarity of a percolation system assumes the existence of a number of subsets with order n (n = 1, 2, 4, ...), which in case of a filled polymer structure are identified as follows [73]. The percolation cluster backbone or cluster network of a matrix physical entanglements. The second subset (n = 2) is the loose-packed matrix, by which is surrounded a cluster network. The third subset (n = 4) is the filler particles backbone, that is specific to filled polymers. In such treatment the critical indexes of percolation cluster β_p, ν_p and t_p are given by (in a three-dimensional Euclidean space) [65]:

$$\beta_p = 1/d_f \tag{45}$$

$$\nu_p = 2/d_f \tag{46}$$

$$t_p = 4/d_f \tag{47}$$

Thus, the values β_p, ν_p and t_p are boundary magnitudes for β_T, indicating that the structural component of a filled polymer defines its behavior. At $\beta_T = \beta_p$ such component is a cluster or, more precisely, a backbone of percolation cluster, identified with a cluster network. At $\beta_p < \beta_T < \nu_p$ the behavior of a filled polymer is defined by the common influence of a cluster and loose-packed matrix. At $\beta_T = \nu_p$ the defining structural component will be loose-packed matrix, at $\beta_T = t_p$ backbone of particles (aggregates of particles) of filler, and at $\nu_p < \beta_T < t_p$ the common influence of two structural components will be observed.

The average value d_f, for filled PHE ~ 2.70 [73], can be obtained from equations (45)-(47), $\beta_p = 0.37$, $\nu_p = 0.74$ and $t_p = 1.48$. Then, by using values of φ_{cl} (see Fig. 11), it is possible, according to equation (44), to calculate β_T for both series of a filled PHE. The dependence of β_T with the volume content of filler φ_f is shown in Fig. 14, from which one follows that at increase φ_f in a narrow interval ($\varphi_f \leq 0.05$) the fast growth of β_T from ~ 0.37 for initial matrix polymer up to ~ 0.82-0.93 for composites with $\varphi_f = 0.044$ is observed. Furthermore, this growth is continued, but much more slowly. Besides in Fig. 14 the shaped horizontal lines show the boundary magnitudes β_p and ν_p for β_T. It is possible to see that the cluster network influences the behavior of a composite only in the case of small φ_f, and for large φ_f the behavior of a composite is defined by the common influence of the filler particles backbone and a loose-packed matrix. This observation has fundamental importance in the sense that it assumes the dependence of properties for the majority of polymer composites (at $\varphi_f > 0.05$) from the structural state of a loose-packed matrix. In [9,11] was shown that the structural state indicated each component can be described by the dimension of regions of extra energy localization D_f. And last, from the data of Fig. 14 it follows that the treatment of a filler surface (reduction of d_{sur}, see Fig. 8) weakens its influence on the behavior of specimens PHE-Gr.

In [114] it was shown that β_T is a function of the molecular mobility degree characterized by the fractal dimension of a chain portion between entanglements D_{ch}. At $D_{ch} = 1$ the indicated portion completely extends between entanglements nodes, its molecular mobility is suppressed and $\beta_T = \beta_p$. For the maximal mobility $D_{ch} = 2$ and in this case $\beta_T = t_p$ the value D_{ch} can be calculated with the help of the equation

$$\frac{2}{\varphi_{cl}} = C_\infty^{D_{ch}}. \tag{48}$$

The dependence $\beta_T(D_{ch})$ for a filled PHE is shown in Fig. 14. The linear increase β_T at raising D_{ch} (increase of molecular mobility) is observed. However, as against unreinforced polymers, the limiting values D_{ch}, mentioned above, are not reached at β_p and t_p. At $\beta_T = \beta_p$, i.e., in case of a percolation cluster, the chains have a certain degree of mobility ($D_{ch} \approx 1,1$). It assumes that the filler loosens a polymer matrix (probably an interphase) even at the greatest possible density of local packing [1]. At $\beta_T = t_p = 1.48$, $D_{ch} \approx 1.55$, i.e., the chain does not reach the greatest possible degree of mobility. This is probably due to the restriction of chains mobility by the filler surface. Thus, the main difference of the initial polymer and the corresponding matrix of a polymer composite is the smaller possible variation D_{ch} for last (D_{ch} = 1.10-1.55), that is caused by the filler influence on a polymer matrix structure [1,65,73].

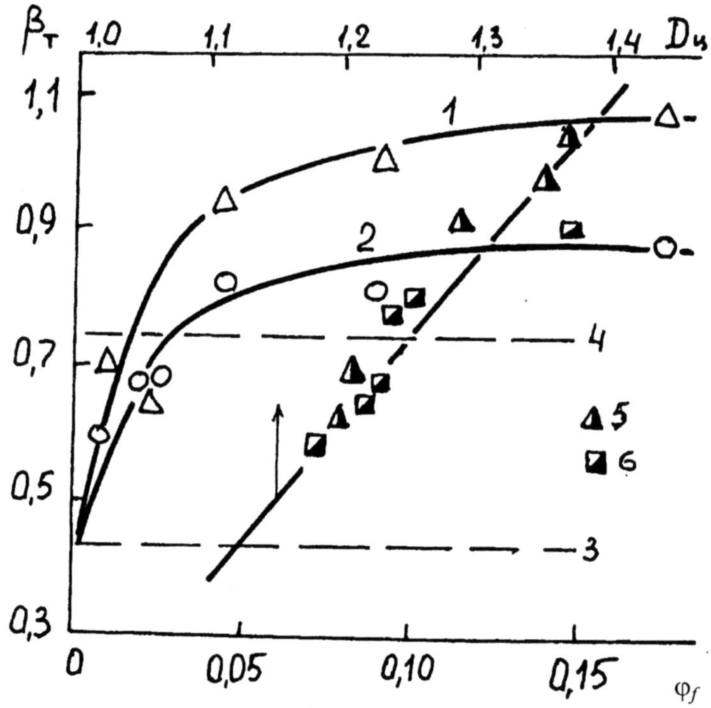

Figure 14. Dependence of critical order parameter β_T of a thermal cluster on volumetric contents of filler φ_f (1, 2) and on fractal dimension of a chain portion between entanglements D_{ch} (5, 6) for PHE–Gr-I (1, 5) and PHE–Gr-II (2, 6). The broken horizontal lines give the values β_p (3) and ν_p (4).

As it was previously indicated, the filler particles (aggregates of particles) backbone is a fractal with dimension D_b. The character of relationships $D_b(\varphi_f)$ and $\varphi_{cl}(\varphi_f)$ [73] assumes a definite relation between parameters φ_{cl} and D_b. As it was expected, the increase of D_b results in a raise of a polymer matrix structure expressed by a decrease in φ_{cl}. At the greatest possible value $D_b = 3$, the local order in a polymer matrix structure is absent ($\varphi_{cl} = 0$). The greatest possible degree of the local order can be calculated according to equation (39) at $\beta_T = \beta_p = 0.37$ and is 0.57. An extrapolation of the plots $\varphi_{cl}(D_b)$ to this value gives $D_b \approx 2.26$ for a system PHE–Gr-II and $D_b \approx 2.0$ for a system PHE–Gr-I. As D_b characterizes the degree of a filler particles aggregation [73], the influence of the filler particles backbone on a polymer matrix structure (decrease of φ_{cl}) will be realized at any aggregation degree distinct from zero for a filler with a non-treated surface and only since some finite aggregation degree for a filler with treated surface [73].

FRACTAL ANALYSIS OF AN INTERPHASE LAYER

The region of the interphase layer between polymer and filler in a filled polymer structure is considered as the result of interaction of two fractals–surface of filler particles and polymer matrix [73]. Generally, this assumption can be considered within the framework of a multifractal formalism.

For the majority of filled polymers the rigidity of a filler considerably exceeds the corresponding parameter for polymers [5] and on the interphase with a filler the polymer layer will be considered close to a rigid elastic filler [4,115,116]. Such approach to an interphase layer will be reviewed below.

As it is known [117], for the interaction of two fractal objects there is a unique linear scale l, determining the spacing interval of the interpenetration of these objects. It is assumed [118] that in filled polymers there is an intrusion of a filler in a polymer matrix and then $l = l_{in}$, where l_{in} is the thickness of the interphase layer. In this case it is possible to record [117]:

$$\left(l_{in}/h\right) \sim \left(R_a/h\right)^{2(d-d_{sur}/d} \tag{49}$$

where h is the lower linear scale of fractal behavior and R_a is the radius of a filler particle.

At first we shall analyze the variation when h is constant and equal to unity. Furthermore, as a measurement of the extension (spreading) of the interphase layer we shall consider its relative thickness (l_{in}/R_a). This is more convenient because of the proportionality sign in relationship (49). The comparison of the values, calculated according to this relationship $(l_{in}/R_a)^T$ and values $(l_{in}/R_a)^e$, obtained during measurement of corresponding characteristics on electron micrographs is shown, There is a good linear relation passing through origin. However, data for each filled polymer give straight lines with a distinct slope [118]. The observed error is due to objective reasons: d_{sur} is a statistical property [66], whereas for calculations we have used its average value [77].

It is apparent that one of the possible causes of obtaining several straight lines, according to relationship (49), is the condition, utilized at their plotting, $h = l =$ const. As it was marked above, h is the lower linear scale of fractal behavior, which for filler particles surface (in particular, graphite) [119] and a polymer matrix [20] is equal approximately to 1 nm (more precisely, 0.3-1.6 nm). It was shown that the incorporation of a disperse filler to a polymer matrix results in "disturbance" of its structure. On the molecular level this effect appears in an increase of polymer characteristic ratio, C_∞ and, therefore, length of a statistical segment l_{st}, estimated from the equation [120]:

$$l_{st} = l_0 C_\infty \tag{50}$$

where l_0 is the length of skeletal bond of the main chain.

In [57] it was shown that the lower limit of fractal behavior is determined by the finite size of structural elements. Apparently, the polymer matrix structure also renders influence on the sizes of the interphase layer, which can be reflected by the incorporation to relationship (49) variable h, equal to l_{st}, as a statistical segment length is the minimum size for describing properties of a polymer chain as a whole. In Fig. 15 the relation of parameters $(l_{in}/R_a)^e$ and

$(l_{in}/R_a)^T\ l_{st}^{2(d-d_{sur})/d}$ is shown. In this case one straight line, describing the relation between theoretical and experimental estimations of an interphase layer for a relative thickness is obtained confirming that it is influenced by the characteristics of both, the filler particles surface and the polymer matrix.

Within the framework of the mechanics of continua [65] the value l_{in} is possible to be expressed as

$$l_{in} = 2R_a\left[\left(\frac{\rho_p}{\varphi_f}\right)^{1/3} - 1\right] \tag{51}$$

where ρ_p is the density of lattice packing, equal to 0.74 [65].

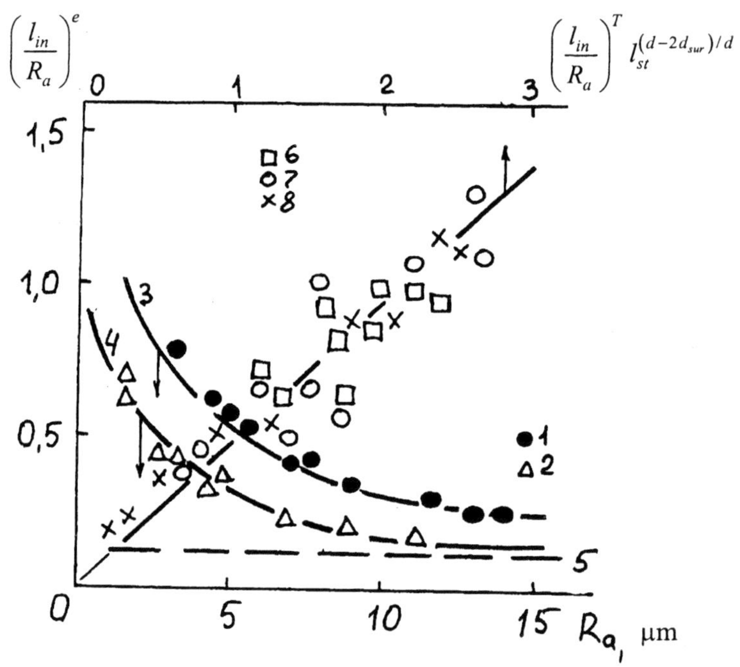

Figure 15. Dependence of the relative thickness of interphase layer l_{in}/R_a on a filler particles radius R_a (1-5) and parameter $\left(l_{in}/R_a\right)l_{st}^{2(d-d_{sur})/d}$ (6-8) for PHE–Gr-I (1,3,6,7) and PHE–Gr-II (2,4,8). 1, 2–experimental data, 3, 4–theoretical data, 5–calculation according to equation (45). $\varphi_f = 0.044$ (7), $\varphi_f = 0.176$ (1-6,8) [118].

From equation (51) it is calculated that at a constant ρ_p and φ_f the interphase layer relative thickness (l_{in}/R_a) is also constant. This is not in agreement with experimental data. In Fig. 15 the dependences (l_{in}/R_a) on R_a for PHE–Gr-I and PHE–Gr-II at $\varphi_f = 0.176$ are shown, where the theoretical estimations are displaced in vertical direction on arbitrary values to fit the experimental dependence. From these plots it follows that the value of the interphase layer relative thickness (l_{in}/R_a) is not constant for a fixed φ_f, and decreases with increase of particles radius R_a. The mechanics of continua [65] does not describe such effect, whereas the fractal model makes it correctly with allowance for both value R_a, and state of filler particles surface (different curves for specimens PHE–Gr-I and PHE–Gr-II at same value φ_f). As it is known [77], the processing of graphite particles results in decreasing of its fractal dimension. It is interesting, as the interphase layer relative thickness in a mechanics of continua treatment (shaped line in Fig. 15) in essence is the lowest limit for the corresponding parameter in case of a fractal model achievable at large R_a. In other words, the increase of values for d_{sur} determines rising of an interphase layer thickness in filled polymers, that follows also from a comparison of curves for PHE-Gr-I and PHE-Gr-II in Fig. 15.

Let us consider the use of relationship (49) for a version of an interphase layer in absence of filled polymers. Such situation is possible in two cases: at $h = 0$ and $R_a = 0$. The first situation corresponds to mathematical fractal with an interval of linear scales 0-∞. In other words, this situation is unreal for filled polymers, which are physical fractals, i.e., their fractal behavior is observed in an interval of finite linear scales with $h = l_{st} \neq 0$. The situation $R_a = 0$ means a filler absence, i.e., represents a trivial case. Besides, the (l_{in}/R_a) value does not depend on R_a (only at $d_{sur} = 3$).

Yakubov [121] has considered the thermodynamics of sorption phenomena on fractal objects and has offered a relationship for its determination if an adsorbed phase relative fraction, which in the present paper is considered as the interphase layer relative fraction υ_{in} [118]:

$$\upsilon_{in} = \rho^{-1} m_0^{(1-3/D)} \tag{52}$$

where ρ is density of a separate particle (in a considered case – graphite), m_0 is the mass of a separate particle, from which the fractal object (aggregate of filler particles) is formed, D is the fractal dimension of object.

The m_0 value can be estimated from electron micrographs of filled polymers chips [59]. The identification of D requires some discussion. In [121] it is assumed that it is necessary to accept fractal dimension of the filler particles aggregate. These aggregates are really fractal objects with $D \approx 2$. However, as has shown by Pfeifer [122,123], the defining effect on the adsorptive layer formation renders not the fractal dimension of the adsorbing object, but dimension of its surface d_{sur}. Therefore, for further calculations we will accept $D = d_{sur}$. Besides υ_{in} represents a fraction of not the whole volume of a filled polymer, but only a fraction of the adsorbed phase, i.e., polymer matrix. Therefore farther we will use υ_{in}, obtained from the equation [118]:

$$\upsilon_{in}^{red} = \upsilon_{in}\left(1-\varphi_f\right) \tag{53}$$

Estimations on equations (52) and (53), for both series of PHE–Gr increase the filler content resulting in growth υ_{in}^{red}, and the greatest increase is observed at rather small values ($\varphi_f \leq 0.10$) with the subsequent approaching to an asymptotic behavior. υ_{in}^{red} at the same φ_f is approximately twice for PHE–Gr-I specimens than for PHE–Gr-II [118]. In order to explain those observed differences shown in Fig. 16, a dependence υ_{in}^{red} (d_{sur}), which is approximated by curves of one kind that allows to determine the limiting values υ_{in}^{red} with allowance for known limits $2 \leq d_{sur} \leq 3$ [124]. So, at $d_{sur} = 2$ (i.e., for a case of a Euclidean plane) $\upsilon_{in}^{red} = 0$, and the maximal value υ_{in}^{red} at $d_{sur} = 3$ is ~ 0.66.

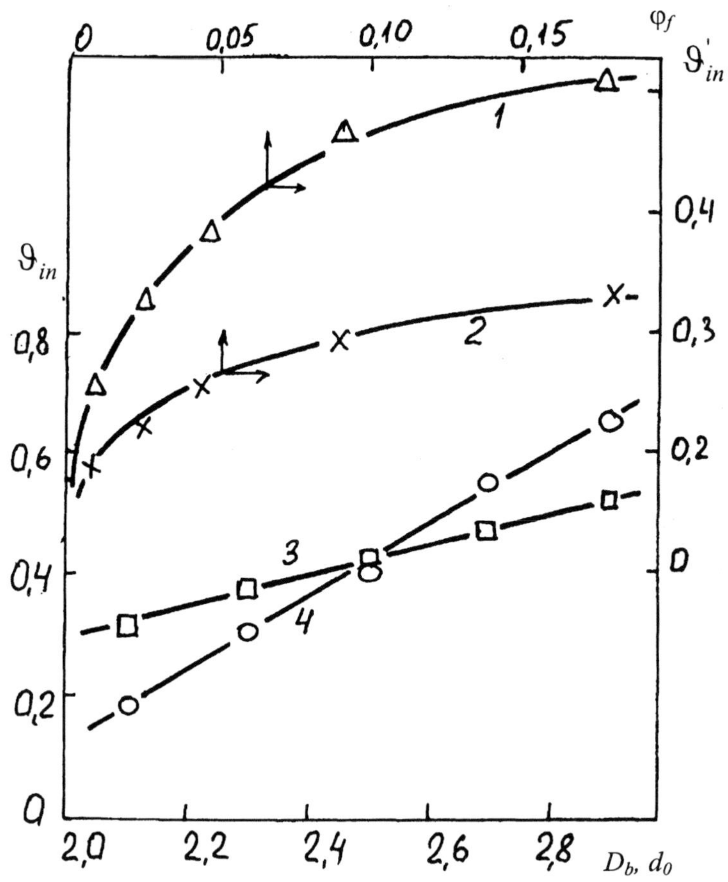

Figure 16. Dependence of the reduced interphase layer υ_{in}^{red} on the contents of a filler φ_f (1, 2) and on fractal dimensions D_b (3) and d_0 (4) (1 -PHE–Gr-I, 2- PHE–Gr-II) [118].

In [125] it was characterized the interphase adhesion level of filled polymers with the help of parameter A, determined as follows:

$$A = \frac{1}{1-\varphi_f}\left(\frac{tg\delta_{comp}}{tg\delta_M} - 1\right) \qquad (54)$$

where $tg\delta_{comp}$ and $tg\delta_M$ are tangents of dielectric loss angles of the filled polymer and polymer matrix, respectively. The increase of parameter A means a decrease of the adhesion level on the interphase for a filler-polymer matrix [125].

The dependences υ_{in}^{red} (A) for both series PHE–Gr are approximated by one straight line passing through the origin. An increase in parameter A (the deterioration of the interphase adhesion) determines the increase of an interphase layer relative fraction. Under these premiscs it is possible to estimate the maximal magnitude A (A^{max}) at $\upsilon_{in}^{red} \approx 0.66$, which is ~ 4.2. At such value A^{max} and experimental magnitude $tg\delta_M \approx 0,1$ the equation (54) allows to estimate the maximal value $tg\delta_{comp}$, which corresponds to the value $tg\delta_M$ at glass transition temperature T_g, that will be the decay of the local order domains in the interphase layer [126] and the achievement if its "unstructured" state. Let us also indicate that the increase of parameter A, according to the equation (53), means a raising of the molecular mobility in a filled specimen in comparison with an initial matrix polymer. This observation assumes more loose molecular packing in a filled polymer. The cited data proof that the incorporation of graphite to PHE results in looser the interphase layer structure. In [118] the analysis of relationships between d_{sur} and D_b for both series of filled PHE specimens is also carried out and has shown, that for increasing D_b there is a linear growth d_{sur}. At $D_b = 2$ these relationships are extrapolated to finite values $d_{sur} = d_0$. From a physical sense of dimension D_b, as it is characteristic of a filler particles aggregation degree, it is possible to draw the conclusion that d_0 is a dimension of the initial (not aggregated) filler particles surface. Such conclusion is confirmed by the fact that for PHE–Gr-I d_0 is 2.10, that is agreement with data for graphite [66]. It is analytically possible to describe dependences D_b (d_{sur}, d_0) as follows [118]:

$$D_b = 2 + 2,55\,(d_{sur} - d_0) \tag{55}$$

and from the data of Fig. 16 the empirical relationship υ_{in}^{red} (d_{sur}) is possible to be presented as

$$\upsilon_{in}^{red} = 0,66(d_{sur} - 2) \tag{56}$$

The combination of equations (55) and (56) gives the empirical relationship determining the dependence of value υ_{in}^{red} with D_b and d_0 [118]:

$$\upsilon_{in}^{red} = \frac{D_b + 2,55d_0 - 7,10}{4,18} \tag{57}$$

The analysis of the dependences υ_{in}^{red} (D_b) and υ_{in}^{red} (d_0) at fixed values of d_0 and D_b, respectively ($D_b = d_0 = 2.5$) (see Fig. 16) has shown that d_0 renders on value υ_{in}^{red} much stronger (approximately 2.5 times) influence than D_b. In other words, the fractality (roughly speaking, the roughness) of a initial (not aggregated) filler particles surface renders stronger influence on υ_{in}^{red} than particles aggregation degree. Besides from equation (56) the condition $\upsilon_{in}^{red} = 0$ is reached only at simultaneous fulfillment of two conditions $d_0 = 2$ and $D_b = 2$, i.e., for absolutely smooth particles of a filler and simultaneous absence of aggregation.

For the explanation of the influence of dimensions of filler particles and polymer surfaces on interphase adhesion in filled polymers the concept of "accessibility" for these surfaces sites for the formation of an interphase must be used. As a first approximation, the degree of such "accessibility" is suggested to be determined by a difference of dimensions (including fractal) of indicated surfaces. The higher this difference the smaller the interphase adhesion degree. Let us explain this idea on a rough, but an obvious case.

Assuming that the filler particles have a rough surface, the dimension of which close to Euclidean dimension $d = 3$ (for example, Al_2O_3 [123]) and the surface of the polymer is perfectly smooth, i.e., $d = 2$. In that case the contact between the indicated surfaces is possible only on tips of the most exposed roughness of filler particles that will reduce the degree of interphase adhesion. In other words, this incorrespondence of dimensions determines the inaccessibility of a largest part of a filler particles surface for interphase bonds formation.

A more precise method for the quantitative characterization of such effect is presented in [87]. It is the concept of "unscreened" perimeter for any object, i.e., a filler particle. This part of the surface is "accessible" for interphase bonds formation [127]. As it is known [65], a filled polymer at the definite contents of a filler φ_f represents percolation of clusters with the first percolation threshold $\varphi_f^c = 0.15\text{-}0.17$. As the maximal magnitude φ_f for the considered filled PHE is equal to 0.176, these systems are below that percolation threshold and equation (21) will be correct, and the interphase sites (nodes) number on a particle surface N_u will be given by (20). The value of fractal dimension of a fractal object surface is adopted to the corresponding parameter of its structure [128] and therefore for a polymer matrix this characteristic is adopted as the fractal dimension of a polymer structure d_f [73]. Thus, it is possible to describe an "accessibility" degree for filler particles surface [118]:

$$\Delta d = |d_f - d_{sur}| \tag{58}$$

The comparison of two parameters, N_u and Δd describing the same effect has shown that an increase in Δd results in a decrease of the number of "accessible" sites and at $\Delta d = 0.5$ or lower the formation of bonds is not expected at all ($N_u = 0$). An extrapolation of the plot $N_u(\Delta d)$ to $\Delta d = 0$ gives a maximal value $N_u = 195$ relative units. Using this value in (20), we obtain a condition $d_f = 3$ at maximal R_a. For smaller values of R_a this condition can not be assumed and gives unreal values of $d_f > 3$. Therefore, this example demonstrates the influence of a filler particles aggregation on the formation of interphase bonds [118].

As it was previously indicated, the role of filler particles backbone consists of modification of the structure of a polymer matrix, which is reflected in the corresponding increase d_f [73]. In this connection there is a question, about what degree of the indicated increase for d_f falls into the interphase layer. The structural changes have happened only in interphase layers of filled polymers, not in the bulk of polymer matrix, in any cases at small φ_f. Let us consider this problem in more detail.

By assuming that the polymer phase of filled polymer consists of two structural components (interphase layer and volume polymer matrix with relative fractions υ_{in} and υ_M), it can be written [129]:

$$d_f = d_f^{M} \upsilon_M + d_f^{in} \upsilon_{in} \tag{59}$$

where d_f^{M} and d_f^{in} are the fractal dimensions of a volume polymer matrix and interphase layer, respectively.

Furthermore:

$$\upsilon_M = 1 - \varphi_f - \upsilon_{in} \tag{60}$$

$$d_f^{in} = d_f^{M} + \Delta d_f \tag{61}$$

where Δd_f is the difference of fractal dimensions of an interphase layer and the volume of polymer matrix ($\Delta d_f = d_f^{in} - d_f^{M}$, as d_f^{in} > d_M). The value of d_f^{in} implies an average of fractal dimension in the interphase layer, since the sharp transition in this case is excepted on the same reasons, which Flory indicated [130] for a case of interphase boundary in semi-crystalline polymers. The value of Δd_f can be estimated from experimental data and $\Delta\varphi_{cl}$ by relationship (30). If we assume a linear increase of fractal dimension in an interphase layer from d_f^{M} on the "volume polymer matrix – interphase layer" up to d_f^{0} on "interphase layer – filler", it is possible to estimate d_f^{0} from a relationship [129]:

$$d_f^{0} = d_f^{M} + 2\Delta d_f. \tag{62}$$

Pfeifer [123] showed that between fractal dimensions of macromolecules in adsorbed (interphase) layer d_f^{0}, filler particles surface d_{sur} and macromolecules in an initial state (melt or solution) D_m there is a following interconnection:

$$\frac{d_{sur} D_m}{d_f^{0}} = d_0 \tag{63}$$

If accepting the value of d_{sur} according to [77], d_0 = 2.13 [66] and d_f^{0} according to equation (61), it is possible to calculate D_m for filler particles aggregate surface according to equation

(63). The calculations have shown [129] that D_m = 2.58-2.54 for PHE–Gr-I and 2.77-2.58 for PHE–Gr-II, i.e., in both cases D_m decreases with the increase d_{sur}, that is connected to growth of an aggregation of filler particles. The indicated relationship is well approximated for filled PHE, which is close to results expected theoretically. Both the indicated fractal dimensions have identical limiting values: $2 \le d_{sur} < 3$ [66] and $2 \le D_m < 3$ [106]. Since a decrease of D_m leads to an increase in d_{sur}, it is possible to expect, that $D_m = 3$ at $d_{sur} = 2$ and $D_m = 2$ at $d_{sur} = 3$. The full correspondence can be reached by raising d_0 up to 2.17-2.19 in equation (57), which is justified with allowance of a large error for d_0 determination, which is 2.13 ± 0.16 [66].

Within the framework of the fractal analysis D_m is determined as follows [106]:

$$D_m = \frac{d_s(d+2)}{2} \tag{64}$$

For linear macromolecules the spectral dimension $d_s = 1$ means their one-dimensional connectivity [107]. From equation (63) follows, that at $D_m < 2.5$ $d_s < 1$, i.e., the polymer melt on a filler particles aggregates surface has not even one-dimensional connectivity, though for volume polymers d_s is much higher than one [20]. It means, that at $D_m < 2.5$ melts with filler particles aggregates are fragmented of a film type with rough topologically edges (samples PHE–Gr-I with $D_m = 2.39$). In the case of samples PHE–Gr-II ($D_m = 2.73$) aggregates are coated with thin (it is even possible to see the structure of the aggregate) polymer film without signs of a fragmentation.

The same aspect of interphase layers formation was discussed in general physical terms [131] namely, chaos and order parameters. The processes of chaotic linear dynamics will often form fractal structures, but it is usually difficult to find a quantitative relation [132]. Apparently, the amorphous polymer structure (or amorphous phase structure in semi-crystalline polymers) gives the basis to assume the presence of a definite degree of chaos. One of possible solutions is the Lyapunov exponent λ [132]. It is a measurement of the exponential rate of divergence or convergence of average trajectories in a phase along a direction of given coordinates. The chaotic processes are characterized by an exponential divergence of adjacent trajectories and as a consequence, at least, one positive Lyapunov exponent. In [113] it was shown that the increase of λ results in raising d_f for polymers structure.

A more strict definition of deterministic chaos is the condition [139]:

$$D_2 < d_f \tag{65}$$

where D_2 is the correlation dimension of structure.

Now it is well-known [13] that the polymers have multifractal structure, in which dimensions are indicated by a condition $D_{q+1} < D_q$ [64]. As $d_f = D_0$ corresponds to $q = 0$, and at $q = 2$ we obtain D_2, a multifractality of polymers structure and the fulfillment of a condition (65) (especially in the region q = 0-2 [13]) is defined, therefore, a chaos in polymers structure is determined [131].

One of the aspects of the chaos change in structure of interphase layers in filled polymers follows from the fractal analysis of adsorption processes [66,122]. As it is assumed by Pfeifer [123], generally for conformations of polymer chains, characterized by its fractal dimension D_{ad}, on a fractal surface with dimension d_{sur} the condition is correct:

$$D_{ad} = \begin{cases} d_{sur}, \text{ for } d_{sur} \approx 2, \\ D_{sol}, \text{ for } d_{sur} \approx 3, \end{cases} \tag{66}$$

where D_{sol} is a fractal dimension of a macromolecular coil in solution. For a poor solvent D_{sol}=2, for good solvent D_{sol}=1.67 [106].

The transition of a polymer coil from solution in a condensed state is accompanied by an environment change (from solvent molecules to coils) that results in a change in its fractal dimension. In a condensed state, it is determined according to the equation (64). The dimension of a macromolecular coil in solution D_{sol} with allowance for of excluded volume effect is given so [106]:

$$D_{sol} = \frac{d_s(d+2)}{d_s+2} \tag{67}$$

The combination of equations (64) and (67) establishes the interconnection of parameters $D_{sol}(D_{ad})$ and d_f, expressed by the equation (36) for linear polymers.

Thus, the dependence $d_f(\lambda)$ and condition (66) establish the general conditions of interphase layers formation in filled polymers. At a flat surface of filler particles, i.e., $d_{sur} \approx 2$, D_{ad} is also at low-level. From equation (36) it follows that the interphase layer with low d_f is in this case formed with a high level of chaos (a large Lyapunov exponent) [131], transformed in a high level of the local order (see equation (30)). At large d_{sur}, approaching to 3, the coils in an interphase layer keep the conformation they had in solution. In this case the level of chaos in an interphase layer is decreased owing to an increase in d_f. Nevertheless, and in this case, a large degree of chaos in an interphase layer will take place at an adsorption from a good solvent and smaller at an adsorption from a poor solvent. However, as a rule, real filled polymers are produced by blending of fillers with a polymer melt. In this case the value of coil fractal dimension is 2.5 [106]. It explains a decrease of filled polymers plasticity in the process of a filler particles aggregation, producing an increase in d_{sur} [73, 131].

INTERPHASE LAYER STRUCTURE FORMATION

The study of interphase layer structure and properties for a polymer charged with filler particles from solution or in melt state was carried out [1]. In such cases diffusion processes play the main role in the formation of an interphase layer structure. In industrial conditions the filled polymers processing is made with usage of injection molding machines, where the conditions of interphase layer formation essentially differ from a free deposition because of high pressures and rates of a melt [133], i.e., the mechanism for the formation of the interphase layer in this case essentially differs [134].

The possibility of simulation of amorphous glassy polymers structure as sets of clusters WS was earlier shown [135,136]. The same method was successfully utilized for simulation of the deposition on fibers and surfaces [137]. In [138] the following relationship between L_{in} and particles number N_i in an interphase layer N_i was obtained:

$$l_{in} \sim N_i^{\varepsilon}, \tag{68}$$

where an exponent ε is ~ 1.7 for depositions controlled by diffusion, and ~ 1 in case the diffusion processes are unessential.

The estimation of N_i is made by the following sequence [134]. The overall length of macromolecules L per unit volume of polymer is determined as [25]:

$$L = \frac{1}{S}. \tag{69}$$

Length of macromolecules in an interphase layer L_{in} is estimated from the expression:

$$L_{in} = \upsilon_{in}L = \upsilon_{in}(1 - \varphi_f)L \tag{70}$$

Then the quantity of particles (statistical segments) N_i in an interphase layer can be obtained from the equation [134]:

$$N_i = \frac{L_{in}}{l_{st}} = \frac{\upsilon_{in}(1-\varphi_f)}{Sl_0C_\infty} \tag{71}$$

As follows from data [134], for filled PHE an exponent in the relationship (68) is ~ 1.1, as it assumes a formation of interphase layers in the indicated systems virtually without participation of diffusion processes. As it was indicated above, the large pressure and a melt motion rate at small processing time is the main reason of this behavior. From equation (68) it can be concluded that the decrease of the interphase layer thickness is quite important. A variation of ε determines the interphase layer structure. An exponent ε can be expressed by the following equation [138]:

$$\varepsilon = \frac{1}{1-d+d_f}. \tag{72}$$

From equation (72) it follows that for ε = 1.7 d_f = 2.59, that is close to dimension of a diffusion-limited cluster WS [137], and at ε = 1 $d_f = d$ = 3, i.e., an interphase layer structure loses its fractal properties. At ε = 1.1 d_f = 2.90, i.e., the formation of a diffusion-limited cluster WS is suppressed at its beginning by a rigid regime of processing. As it is known [25], raising d_f means a decrease of the local order degree in an interphase layer, i.e., weaking its structure.

Equations (68) and (71) jointly allow estimating the influence of the characteristics of a polymer matrix, namely C_∞ and S, on an interphase layer. Assuming values for υ_{in}, φ_f, l_0 and ε constant (ε = 1.1) and in turn varying values for C_∞ and S, it is possible to show, that an increase both in C_∞ and S results in a decrease in l_{in} Similar dependences for l_{in} are obtained at ε in an interval 1.0-1.7, and the increase in ε results in more strong decay l_{in} at increasing C_∞ or S.

Description of Oriented Composites Structure and Properties

The research in oriented polymers has always show large attention within the framework of classic representations on orientation processes [139]. The processes of orientation of polymers containing fillers were much less often studied [76]. The fractal analysis for the description of structure and properties of polymerization-filled polymers is reviewed on the basis of ultra-high-molecular polyethylene (UHMPE) and related composites, produced by solid-state extrusion [140].

Structural changes in oriented PE composites are not often studied by the fractal analysis, though representation of a macromolecular chain as fractal is obvious [141]. According to [57], a broken line (length L) with spacing interval between ends R is possible to be represented as follows:

$$\frac{L}{a} = \left(\frac{R}{a}\right)^D \tag{73}$$

where a is the scale of length measurement, D is the fractal dimension of a broken line ($1 \le D < 2$).

If applied to a part of a macromolecule having length L_e [103] the equation (73) will present a form [142]:

$$\frac{L_e}{l_{st}} = \left(\frac{R_e}{l_{st}}\right)^{D_e} \tag{74}$$

Here R is the spacing interval between entanglement nodes (R_e), and a the statistical segment length l_{st} ("natural" scale of length for a polymer chain [25]). Equation (74) allows considering a chain fragment between entanglement nodes with a molecular weight MW_e, as fractal with dimension D_e. The self-similarity of such fragment of a polymer chain was demonstrated [143].

Since polymers in a solid state are thermodynamically non-equilibrium systems [144], their behavior at deformation should be considered from a point of view of thermodynamics of strong non-equilibrium solids. According to [145], this deformation is determined by processes of formation and evolution of dissipative structures (DS), providing an optimum regime of dissipation of energy. DS in a deformed body shows the existence of universal hierarchy of spatial scales (structural levels). It is assumed [145] that even in elastic-isotropic bodies exist not less than three independent length scales. For polymers it is natural to accept length of real skeletal bond l_0, l_{st} and R_e [25, 26]. During deformation the first two scales do not change and R_e is proportional to molecular (microscopic) draw ratio λ_{mol} (in one orientation direction). Then an auto-model factor Λ_{23} for the second and third scales can be expressed [142]:

$$\Lambda_{23} = \frac{R_e \lambda_{mol}}{l_{st}} \tag{75}$$

Since a change of $\left(R_e / l_{st}\right)^{D_e}$ during orientation is expected, the value L_e/l_{st} remains to a constant. From equations (74) and (75) we shall calculate [142]:

$$\lambda_{mol} = \frac{l_{st} \lambda^{2/D_e}}{R_e} \tag{76}$$

It is taken into account that extrusion (macroscopic) draw ratio λ is possible to be presented as $n_{st}^{1/2}$ (where n_{st} is number of statistical segments between entanglement nodes, $n_{st} = L_e/l_{st}$).

Equation (76) establishes the interconnection between extrusion (macroscopic) and molecular (microscopic) draw ratios, that allows to made quantitative assessment of extrudates properties. Let us mark that, for filled polymers the orientation processes only happen in the polymer matrix. It is therefore necessary to use the corrected value of a molecular draw ratio λ_{mol}^{cor} [146]:

$$\lambda_{mol}^{cor} = \frac{\lambda_{mol}}{1 - \varphi_f} \tag{77}$$

The most sensitive parameter for the description of orientation processes of a polymer chain is the dimension D_e. The calculations according to (76) demonstrate that with an increase of λ there is a raise of D_e. At the same time, from equation (74), the increase of R_e at fixed L_e and l_{st} should result in a fast decrease of D_e. In order to understand the observed effect, we could remind the physical sense of D_e for a molecular chain. As follows from (74), the condition $D_e = 1$ assumes $R_e = L_e$, i.e., the chain is completely extended between entanglement nodes and its deformation capacity (mobility) is completely suppressed. At $D_e = 2$ the chain has the greatest possible mobility. On the first view, the increase of chain mobility at rising of a draw ratio is represented unreal. However, such effect can be the result of breakages of polymer macromolecules during extrusion, that means a decrease of a molecular weight, or increase effective of MW_e during extrusion – disentanglement of macromolecules [147]. However at used extrusion rates [148] and molecular weights of extruded materials (~10^6) this second effect can be eliminated from consideration. In essence, the effect of chain breakages at extrusion is completely similar to "geometrically necessary" loss of entanglements of polymer in craze fibrils [149]. The linear correlation between crystallinity degree increase ΔK_r in orientation process and fractal dimension of a chain D_e for UHMPE is observed. It means that the macromolecules breakages during extrusion, increasing the chain mobility, promote the orientation crystallization of UHMPE, and this is the main condition to increase K_r with the orientation of polymers permitting packing of its segments in crystallites [142].On the physical nature this effect is completely similar to growth of K_r with decrease of polymer molecular weight [144]. The increase of λ (or λ_{mol}) promotes this process, but not at any condition. The greatest chain breakages number will be realized at a dense entanglements network, i.e., at large molecular weights, or if there are specific conditions, one of which can be the presence of a filler [150].

Let us consider the influence of this last factor on the molecular orientation process of polymerization-filled for ultra-high-molecular polyethylenes (componors). As was shown in [151], the increase of λ_{mol}^{cor} at growth φ_f and a fixed value λ is observed. At the same time, λ_{mol}^{cor} depends on the filler type. At identical λ, molecular draw ratio is raised in a sequence kaolin $\rightarrow$ bauxite $\rightarrow$ aluminum powder (Al) [151]. This effect is probably connected to the well-known dependence of filled polymers properties to the adhesion level on an interphase boundary and, therefore, with the boundary strength [92,150]. The macromolecules breakages on interphase boundaries result in a decrease of macromolecular entanglements network density, increasing the limiting draw ratio in comparison with matrix polymer and, therefore, the value for λ_{mol}^{cor}.

In [151] the estimation of the fractal dimension of filler particles surface, d_{sur} was made, and dimensions of filler particles unscreened perimeter d_u as well as the number of unscreened sites on it, m, according to equations (17) and (18) were calculated. Calculations resulted in values for d_u and m (in relative units) 1.697; 1.781; 1.739 and 7.64; 10.61; 9.00 for kaoline, bauxite and Al respectively. The analysis of interconnections between a surface structure of filler particles and oriented componors properties, expressed by the parameter λ_{mol}^{cor}, has shown that the dependence of normalized value (λ_{mol}^{cor}/m) on λ is described by an unique curve [151]. Therefore, the value λ_{mol}^{cor} is inversely proportional to m, i.e., contact points between the filler and polymer matrix. Therefore, the molecular draw ratio is raised at the increase of filler concentration and depends on the surface structure of its particles.

As it is known [152], concepts of fractality and order are intimately interdependent. A study of this relation has special importance for polymers by two circumstances. At first, the polymers are fractals in scale ~ 3-50 Å. At second, polymer is never completely ordered or disordered: even at temperatures higher than its glass transition temperature, it has a local order [153]. At the same time it is impossible to obtain polymer having 100 % crystallinity [144]. Furthermore, crystallizing polymers have complicated structure, consisting of amorphous and crystalline phases. Within the framework of the cluster model of amorphous state structure polymers [100], the first structure of the indicated phase represents the local order domains (cluster) surrounded by a loose-packed matrix [154,155]. The situation is complicated because the large number of widely used semi-crystalline polymers (polyethylenes, polypropylene) at room temperature which have a viscous loose-packed matrix. The indicated circumstances determine the importance of the description of crystallizing polymers with the help of a general physical parameter – its fractal dimension. In [156,157] the interdependence of d_f and the structural states was studied for a number of polyethylenes.

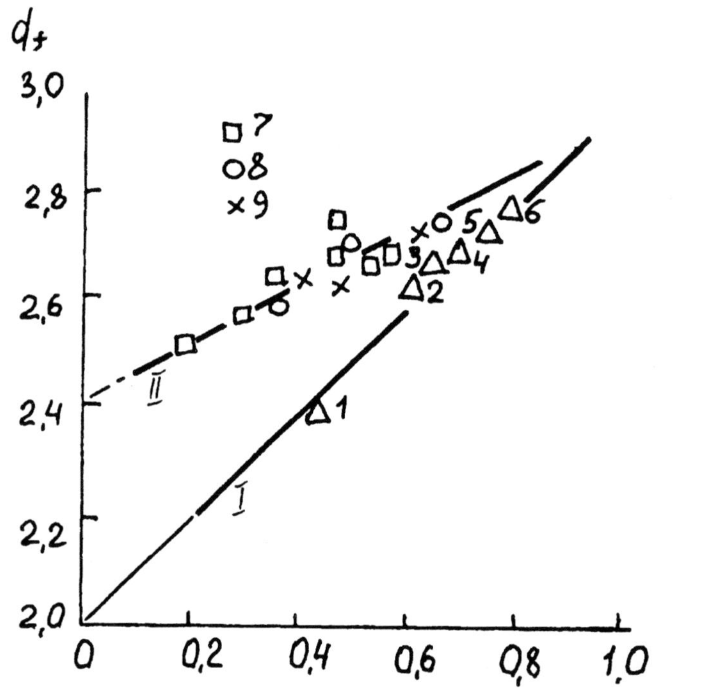

Figure 17. Dependences of fractal dimension of structure d_f on crystallinity degree K_2 (1-6) (1 – LDPE, 2 – UHMPE – bauxite, 3 – HDPE-273, 4 – UHMPE, 5 – HDPE-276, 6 – HDPE-277) (a) and on reduced fraction of a loose-packed matrix $\varphi_{\text{lm}}^{\text{red}}$ (7-9) (7 – impact tests of specimens with a sharp notch, 8 – without a notch, 9 – tension tests of film specimens) (b) for polyethylenes [159].

In Fig. 17a the relationship between the crystallinity degree K_ρ, determined on density of specimens and the fractal dimension of structure d_f for a number of polyethylenes is shown. The value d_f is determined according to equation (9). On the first view, the data will excellently agree with results [107] – a completely disordered polymer present a fractal dimension 2 and a completely ordered polymer (K_ρ = 1,0) – d_f = 3. However, it is necessary to make some remarks about this correlation. At first, for plotting the graph in Fig. 17a the value for K_ρ utilized allows to calculate not only the long-range order regions (crystallites), but also the existence of intermediate (local) order domains [158]. Usage of X-ray crystallinity degree K_r can result in essential deterioration of this correlation. So, for UHMPE K_ρ = 0.72 and K_r = 0.53 at identical d_f. For example, in impact tests of (HDPE-273) with varied length of a sharp notch the decrease of d_f was observed under the obvious condition K_ρ = const [154]. In addition, for by solid-state extrusion specimens UHMPE and componors the increase on K_ρ is observed at a practically invariable value of d_f [146,148]. All these observations lead to assume that the fractal dimension of semi-crystalline polymers structure (including filled) depends not only on the long-range order degree, i.e., degree of crystallinity, but also on the structure of the polyethylenes amorphous phase, i.e., on the degree of the local order [156].

In Fig. 17b the dependence of d_f, calculated according to equation (9), on a loose-packed matrix reduced fraction with $\varphi_{l.m.}^{red}$ is shown. The value $\varphi_{l.m.}^{red}$ is determined as follows. Within the framework of a cluster model, it is supposed that a semi-crystalline polymer consists of two phases – amorphous and crystalline (relative fraction of each one φ_{am} and $\varphi_{cr} = K_r$, respectively, and $\varphi_{am} = 1 - \varphi_{cr} = 1 - K_r$). The amorphous phase consists of two structural components – clusters and loose-packed matrix, where relative fractions φ_{cl} and $\varphi_{l.m.}$ are connected by a relationship [156]:

$$\varphi_{l.m.} = \varphi_{am} - \varphi_{cl} = 1 - K_r - \varphi_{cl} \tag{78}$$

It was also assumed that the loose-packed matrix relative fraction should be calculated on the whole polymer and not just on an amorphous phase:

$$\varphi_{l.m.}^{red} = \frac{\varphi_{l.m.}}{1 - K_r} \tag{79}$$

On Fig. 17b the results for impact tests of HDPE specimens with notches of different length at T = 293 K are shown. The data of tension tests of specimens without notch and film specimens at T = 293, 313 and 333 K are simultaneously shown. This relationship can be presented as [157]:

$$d_f = 2,44 + 0,45\varphi_{l.m.}^{red} = 2,44 + \frac{0,45\varphi_{l.m.}}{1 - K_r} \tag{80}$$

As shown in Fig. 17b data present a number of characteristic features. At first, they demonstrate that the value of $d_f = 2$ for polyethylenes is unreachable. The reason is that $d_f = 2$ is correct for the ideal linear non-ordered polymer, i.e., this is only theoretical. This dimension corresponds to the spectral dimension of a single chain, equal to 1 [107], instead of the polymer volume. At second, at $\varphi_{l.m.}^{red} = 1$, $d_f = 2.92$, i.e., does not reach 3. As follows from equation (7), it corresponds to $\nu = 0.46$, which is very close to the maximal value of Poisson's ratio for real solids, 0.475 [57]. And the most relevant, equation (80) demonstrates a different dependence for d_f on a degree of the local and long-range order – the increase of a degree firstly reduces d_f, and the increase of crystallinity degree raises, that is in agreement with results on Fig. 17b. This model has allowed making the correct description of structural changes of componors in the solid-state extrusion.

Let us discuss the fractal approaches to fracture and thermal shrinkage of oriented filled polymers. In the beginning we shall consider the fracton concept of fracture [159], as the fundamental treatment of this process for polymers. It is known [160], that the dilaton concept of solids fracture assumes the failure of a negative fluctuation of density (dilaton), whose length is determined by the length of the free run of phonons Λ. In this case, the overload factor æ on failure bonds can be expressed as follows [161]:

$$æ = \frac{\Lambda}{a} \tag{81}$$

where a is interatomic spacing interval.

For oriented polymers Λ is about 100 Å [161]. However, in [162] for non-oriented polymers subject to high-rate fracture, it was shown that $\Lambda \cong a$ (i.e., æ = 1) and such dilaton, consisting of two adjacent atoms, was called "degenerated". It was also demonstrated [163] that experimental values of stress of a thermal fracture were essentially lower than those theoretically calculated (in 2 ÷ 3 times). One more relevant feature of non-oriented polymers fracture in impact tests are the low values for æ (≅ 0,2 ÷ 1,0). This means that the stress on fractured bonds is much lower than the nominal fracture stress. In addition, it was shown [164], that æ is decreased with the increase of testing temperature and at transition from brittle to ductile fracture [162]. The development of polymer technology [13,20,106] and specially the proposal by Alexander and Orbach [107], who offered "fracton" conception, allowed to perform a fundamental treatment of polymers fracture process [159] including the dilaton concept [160,161] as a particular case. They showed that the vibrational excitations on fractals are localized by a medium fractal geometry and called such localized states as "fractons". It was also demonstrated [20] that the fracton regime is localized from a several angstroms to several tens angstroms and this last value will excellently agree with the range of distances between macromolecular entanglement nodes R_e. Let us remind that the breakage of chain fragments between those nodes represents the fracture of polymers on the molecular level. The localization of the excited states (phonons) in that range of scales means that the phonon can not be displaced on the spacing interatomic range, $\Lambda = a$ and æ ≅ 1 according to equation (81). This condition is observed by the fractalitity of the chain fragment between points of its topological fixation (nodes of chemical cross-linking, macromolecular "hookings", clusters etc.). The transition to usual behavior of phonons, i.e., $\Lambda > a$ and æ > 1, will be observed in that case, when the indicated chain fragment loses the fractal properties and becomes an Euclidean object, ($D_e = 1$) [159].

Let us consider the causes of æ < 1 in non-oriented polymers [162]. As it is known [114], D_e characterizes the degree of molecular mobility (deformability) of a considered chain fragment. The increase of the molecular mobility results in the corresponding raising of the relaxation of a specimen fracture stress σ_f [165]. Such treatment assumes the existence of a correlation between æ and D_e. This assumption is confirmed by the data on Fig. 18, where the dependence æ(D_e) for 10 different polymers is shown. As it can be seen, æ grows faster, than D_e, indicating on a strong dependence of a stress relaxation on molecular level. This relationship can be presented as follows [159]:

$$æ = D_e^{-2} \tag{82}$$

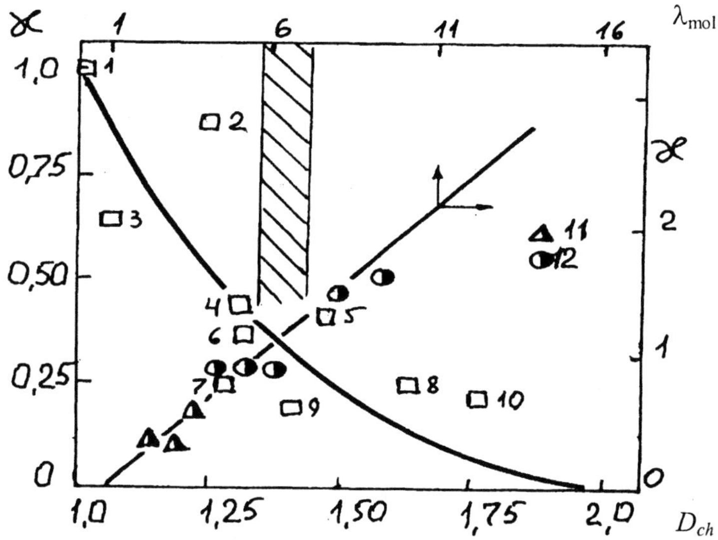

Figure 18. Dependence of the local overload coefficient æ on fractal dimension of a chain portion between entanglements (1 – polyvinylchloride, 2 – polyethylene, 3 – polypropylene, 4 – polystyrene, 5 – polycarbonate, 6 – polymethylmethacrylate, 7 – polytetrafluoroethylene, 8 – polyethylenterephtalate, 9 – polyamide-6, 10 – polysulfone) and molecular draw ratio λ_{mol} for UHMPE (11) and UHMPE–Al (12). The shaded region is an interval of literature values C_∞ [159].

Simultaneously in Fig. 16 the dependence of æ on a molecular draw ratio λ_{mol} for extrudates of UHMPE without and with filler (aluminum powder), demonstrating a linear correlation æ(λ_{mol}), at $\lambda_{mol} = 1$ is extrapolated to æ = 0. It means that fracture of polymer without a preliminary extension of a chain is impossible. It also assumes a definite, not zero, strain before fracture for non-oriented polymers specimens. A maximal λ_{mol} can be expressed as [149]:

$$\lambda_{mol}^{max} = \frac{L_e}{R_e} \tag{83}$$

In [25,27] it was shown that the ratio for the right member of equation (83) represents an auto-model factor of polymer structure, which is equal to the characteristic ratio C_∞, i.e., it is possible to consider $\lambda_{mol} \approx C_\infty$. A maximal molecular draw ratio λ_{mol} is reached at the full chain extension between entanglement nodes and consequently it corresponds to $D_e = 1$ and æ = 1, as it was indicated above.

The shaded area in Fig. 18 indicates an interval of values C_∞ for polyethylenes, from C_∞ = 5.7 [166] up to 7.0 [103]. As it is possible to indicate for this interval of values $\lambda_{mol} \approx C_\infty$ the magnitude æ reaches the unity, which means a full extension of chain fragmentation between entanglements. The transition from fractal to Euclidean behavior of this fragment will result on mechanical overload and change of a fracture mode on the molecular level from fracton to dilaton. This is possible even it is intuitively difficult to explain the mechanical overload on the not extended chain fragment.

Now we shall consider the cause of chain breakages at low stresses, which can be on an order lower than the macroscopic fracture stress σ_f (i.e., at hypothetical æ = 0.1, see Fig. 18) [169]. The lack of harmonicity in the fracture site is explained by an effect identical to the mechanical overload. Quantitatively this effect expresses the ratio of thermal expansion coefficient in the fracture site to the modal thermal expansion coefficient [162]. Another cause is the close interdependence of local yielding and fracture processes [159].

In [92,167] the change of σ_f as a function of λ for componors UHMPE-Al also produces a monotonic decrease of extrudates density ρ [167]. Thus the limiting draw ratio λ_f corresponding to a specimen fracture in mechanical tests, is raised with λ. Such behavior λ_f differs from the traditionally observed for oriented polymers, when the growth λ reduces λ_f owing to the exhaustion of molecular chains mobility [139]. So, it was established [148] that for extrudates UHMPE the increase of λ from 3 up to 5 reduces λ_f from 1.18 to 1.12.

The quoted facts have allowed proving that the fracture process of extruded componors is directly connected to filler presence because of loosing of polymer-filler boundaries and formation of multiple microcracks. Deformation of specimens during mechanical tests leads to an aggregation of microcracks formed during extrusion and their final failure.

Availability of the dependence $\rho(\lambda)$ and knowledge of the fracture mechanism allow to use a model for the fracture process description [168]. According to [62]:

$$\rho = \rho_0 \lambda_f^{-\alpha} \tag{84}$$

where ρ_0 is undeformed componor density, and

$$\alpha = d - d_r \tag{85}$$

where d_r is determined according to equation (7). Thus, fractal model [168] allows the adequate description of fracture processes of extruded filled polymers [92,167].The calculation of σ_f is made on the density of extruded specimens, not subjected to further deformation in mechanical tests. It means that the fracture of interphase boundaries is possible at extrusion causing the specimen fracture.

The investigation of thermo-shrinkage characteristics gives valuable information on the structural rearrangement caused by orientation processes in polymeric materials [139]. However, most papers have studied only qualitative rules of these processes. Therefore, it is necessary to use the methods of the fractal analysis for the quantitative description of thermo-shrinkage of extruded UHMPE and componors [169].

Ball [170] studied the elasticity of colloidal aggregates within the framework of fractal models and introduced two characteristic scales of length for the structure (a_T and ξ) assuming that the structure did not change for scales smaller than a_T and colloidal aggregates are homogeneous for scales larger than ξ. These assumptions make possible to obtain a relationship between the linear shrinkage ψ and the structural parameters of a polymer after gel formation:

$$\psi = \left(\xi / a_{\mathrm{T}}\right)^{\left(d'_f - d_f\right)/d'_f} \tag{86}$$

where d_f and d'_f are the fractal dimensions of the polymer structure before and after gel formation. As it was already indicated, unlike mathematical fractals, for physical (real) fractals there are two natural limiting length scales, a_{T} and ξ, [170]: the lower scale is the length of the statistical segment l_{st} and the upper scale is the spacing interval between entanglement nodes R_{e} [25]. Since equation (86) includes only structural parameters and does not contain factors that indicate the character of the action, we can write [169]:

$$\psi = \left(R_{\mathrm{e}} / l_{\mathrm{st}}\right)^{\left(d'_f - d_f\right)/d'_f} \tag{87}$$

The $(R_{\mathrm{e}}/l_{\mathrm{st}})$ ratio is the auto-model factor Λ_i of the polymer structure:

$$\Lambda_i = \frac{R_{\mathrm{e}}}{l_{\mathrm{st}}} = \frac{L_{\mathrm{e}}}{R_{\mathrm{e}}} \tag{88}$$

Since the $(L_{\mathrm{e}}/R_{\mathrm{e}})$ ratio is the maximal draw ratio of the molecular chain λ_{mol} between the entanglement nodes (equation (82), equation (87) reduces to the form [169]:

$$\frac{\xi}{a_{\mathrm{T}}} = \lambda_{\mathrm{mol}} \tag{89}$$

A comparison of the experimental values of ψ and ψ_{T} calculated according to equation (83) for UHMPE, UHMPE + Al and UHMPE + bauxite shows a satisfactory correspondence between them [169]. Thus, the thermal shrinkage of filled UHMPE is defined by two parameters: d_f, which characterizes the change of supermolecular structure during the extrusion process, and λ_{mol}, which describes structural changes at the molecular level.

FRACTAL MECHANICS OF THE FILLED POLYMER

The Elasticity Modulus

The elasticity modulus, E, of filled polymers can be described as a function of the dimension of regions of extra energy localization D_f (equation (31). In Fig. 19 (curve A) it is shown the dependence of the relative elasticity modulus E/E_{m} (where E_{m} is the elasticity modulus of matrix polymer) on the values of D_f and φ_{f} for PHE–Gr-I, PHE–Gr-II and epoxy polymer, filled with SiO_2 [105]. The data points lie on one common curve adjusting the relationship $E/E_{\mathrm{m}}(\varphi_{\mathrm{f}})$ for those specimens with an ideal interphase adhesion (Kerner equation) [5]. At the maximal value $D_f \approx 11$ ($\nu = 0.45$) [73] the E/E_{m} ratio is about 7, that is in agreement with the data for filled polymers [65]. Thus, on Fig. 19 (curve A) the dependence of E on a "disturbance" degree of a polymer matrix is represented.

Other definition for E assumes its dependence on filler particles aggregation degree, described by θ (equation (18)). In Fig. 17 (curve B) the dependence of elasticity modulus E of filled PHE with the reciprocal of θ is shown. The increase of filler particles aggregation degree (increase θ^{-1}) results in growth of E [97].

Data for specimens of filled PHE are approximated by a linear correlation, which at $\theta^{-1} = 0$ is extrapolated to value $E \approx 1$ GPa, that is approximately equal to the elasticity modulus of a matrix polymer [109].

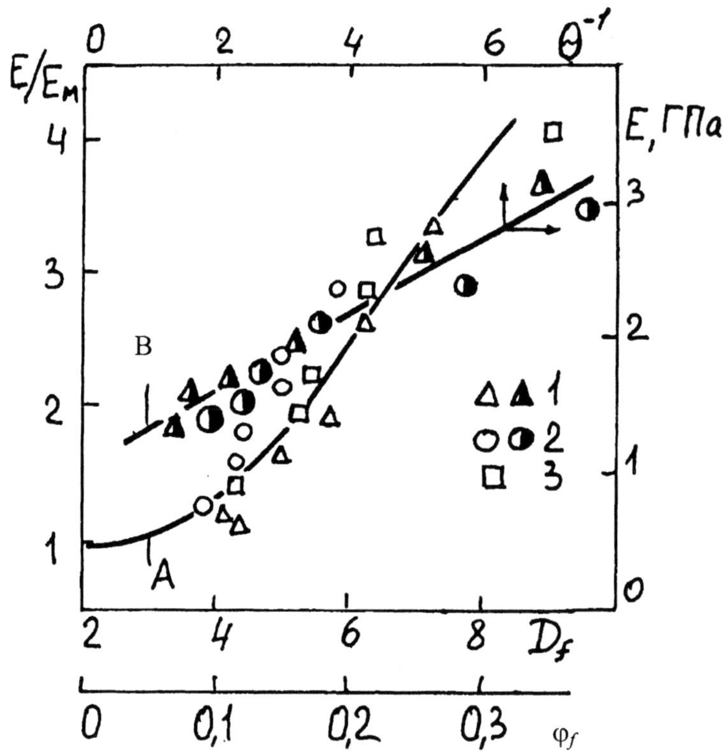

Figure 19. Dependence of elasticity modulus E on the dimension of extra energy localization regions D_f (1, 2, 3), volumetric contents of filler φ_f (line A) and aggregation parameter θ (line B) for PHE–Gr-I (1), PHE–Gr-II (2) and EP-S (3) [73].

Yield Stress

For the estimation of yield stress, σ_Y, of filled polymers the following fractal relationship was obtained [171]:

$$\sigma_Y = 958(D_b - 2)\left(\frac{3-d_f}{d_f}\right), \text{ MPa} \tag{90}$$

In Fig. 20 the comparison of the experimental σ_Y^e and calculated according to equation (90) σ_Y^T of yield stress values for filled PHE is shown. As it is seen, equation (89) gives an adequate description.

Between dimensions d_f and D_b there is a simple relationship (in any case, for graphite-reinforced PHE) [171]:

$$d_f = 1{,}74 + 0{,}38\ D_b \tag{91}$$

The combination of (90) and (91) allows obtaining a functional dependence σ_Y on d_f [171]:

$$\sigma_Y = 2520\left(d_f - 2{,}5\right)\left(\frac{3 - d_f}{d_f}\right),\ \text{MPa} \tag{92}$$

Concerning equations (90) and (92) it is necessary to make some remarks. At first, the fractality of a polymer matrix structure and filler particles backbone is observed in different intervals of linear scales. In first interval it is 3 ÷ 50Å [20], in the second from the size of the least particles up to spacing interval between particles (~ 4 × 10^{-6} m) [73]. The connection between these fractals provides a filler particles surface, whose self-similarity interval is approximately equal to 15 ÷ 50 000 Å [118]. Secondly, the empirical constants in equations (90) and (92) (985 and 2520 MPa, respectively) assumes their validity only for filled PHE. At third, equation (92) demonstrates the dependence of yielding process parameter σ_Y only on d_f, i.e., the yielding process is controlled by a linear scales interval of a polymer matrix structure. This interval represents simultaneously linear scales of both, the fluctuation free volume [27] and cluster structure [162]. On an insert of Fig. 20 the tendency of change of σ_Y with d_f, calculated according to equation (92) for filled PHE is shown. As it is possible to see, the theoretically obtained tendency agree with the corresponding tendency of experimental data – approximately at $d_f = 2{,}75$ the maximum σ_Y is reached.

The Fracture Stress

The fracture stress, σ_Y, is described in the form of a power law [5]:

$$\sigma_f = \sigma_{fm}\left(1 - a\varphi_f^n\right) \tag{93}$$

where σ_{fm} is the strength of a polymer matrix, a and n are constants dependent on the share and arrangement of particles in model of filled polymer.

Apparently, equation (92) assumes a reduction of the fracture stress σ_f at increase of φ_f. The analysis of the experimental dependences $\sigma_f(\varphi_f)$ for filled PHE has shown that the fracture stress practically does not depend on the filler content (for $\varphi_f \leq 0{,}176$) and, therefore, can not be described by equations such as (93). The indicated type of equations assumes a poor adhesion on the interphase boundary and absence of a stress concentration on this boundary. In other words, the equations of such type assume a decrease of values of σ_Y at increase φ_f owing to decreasing of effective cross section of a polymer matrix with the introduction of a dispersed filler.

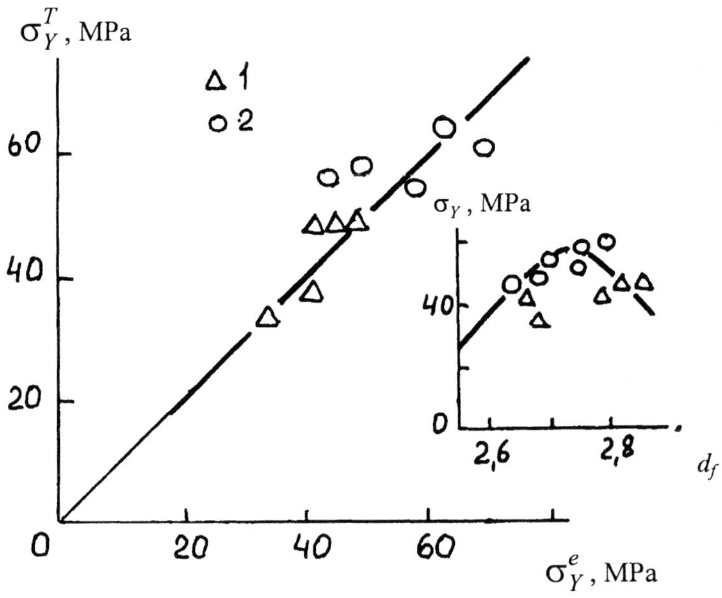

Figure 20. Relation of experimental σ_Y^e and calculated according to equation (90) yield stress for PHE–Gr-I (1) and PHE–Gr-II (2). In the insert: comparison of experimental and calculated results according to equation (92) (line) dependences $\sigma_Y(d_f)$ for the same materials [171].

For the specimens of filled PHE it was shown [59] that the dependences $E(\varphi_f)$ are well described by the Kerner equation (see Fig. 19), which assumes the existence of interphase connections. Therefore, we should consider the existence of adhesion on the polymer-filler interphase and the ability of the applied stress transport to go through this boundary by the shear mechanism. On the indicated case, the fracture stress of filled polymers will be a function of shearing strength of a polymer matrix τ_m and strength of interphase connection, σ_a. The interdependence of these parameters is given by the Leidner-Woodhams equation

$$\sigma_f = (\sigma_a + 0{,}83\ \tau_m) + \sigma_a K\ (1 - \varphi_f) \qquad (94)$$

where K is coefficient of stress concentration.

A drawback of equation (94) is the difficulty of independent experimental determination of σ_a. Nevertheless, this equation can be used for the estimation of σ_a with known σ_f, which are easier for experimental determination. Two assumptions must be considered for the solution of this problem [118].

At first, as the matrix polymer PHE is plastic with sharp and definite macroscopic yield stress σ_Y, then a value for τ_m (yield shearing stress) of a polymer matrix τ_Y was used.

At second, as it is known [5], K does not depend on the filler particles size, which increases φ_f for a filled PHE specimens owing to an aggregation of the initial filler particles (equation (28)) and therefore it is possible as a first approximation to consider it as a constant. In [118] it is accepted $K = 2$. Such estimation can produce a slight influence on absolute values σ_a, but with no influence on the tendency of change with a variation of φ_f. The calculation of an interphase connection strength, σ_a, has shown that σ_a decreases at increase φ_f for both series of filled PHE specimens: $\sigma_a = 4.9 \div 8.0$ MPa for PHE–Gr-I and $\sigma_a = 8.0 \div 11.4$ MPa for PHE–Gr-II.

The properties of an interphase layer in filled polymers are defined by a surface structure of filler particles (aggregates of particles), which can be described by its fractal dimension d_{sur} [70]. The analysis of the dependence $\sigma_a(d_{sur})$ for filled PHE has shown that this dependence is approximated only by one straight line for both series of filled PHE and a decrease of interphase connection strength σ_a at increase of d_{sur} is observed [118]. For $d_{sur} = 2$ (i.e., smooth Euclidean flat surface of filler) we shall obtain a maximal value $\sigma_a \approx 13.4$ MPa for filled PHE. For $d_{sur} = 3$ (i.e., extremely rough surfaces of filler) we obtain $\sigma_a = 0$, i.e., an absence of a polymer-filler connection. An increase of d_{sur} with φ_f is due to the aggregation process of the initial filler particles (equation (17)). Thus, regulating the indicated processes, it is possible to influence the number of interphase connections σ_a and, therefore, the filled polymer strength σ_f (equation (93)) [118]. In order to calculate the strength upper limit σ_f^{max} it is necessary to obtain the maximal values of σ_a and $\tau_m(\tau_Y)$ simultaneously. As follows from [118], the maximal value $\sigma_a \approx 13.4$ MPa is reached at $d_{sur} = 2$, i.e., at ideally smooth surface of filler particles (that eliminates their aggregation). The incorporation of dispersed filler in polymer results that yield stress σ_Y is raised with φ_f [171]. Therefore, in order to obtain the greatest possible values σ_Y, it is necessary to avoid modification of matrix polymer structure. It can be achieved by an even distribution of filler particles, i.e., it is necessary to avoid their aggregation [175].

Having determined a proportionality coefficient between σ_Y and E under the data of mechanical tests of filled PHE and using experimental values for E [159], it is possible to estimate value σ_f^{max} under the condition $\sigma_a = 13{,}4$ MPa. The analysis of the dependence $\sigma_f^{max}(\varphi_f)$ shows the essential increase of σ_f^{max} in comparison to σ_f at identical φ_f, specially at large values. However this dependence $\sigma_f^{max}(\varphi_f)$ is valid only in the case that the experimental elasticity modulus, E, is used. In order to avoid filler particles aggregation and, therefore, "disturbance" of the polymer matrix structure, it can result in decreasing of E and σ_Y (see Fig. 20 and equation (89)). Simultaneously from the dependence $\sigma_f^{max}(\varphi_f)$ under condition of E = const it is necessary to expect σ_f^{max} at increase φ_f at an ideal adhesion. All these data assume a complicated relation between a filled polymers structure and E and σ_Y, that in practice required a definite optimum relationship between these factors [118].

Impact Toughness

The effect of the polymer toughness decrease (brittlement) with the incorporation of particulate filler is well-known [105,172]. In [159] it was shown that the incorporation of PHE up to 40% mass of dispersed graphite leads to a decrease in impact toughness A_p of specimens without a notch in 4 ÷ 7 times, and this effect is more clearly observed for PHE–Gr-I. It is also explained by the lower level of adhesion for a polymer-filler system than for PHE–Gr-II. The characterization of the level of this adhesion (equation (53)) is obtained by the following relation [118]:

$$A_p \approx \frac{19}{A^{1/3}}, \text{ kJ/m}^2. \tag{95}$$

For explanation of the brittleness effect of filled polymers the fractal model is proposed [173, 174]. The filler role consists of a "disturbance" of the polymer matrix structure and the filled polymer properties are defined only by structural characteristics of a modified matrix. As it is known [162], the impact toughness of polymers (and a filled polymer is considered as polymer with changed structure) is determined by a level of the impact energy dissipation at plastic deformation. This circumstance allows using an estimation of a fracture surface fractal dimension d_r and the following relationship [175, 176]:

$$d_r = \frac{2 - \ln(1 - \eta_d)}{\ln \Lambda_i} \tag{96}$$

where η_d is the energy fraction consumed in dissipative processes, Λ_i is the structure of the auto-model factor.

Equation (95) assumes that the impact energy dissipation is the sole cause of fracture surface fractality. In other words, the impact energy dissipation at plastic deformation is a sole source of polymer toughness. For polymers this assumption is valid for a large approximation. As following on a level of energetic consumptions the mechanism of energy dissipation (the chains breakage) consumes energy on three order of magnitude lower [165].

If we consider the physical of parameters η_d and Λ_i included in equation (95), with reference to polymers, within the framework of the fractal concept of polymers plasticity [147], it was shown that only a part of a volume $(1 - \chi)$ is only subjected to plastic deformation. In [178] it was demonstrated that the indicated volume part is consisting of the densely packed regions of polymer, i.e., clusters. This condition can be written as follows [178]:

$$(1 - \chi) = \varphi_{cl} \tag{98}$$

As the brittle effect (A_p decreasing) is accompanied by a simultaneous reduction both in η_d [176], and $(1 - \chi)$ [179], with identical allowance variation limits η_d and $(1 - \chi)$ (from 0 up to 1) it is possible to assume the following equation [173]:

$$\eta_d = (1 - \chi) = \varphi_{cl} \tag{98}$$

As was mentioned above, for polymer cluster structures the approximation $\Lambda_i \approx C_\infty$ is valid [26]. For PHE $C_\infty = 5$ [166] and it is further assumed that the filler incorporation does not change C_∞. Therefore, equation (96) becomes [173]:

$$d_r = 2 - \frac{\ln(1 - \varphi_{cl})}{\ln C_\infty} \tag{99}$$

As $(1 - \varphi_{cl})$ represents the loose-packed matrix relative fraction $\varphi_{l.m.}$, the equation (99) can be written in the equivalent form [173]:

$$d_r = 2 - \frac{\ln \varphi_{l.m.}}{\ln C_\infty} = 2 - \frac{\ln \chi}{\ln C_\infty} \tag{100}$$

where χ is the volume fraction of polymer subjecting to elastic deformation [177].

The impact toughness A_p is a linear function of d_r for polymers [174] and therefore the calibration plot $A_p(d_r)$ can be plotted as follows [174]. At $d_r = 2$, i.e., for smooth fracture surface [170], $A_p = 0$ [180]. If the specimen does not failure in impact tests, it is assumed [177] that for the superplastic state will be realized, [57]:

$$\frac{2(1 - \nu)}{1 - 2\nu} = 40. \tag{101}$$

The limiting value d_r, at which there is a possible fracture is determined according to equation (8). At the greatest possible $\nu = 0.475$ [57], $d_r = 2.974$ and at larger d_r the polymer is not fractured. The impact toughness A_p^e for such specimen can be defined as the ratio of energy of all instrument dial to gross-sectional area [173]. The application of such calibration plot allows to estimate a theoretical value d_r, calculated according to equations (99) and (100), and to compare them to the experimental results, A_p^e. In [167, 168] it is shown that the fractal model describes well the experimental data obtained in impact tests of a filled PHE.

Interphase Layer Fracture

The process of quasi-brittle fracture in polymer composites begins with the critical structural defects (CSD) formation [181,182] and there are several variants of interdependence in the mechanism of formation [172]. There are two probable mechanisms. The first one assumes that CSD appears in polymer matrix and the filler particles limit their growth [171]. Such mechanism means a decreasing size of CSD, a_c when the content of particulate filler, φ_f increases. The second mechanism assumes the formation of CSD in interphase polymer matrix-filler [187] and, in this case, the increase of a_c must be observed in accordance with the well-known filler particles aggregation effect [77].

For filled PHE specimens the second effect was observed, accompanied by aggregation as it was proved by electron microscopy studies [177]. Therefore, for those composites the investigation and description of state and characteristics of the interphase layer, defining a_c, have special relevance, where each of them influences strongly on the mechanical properties of PHE–Gr composites specimens.

As it is known [184], the failure interface is present when its strength is lower than the volumetric strength of a polymer matrix and this condition is the separating boundary between two mechanisms of formation of CSD. Within the framework of Griffith's criterion it can be expressed by [184]:

$$\left(\frac{E_{12}G_{in}}{a_{12}}\right)^{1/2} < \left(\frac{E_2 G_{Ic2}}{a_2}\right)^{1/2} \quad (102)$$

where indexes 1 and 2 are related to the different phases of the composite (phase 1 is stronger than phase 2). This means that index 1 is related to the filler (graphite), and index 2 to the polymer matrix (PHE). In (102) the following notation is utilized: E_{12} and E_2 are elasticity modulus of the interphase layer and PHE; G_{in} and G_{Ic2} are critical strain energy release rates of the interphase layer and PHE; a_{12} and a_2 are CSD sizes for filled PHE and matrix PHE, respectively.

In the absence of interfacial chemical bonds it is accepted [184]:

$$E_{12} \approx \left(E_1 E_2\right)^{1/2}, \quad (103)$$

and

$$G_{in} \approx \left(G_{Ic1} G_{Ic2}\right)^{1/2}. \quad (104)$$

When considering these approximations the inequality (102) becomes [118]:

$$\left(\frac{a_2}{a_{12}}\right) < \left(\frac{E_2 G_{Ic2}}{E_1 G_{Ic1}}\right)^{1/2}. \quad (105)$$

If as the lowest limit for a_{12} in the inequality (105) we assume the equality sign, the values E_1 and G_{Ic1} for graphite are constant. E_2 and G_{Ic2} for PHE are also assumed constant, as the existing theories of filled polymer suppose identical structure for the initial polymer and the polymer matrix [5]. As it is known [9], the Griffith's equation is valid in a case of quasibrittle fracture and therefore for ductile PHE the impact tests were carried out on the specimens with a sharp notch of length $a = 0.22$ mm, i.e., $a_2 = a = \text{const}$. Thus, equation (105) assumes a constant value a_{12}, which will not agree with experimental results, as a_{12} is varied within large limit for filled PHE specimens: from ~ 30 up to 150 microns [59]. Therefore, approximations (103) and (104) are too rough for the description of real composites properties (at least, composites PHE–Gr) [185,186].

For an explanation of the observed effect of this change (a_c as a function of φ_f) there were used some hypothesis, according to which the level of an interphase adhesion and the value dependent on it, G_{in}, is a function of Δd (equation (59)), keeping approximation (103) invariable. Then for an estimation of G_{in} it is possible to use the following version of the equation (10):

$$G_{in} \approx L_{av}^{\Delta d} \tag{106}$$

G_{in}, calculated according to equation (106), is adopted as the theoretical value of this parameter $\left(G_{in}^{T}\right)$, and G_{in}, estimated according to (102) will be its upper limiting value as experimental $\left(G_{in}^{e}\right)$. The comparison of these values for filled PHE (Fig. 21, curves 1, 2) has shown a good correspondence. Using values calculated according to (105) G_{in}^{T}, according to (101) it is possible to calculate the theoretical size of CSD $\left(a_c^{T}\right)$ and to compare it with those obtained experimentally (a_c^{e} [159]) (Fig. 21, curves 3, 4). A good correspondence between the theoretical and experimental data is observed [118, 185, 186].

MEASUREMENTS OF FRACTAL (MULTIFRACTAL) PARAMETERS OF THE FILLED POLYMER STRUCTURE

Dimension of a Filler Particles Backbone

Measurements of the fractal dimension D_b of filler particles backbone can be made using a known relationship [124, 184]:

$$D_b = \frac{\ln N}{\ln \rho} \tag{107}$$

where N is the number particles by the size ρ.

A greater size of particles has been measured on electron micrographs, and was used as ρ [64,73]. The results of measurements were joined in 10 groups for the subsequent calculation of average values, N and ρ. For filled PHE the linear dependences $N(\rho)$ in double log-log coordinates were obtained, with a slope which the values D_b are determined.

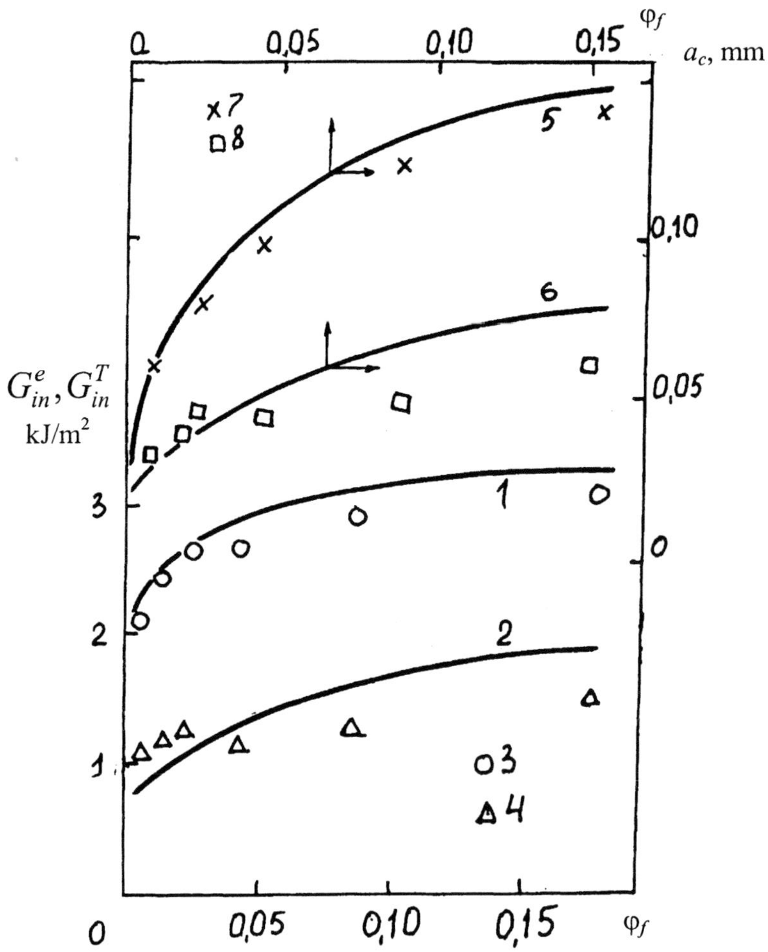

Figure 21. Dependence of critical strain energy release rate on interphase layer G_{in} (1-4) and critical structural defect size a_c (5-8) on a volumetric contents of filler φ_f for PHE–Gr-I (2, 4, 5, 6) and PHE–Gr-II (1, 3, 6, 8) [185].

It is obvious, that at such method of calculation of D_b the fractal dimension in a two-dimensional Euclidean space is determined, whereas the real material should be considered in a three-dimensional Euclidean space. For recalculation of D_b on a case of three-dimensional space the relationship is changed [58]:

$$D3 = \frac{d + D2 \pm [(d - D2)^2 - 2]^{1/2}}{2}, \tag{108}$$

where $D3$ and $D2$ are corresponding fractal dimensions in three and two-dimensional space, $d = 3$. D_b in two-dimensional space ($d = 2$) for a filled PHE varies within the limits 0.43 ÷ 1.60. It means that D_b, obtained by the indicated method falls into the top branch of a relationship $D3$-$D2$ (see Fig. 7 of paper [58]). It means that $D2$ is equal to dimension of one of multipliers of a Cartesian product, the result of which is $D3$ fractal itself. Thus, the application of equation (108) in this case is justified.

Estimation of Self-Similarity

As it was indicated above, any (physical) fractal has fractal properties only in a definite interval. Therefore, after determination of the object dimension the second condition of fractality is the self-similarity evidence of an object in this scale interval [13]. The third condition is a correct choice of the change of the interval.

For confirmation of filler particles backbone self-similarity a special technique can be used [118]. The essence consists in an enlarged microphoto of the fracture surface which is covered by a grid of squares of length α; varying from 4.5 up to 24 mm with a constant ratio $\alpha_i/\alpha_{i+1} = 1.5$, and the number of squares N_i containing (completely or partly) the filler particles is counted. For each measurement, five arbitrary positions of the grid with respect to each microphoto were chosen. If the filler particles backbone is a fractal, then the following relationship must be fulfilled [188]:

$$N_i \sim S_i^{-D_b/2} \qquad (109)$$

where S_i is the square area equal to α_i^2.

In Fig. 20, relationship (109) in double log-log coordinates for PHE–Gr-I with the contents of filler $\varphi_f = 0.044$ and 0.176 is shown. These plots are linear, that allows determining D_b for a two-dimensional Euclidean space. The recalculation of the obtained values of D_b in the corresponding three-dimensional space according to equation (108) has given values 2.62 and 2.73, and $D_b = 2.45$ and 2.79, obtained for the same composites according to equation (106).

For self-similar fractal curves it should be satisfied the condition (at $\alpha_i/\alpha_{i+1} = \text{const}$) [189]:

$$N_i - N_{i+1} \sim \alpha^{-D} \qquad (110)$$

where D is the fractal dimension of the curve.

As in the considered case we use an object with topological dimension 2, equation (110) should be written [190]:

$$N_i - N_{i+1} \sim S_i^{-D_b}. \qquad (111)$$

In Fig. 22 is shown the relation for PHE–Gr-I and PHE–Gr-II, which are linear and pass through the origin. According to (111), the self-similarity of filler particles backbone in the selected interval α_i is observed. Apparently, this self-similarity is statistical [190]. The points corresponding to $\alpha_i = 4.5$ mm do not belong to a common straight line. It means that within the scale range 4.5 – 24 mm the interval of self-similarity of the filler particles backbone is restricted to 7 – 24 mm, or, as observed in the microphotos, ~ 17.5 ÷ 60 μm.

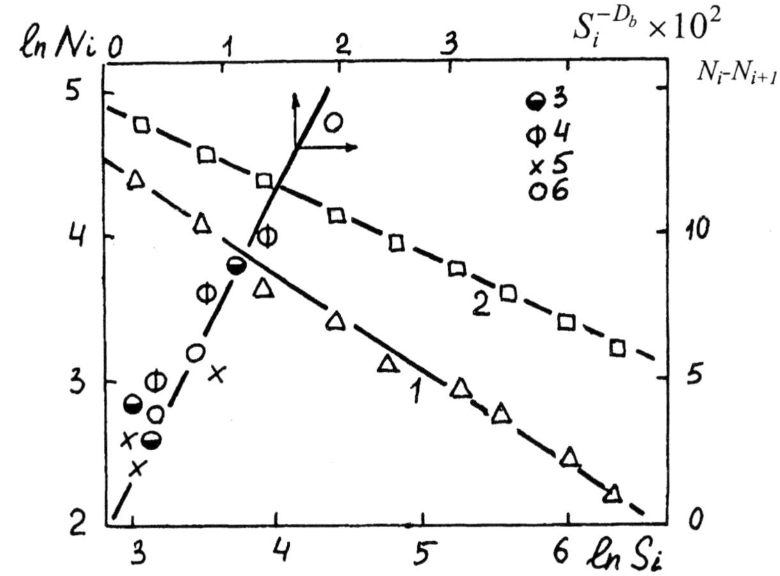

Figure 22. Dependence of covering squares number N_i on their area S_i corresponding to relationship (109) (1, 2) and difference ($N_i - N_{i+1}$) on the value $S_i^{-D_b}$ corresponding to relationship (111) (3-6) for PHE–Gr-I (1-4) and PHE–Gr-II (5, 6) with filler contents $\varphi_f = 0.088$ (1, 3, 5) and 0.176 (2, 4, 6).

As the natural limits of existence of filler particles backbone as a structure, it should be accepted the following general rule [57]: the lower limit is associated to the finite size of the structural elements, while the upper limit is connected with the non-uniform tendency to a fractal dimension limit [23,64]. The lowest limit was taken as the smallest size of the filler particles, which is similar to the graphite powder size, i.e., about 10 μm. As an upper limit of filler particles backbone the existence of the greatest spacing interval between particles λ_p can be determined [65]:

$$\lambda_p = \left[\left(\frac{4\pi}{3\varphi_f}\right)^{1/3} - 2\right]\frac{\rho}{2}. \tag{112}$$

It is easy to see that the maximal value of $\lambda_p \left(\lambda_p^{max}\right)$ is reached at a minimal φ_f and maximal ρ. The effect of the ρ value was stronger than that of φ_f due to a pronounced aggregation of filler particles at high φ_f and the power dependence of λ_p on φ_f in equation (112). Therefore, for estimation of λ_p^{max} it was supposed $\varphi_f = 0.176$ when the largest particles were $\rho \approx 25$ μm. Then, from equation (112), we obtain $\lambda_p^{max} = 55$ μm. Thus, the natural interval of the filler particles backbone is 10 ÷ 55 μm and, as follows from the above estimations, it practically coincides with the interval of self-similarity of the backbone, i.e., 17.5 ÷ 60 μm. Above λ_p^{max} the composite is treated in terms of the mean field approximation as a macroscopically homogeneous system [105].

In [122] it was shown that the minimal scale range of S_i should contain at least one self-similarity iteration. In this case, the condition for the ratio of maximal S_{max} and minimal S_{min} areas of the covering squares should be satisfied [122]:

$$S_{max}/S_{min} > 2^{2/D_b} \tag{113}$$

It is obvious, that the maximal range is obtained for minimal values of D_b. Then, taking into account the limitation S_{max} = 576 mm^2 and S_{min} = 49 mm^2 defined above, we have 576/49 > 2^2 or 11,76 > 4, i.e., the scale range is chosen correctly.

The number of interactions of the self-similarity μ can be found from the relationship [112]:

$$\left(S_{max}/S_{min}\right)^{D_b/2} > 2^{\mu}. \tag{114}$$

Using the above values of equation (114) parameters, we obtain μ = 3.577, i.e., under conditions of experiment the number of self-similarity iterations is more than one, which confirms that the estimation of D_b is correct.

Dimension of a Surface of Filler Particles Aggregates

The measurements of the fractal dimension of filler particles aggregates in two-dimensional Euclidean space ($d_{sur}2$) is carried out on a contour of particles projection on a fracture surface obtained from the electron micro graphs, according to "cells" methods[188]. The enlarged micrographs of filler particles boundary covered with a grid of squares of side length α_i, varying from 4.5 mm up to 24 mm with a constant ratio α_i/α_{i+1} = 1.5, and afterwards the squares number N_i containing (completely or partly) the filler particle boundary were counted. For each measurement, five arbitrary positions of a grid concerning a micrograph were selected. If a filler particle boundary is a fractal curve, the following relationship should be fulfilled [188]:

$$N_i \sim \alpha_i^{-d_{sur}/2}. \tag{115}$$

In order to obtain the fractal dimension of a surface of filler particles aggregates in a three-dimensional Euclidean space equation (108) will be used. The check of self-similarity of the indicated surfaces is made according to (110). A surface of the graphite aggregate for a filled PHE having statistical self-similarity in a range of linear scales ~ (1 ÷ 6) × 10^{-7} m. can be observed.

Dynamic Dimension of Structure

There are a number of techniques to determine the fractal dimension d_f of polymers (polymer matrixes) structures, for instance, small angle X-ray [192]. As it was indicated by Tsallis [192] a measurement of fractal dimension of real materials by direct application of mathematical definitions could appear extremely work-consuming and often impossible. The situation becomes complicated by the known fact [186] of the existence of two types of fractal dimension – statistical (only geometrical) and dynamic. Therefore, for glassy polymers by their thermodynamic non-equilibrium of their structure d_f is a function of the external effects – temperature, strain rate, pressure, etc [193]. Therefore, the simplest way for the estimation of d_f is the use of glassy polymers properties, which are considered only determined by structural level in scales 3 ÷ 50Å [194].

The relation of yield stress σ_Y and elasticity modulus E for glassy polymers can be expressed as follows [162]:

$$\frac{\sigma_Y}{E} = \frac{(1-2\nu)}{6(1+\nu)}. \tag{116}$$

The combination of equations (9) and (116) at $d = 3$ allows to obtain the following equation:

$$\frac{\sigma_Y}{E} = \frac{3-d_f}{3d_f} \tag{117}$$

from which it is possible to obtain dynamic d_f by results of mechanical tests.

As it is known [194], yield strain ε_Y can be determined by two ways. First of them and more often used with materials which at deformation find out a maximum of stress in a yielding point (so-called "upper yield stress") and in this case ε_Y is the strain corresponding to an indicated maximum of stress $\left(\varepsilon'_Y\right)$. For a considerable number of rigid chain polymers and polymers in condition of impact tests ε'_Y is the strain corresponding to the point of intersection of tangents to portions of elasticity and cold flow $\left(\varepsilon''_Y\right)$. When taking into account that in the latter case as σ_Y corresponding to this point stress is accepted, it is possible to write [193]:

$$\varepsilon''_Y = \frac{\sigma_Y}{E} \tag{118}$$

In [194] it was shown that the two ways of values are connected by a simple equation:

$$\varepsilon'_Y = 3\varepsilon''_Y. \tag{119}$$

The combination of equations (117) and (119) allows obtaining a final relationship for the determination of dynamic fractal dimension d_f of polymers (polymer matrixes) structure under a yielding process characteristic ε_Y (defined as ε'_Y) [193]:

$$\frac{3-d_f}{d_f} = \varepsilon'_Y. \tag{120}$$

For ideal rubbers $d_f = 3$ [177] and $\varepsilon_Y = 0$, that means an absence of yielding.

The comparison of values for d_f determined by method of small angle X-ray [191] and calculated according to equation (120) show a good correspondence.

Multifractal Parametrization

a) Cantor set

For calculation of the multifractal characteristics of filled polymers as mathematical model the Cantor set is utilized (Fig. 1) [51,52,195]. At the construction of Cantor set from an initial section of length 1, the length of two stayed sections will be ~ 0.677 [30]. Then this value can be divided proportionally by a filler particle size and the spacing interval between surfaces of adjacent filler particles, using the average values. They will correspond to scales l_1 and l_2. The general probability of filler polymers fracture p, apparently, is equal to unit. This value is divided under the condition of $p_1 + p_2 = p$ as follows [51]. If the adhesion degree in a system "polymer matrix-filler" is large, the crack can move in a equiprobable way both on the matrix, and on the interphase layer, i.e., $p_1 = p_2 = 0.5$. This condition is valid for PHE–Gr-II with activated filler. For PHE–Gr-I without processing of the filler the condition $p_1 > p_2$ was accepted, i.e., the failure of interphase boundary is more probable than the matrix (as conditions eliminate fracture of a filler particles). Several values for p_1 (0.7; 0.8; 0.9 and 0.95) and p_2 (0.3; 0.2; 0.1 and 0.05) are utilized. Furthermore, by applying the scheme of the multifractal diagram construction [30], it is necessary to use the following relationships:

$$\ln(n/m)\ln(l_1/l_2) - \ln(n/m-1)\ln(l_1) = q[\ln(p_1)\ln(l_2) - \ln(p_2)\ln(l_1)] \tag{121}$$

$$\alpha = \frac{\ln(p_1) + (n/m-1)\ln(p_2)}{\ln(l_1) + (n/m-1)\ln(l_2)}, \tag{122}$$

$$f = \frac{(n/m-1)\ln(n/m-1) - (n/m)\ln(n/m)}{\ln(l_1) + (n/m-1)\ln(l_2)}, \tag{123}$$

$$(q-1)D_q = q\alpha(q) - f(q) \tag{124}$$

where n and m are quantities of each of Cantor's set segments, q is an index, α is scaling exponent describing concentration of singularities, f is the dimension of singularities α, D_q are generalized dimensions Renyi.

For computer calculation and construction of multifractal diagrams an algorithm and program are designed [51] in accordance to which values l_1, l_2 and p_1 ($p_2 = 1 - p_1$) with allowance for studied structure parameters, and then with the use of equation (121) at two values q, equal to –40 and + 40, values for α are calculated. Furthermore, according to equation (124) D_∞ at $q = +40$ and $D_{-\infty}$ at $q = -40$ are calculated. If $D_\infty \neq D_{+40} \neq \ln p_1/\ln l_1$, changing l_1, l_2 and p_1 the calculation is finished by the plots construction, which are similar to those shown in Fig. 5.

b) Sierpinski Carpet

For multifractal parameterization of inhomogeneous structures as the mathematical model, Sierpinski carpet is chosen (Fig. 3) [13,124], and the objects of study – electron micrographs of structure, can be converted by scanning in graphic file with "BMP" format.

For the calculation of the multifractal characteristics of two-dimensional structures it is necessary to present a combination of zero points and units, as each element of structure receives only two possible values, which correspond to one bit of information. Thus, the area occupied by only white (or only black) pixels is compared to a standard measurement. At the same time it is known, that scanners and digital video cameras work in a graphic Grayscale regime, at which each pixel is represented by 1 byte. It corresponds to 256 gradations of a gray scale. Therefore at multifractal parameterization of such structures it is important define correctly the threshold value of gray, at which we should convert images from a Grayscale mode to a black- and – white mode, where each point of the image will be characterized only by two possible states.

For the analysis of contrast micrographs of structures we have used a procedure of the 256 – colour image on the monochrome format. The file in graphic format BMP (size 512 × 512) transfer from the camera to a video memory PC and by changing the current graphic pallet the necessary threshold value of gray level can be chosen, The tints with the greater intensity were equated to white color and those with a lower intensity are considered black. After that, the obtained monochrome image replicated in the operative memory, where it was represented by two-dimensional massive 512 × 512 byte files describing the given structure, is obtained. From equation (4), the exponents of weight $\tau(q)$ represent a derivative of the functional dependence of a log cells weighted number $N(q, \delta)$ on log of the cell size δ. The value for $\tau(q)$ is calculated as follows: the studied structure covered with a set of square cells with the side δ_k = 2, 4, 8, 16, 32, 64, 128, 256 squares and for each set d_k ($k = 1, \ldots, 8$) the calculus of the characteristic function $N(q, \delta)$ as the normalized number of points occupied by the investigated set in the given cell was carried out. The normalization was made by calculation of the value of the total number of points of one particular color. The calculations were made for all $k = 1,\ldots,8$ and the plotted relation $\ln(N(q, \delta))$ on $\ln(\delta_k)$, then the slope was calculated by the least squares method which represent an exponent of weight τ for a given q. After the realization of similar operations for all q in an interval from $-\infty$ up to ∞ with a step 1 plotted relation $\tau(q)$, then under equation (7), we can calculate values for f, α and D for each q. The $\alpha(q)$ were calculated with the help of numerical derivation.

With the purpose to test this technique we tested the multifractal spectra for a model Sierpinski carpet (Fig. 3a) with exactly known fractal dimension (D_{theor} = ln 12/ln 4 ≈ 1.7925), measurements were made for a set of scales δ_k = 2, 4, 8, 16, 32, 64 on a massive 128 × 128 of squares. As well as it was necessary to expect for a geometrically regular fractal, the spectrum $f(\alpha)$ has degenerated in a point where the dependence $D(q)$ – in a straight line and the values $D = f = \alpha$ are equal to D_{theor}. However, at usage of additional scales δ_k, not being integer divisors of the image side length, the measured values f_0, α_0 and D_0 differed from theoretical on 1 – 2 %. The obtained spectra found out a weak multifractal behavior, that suggested the existence of the scale effect intrinsic to a given technique (the condition $\delta_k \to 0$ is not reached). By normalization of the area really covered to the given scales it was shown that can be a little different from the common area of the investigated structure.

At the multifractal analysis of two-dimensional structures, as was mentioned above, an original image from 256-colour format was converted in monochrome with the area covered with points of one of two possible colors (black or white). Some lacks of such calculations can be considered, such as the information on the image is lost, as the relief of three-dimensional image was replace by a flat one; at second, by the selection of different magnitudes of threshold value of a gray level the different monochrome images could be obtained; In the case of multifractal parameterization of compact aggregated structures, for example, filled polymers, where interphase boundaries of structural components are blurred, the given technique is inapplicable, as the two-dimensional Euclidean area, strictly speaking, can not be fractal. At increase of the number of iterations, the perimeter (line) of a Koch figure diverges, and the area remains finite, as all the figure can be contained by a circumference of definite radius.

All those problems can be avoided if we analyze not black – and – white, but initial 256 – color volumetric image of the structure, interpreting the value of tint gray for each pixel of the image as "depth" or distance up to a reference point. Thus, more dark areas described by smaller intensities of gray color, will correspond to more remote surface points of studied structure. More light areas described by large intensities will correspond to surface points located closer to the spectator. Thus, the studied structure surface "is immersed" in a layer of thickness 256 arbitrary units of "depth", each of which corresponds to one gray gradation. The area of this surface at tendency to zero of the measurement scale will deviate, i.e., the surface will find out fractal and (or) multifractal properties.

With allowance of all the mentioned techniques of parameterization of inhomogeneous and complicated structures immersed in a three-dimensional Euclidean space, the main statements are described on formalism. The investigated structure (surface in a three-dimensional Euclidean space) covered with a set of elementary parallelepipeds, the basis represented which squares with the side δ_k = 2, 4, 8, 16, 32, 64, 128, 256 pixels, and height lied in range Z_k = 1, 2, 4, 8, 16, 32, 64, 128 gray gradations for each δ_k respectively. The values of the characteristic function $N(q, \delta)$ calculated by summation for all cells, fills a parallelepiped by the size 512 × 512 × 256. Normalization is made in reference to the total number of image points. Values for f, α and D for each q in an interval from $-\infty$ up to ∞ are determined according to equation (6).

Additionally with the help of the described techniques, the studied structure surface area in arbitrary units "the size of a pixel of the image per unit of gray level" is calculated. Thus a surface is approximated by a set from 512 × 512 of rectangular prisms, based on square pixels, and the lengths of the lateral sides equaled to the difference between "height" of the given pixel basis and basis of four nearest neighbors. Thus, the surface area S consist of constant and not fractal component S_{nf}, equal to the total quantity of the image pixels and fractal part $S - S_{nf}$, dependent on the roughness degree of a studied structure surface.

This technique was performed by the way of a computer program [60], with the help each one investigates inhomogeneous structures of oriented polymethylmethacrylate, deformed epoxy polymers and carbon fibers [28,196,197].

CONCLUSIONS

Considering a particulate filled polymer as a heterogeneous system, the possibility of using fractal analysis methods, methods of synergetics and an irreversible aggregation models for the description of filled polymers and their components structure is shown. The complexity of filled polymers structure and their polyfractality predetermines the application of a multifractal formalism. The necessity of such approach is connected to a dynamic non-equilibrium state of different components of filled regions, which are the result of an interaction of filler and polymer matrix. The role of a filler particles is the aggregation during production of filled polymers and its influence on the structural characteristics of these materials are shown. A feature of oriented filled polymers is the defining role of the fractal dimension of a chain fragment between entanglement nodes. The polyfractal model of filled polymers structure allowing a description of their properties is discussed. The experimental methods of measurement of fractal and multifractal parameters of filled polymers structure are listed.

REFERENCES

[1] Gladkov S.O. *The Physics of Composites.* Moscow, Nauka, 1999.
[2] Pomogailo A.D. *Uspekhi Khimii*, 66, 750 (1997).
[3] Beloshenko V.A., Askadskii A.A., Varyukhin V.N. *Uspekhi Khimii*, 67, 410 (1998).
[4] Lipatov Yu.S. *Physicochemical Bases of Polymer Filling*. Moscow, Khimia, 1991.
[5] Ahmed S., Jones F.R. *J. Mater. Sci.*, 25, 4933 (1990).
[6] *Handbook of Fillers and Reinforcement for Plastics*. Ed. Katz H.S., Milewski J.V. Amsterdam, Van Nostrand Reinhold, 1979.
[7] *Multicomponent Polymer Systems*. Ed. Gjuld R.F. Washington, F.C.S., 1972.
[8] Mandelbrot B.B. *The Fractal Geometry of Nature*. New York, W.H.Freeman and Company, 1988.
[9] Zosimov V.V., Lyamshev L.M. *Uspekhi Fizich. Nauk*, 1765, 361 (1995).
[10] Shreder M. *Fractals, Chaos, Power Series*. Moscow-Izhevsk, RC Lynamics, 2001.
[11] Kronover R.M. *Fractals and Chaos in dynamic systems*. Moscow, Postmarket, 2000.
[12] Shogenov V.N., Kozlov G.V. *Fractal Clusters in Physicochemistry of Polymers*. Nalchik, "Polygraphservice and T", 2002.
[13] Feder E. *Fractals*. New York, Plenum Press, 1989.
[14] Meakin P. *Phys. Rev.* A, 34, 710 (1986).
[15] Morosov A.D. *Introduction in Fractals Theory*. N.Novgorod, Publ. NNSU, 1999.

[16] Vstovskii G.V., Bunin I. Zh., Kolmakov A.G., Tanitovskii I. Yu. *Dokl. RAN*, 343, 613 (1995).
[17] Kolmakov A.G. *Metally*, (6), 37 (1996).
[18] Vstovskii G.V. *Found. Phys*., 27, 1423 (1997).
[19] Bunin I. *Zh. Metally*, (6), 29, (1996).
[20] Zemlyanov M.G., Malinovskii V.K., Novikov V.N. *a.a. Zh. Eksp. Teor. Fiz*, 101, 284 (1992).
[21] Shamurina M.V., Roldugin V.I., Pryamova T.D. *a.a. Kolloid. Zhurn*, 56, 451 (1994).
[22] Shamurina M.V., Roldugin V.I., Pryamova T.D. *a.a. Kolloid. Zhurn*. 57, 580 (1995).
[23] Rammal R., Toulouse G. *J. Phys. Lett.* (Paris), 44, L13 (1983).
[24] Nemilov S.V. *Fizika i Khimia Stekla*, 13, 801 (1987).
[25] Kozlov G.V., Novikov V.U. *Synergetics and Fractal Analysis of Gross-linked Polymers*. Moscow, Klassika, 1988.
[26] Novikov V.U., Kozlov G.V. *Uspekhi Khimii*, 69, 378 (2000).
[27] Novikov V.U., Kozlov G.V. *Uspekhi Khimii,* 69, 572 (2000).
[28] Novikov V.U., Kozitskii D.V., Deev I.S., Ivanova V.S., Kobets L.P. *Plast. Massy,* (1), 7 (2001).
[29] Hentschel H.G.E., Procaccia I. *Physica D*, 8, 435 (1983).
[30] Halsey T.C., Jensen M.H., Kadanoff L.P. *a.a. Phys. Rev. A*, 33, 1141 (1986).
[31] McCauley J.L. *Int. J. Modern Phys. B*, 3, 821 (1989).
[32] Paladin G., Vulpiani A. *Phys. Rep.,* 156, 147 (1987).
[33] Aharony A. *Physica A*, 168, 479 (1990).
[34] Grassberger P. *J. Stat. Phys.,* 51, 135 (1988).
[35] Gosenza M.G. *Phys. Rev. A*, 39, 2734 (1989).
[36] Su Z. *Phys. Rev. A,* 36, 3515 (1987).
[37] Broggi G. *Phys. Rev. A*, 39, 434 (1989).
[38] Vicsek T. *Physica A*, 168, 490 (1990).
[39] Manna S.S., Vicsek T. *J. Stat. Phys*., 64, 525 (1991).
[40] Vstovskii G.V., Bunin I. *Zh. J. Adv. Mater*, 1, 230 (1994).
[41] Giona M. *Phys. A*, 24, 367 (1991).
[42] Godreche C., Luck J.M. *J. Phys. A*, 23, 3769 (1990).
[43] Salejda W. *Int. J. Modern Phys. B*, 5, 825(1991).
[44] Vstovskii G.V., Kolmakov A.G. *Fizika i Khimia Obrab. Mater*., (6), 69 (1995).
[45] Novikov V.U., Kozistkii D.V., Deev I.S. *a.a. Materialovedenie*, (11), 17 (2000).
[46] Williford R.E. *Scripta Metal.,* 22, 1749 (1988)
[47] Ivanova V.S., Kuseev I.R., Zakirnichnaya M.M. Synergetics and Fractals. *Universality of Materials Mechanical Behavior.* Ufa, Pull. UGNTU, 1998.
[48] Novikov V.U. In book: "*Fractals and Applied Synergetics*". Moskow, Publ. MSOU, 2001, p. 27.
[49] Olemskoi A.I., Flat A.V. *Uspechi Fizich. Nauk*, 163, 1 (1993).
[50] Novikov V.U. *Materialovedenie* (2002, in press).
[51] Kozlov G.V., Novikov V.U., Mikitaev A.K. *Probl. Machinostr. i Avtomatiz*., (3-6), 35 (1996).
[52] Novikov V.U., Kozlov G.V., Bilibin A.V. *Materialovedenie*, (10), 14 (1998).
[53] Underwood E.E., Banerji K. *Mater. Sci. Engng*., 80, 1, (1986).
[54] Mu Z.Q., Lung C.-W. *J. Phys. D*, 21, 848 (1988).

[55] Zhang S.-Z., Lung C.-W. *J. Phys. D*, 22, 790 (1989).
[56] Tanaka M., Iizuka H. *Zt schr. Metallk.*, 82, 442 (1991).
[57] Balankin A.S. *Synergetics of Deformable Body*. Moscow, MO SSSR, 1991.
[58] Vstovskii G.V., Kolmakov A.G., Terent'ev V.F. *Metally*, (4), 164 (1993).
[59] Kozlov G.V., Abaev A.M., Novikov V.U. *Materialovedenie*, (5), 31 (1997).
[60] Novikov V.U., Kozistkii D.V., Ivanova V.S. *Materialovedenie*, (8), 12 (1999).
[61] Semenov B.I., Agibalov S.N., Kolmakov A.G. *Materialovedenie*, (7), 25 (1999).
[62] Malyshev V.N., Kolmakov A.G., Bunin I. *Zh. Fizika i Khimia obrab. Mater.*, (5), 77 (1997).
[63] Ivanova V.S. *Synergetics and Fractals in Radiative Material Science*. Moscow. Intercontact Science, 1997.
[64] Balankin A.S., Isotov A.D., Lasarev V.B. *Neorganich. Mater.*, 29, 451 (1993).
[65] Bobryshev A.N., Kozomazov V.N., Babin L.O., Solomatov V.I. *Synergetics of Composite Materials*. Lipestk, NPO ORIUS, 1994.
[66] Pfeifer P., Avnir D. *J. Chem. Phys.*, 79, 3558 (1983).
[67] Zubarev A.Yu. *Kolloid. Zhurn.*, 54, 57 (1992).
[68] Kryuchkov Yu.N. *Kolloid. Zhurn.*, 53, 752 (1991).
[69] Kuznestov S.Yu., Ur'ev N.B. *Kolloid. Zhurn.*, 53, 755 (1991).
[70] Kulak M.I. *Dokl. BSSR*, 35, 704 (1991).
[71] Ladyzhenskii I.Ya. *Kolloid. Zhurn.,* 54, 80 (1992).
[72] Vysotskii V.V., Roldugin V.I., Pryamova T.D. *a.a. Kolloid. Zhurn.*, 57, 580 (1995).
[73] Novikov V.U., Kozlov G.V. *Mekhanika Kompozith. Mater.*, 35, 269 (1999).
[74] Kozlov G.V., Gazaev M.A., Novikov V.U., Mikitaev A.K. *Pisma ZhTF*, 22, 31 (1996).
[75] Long Q.Y., Suqin L., Lung C.-W. *J. Phys. D*, 24, 602 (1991).
[76] Sumita M., Tsukumo Y., Miyasaka K., Ishikawa K. *J. Mater. Sci.,* 18, 1758 (1983).
[77] Kozlov G.V., Ovcharenko E.N., Lipatov Yu.S. *Dokl. NAN Ukraine*, (11), 128 (1999).
[78] Mikos A.G., Peppas N.A. *J. Chem. Phys.*, 88, 1337 (1988).
[79] Witten T.A., Sander L.M. *Phys. Rev. Lett.*, 47, 1400 (1981).
[80] Weitz D.A., Huang J.S., Lin M.Y., Sung J. *Phys. Rev. Lett.*, 53, 1657 (1984).
[81] Mashukov N.I., Mikitaev A.K., Gladyshev G.P. *a.a. Plast. Massy*, (11), 21 (1990).
[82] Shiyan A.A. *Fizika Tverd. Tela*, 47, 2517 (1995).
[83] Botet R., Jullien R. *Phys. Rev. Lett.*, 55, '943 (1985).
[84] Kozlov G.V., Shogenov V.N., Afaunova Z.I. *a.a. Electron. Zhurn.* "Issledovano v Rossii". 1999, 033, http: //Zhurnal mipt, rssi, ru/articles/1999/033, pdt.
[85] Matsushita M., Honda K., Toyoki H., Hayakawa Y. *J. Phys. Soc. Japan*, 55, 2618 (1986).
[86] Sahimi M., McKarnin M., Nordahl T., Tirrell M. *Phys. Rev. A*, 32, 590 (1985).
[87] Meakin P., Stanley H.E., Coniglio A., Witten T.A. *Phys. Rev. A*, 32, 2364 (1985).
[88] Tokuyama M., Kawasaki K. *Phys. Letters*, 100A, 337 (1984).
[89] Vannimenus J. *Physica D*, 38, 351 (1989).
[90] Aharony A., Harris A.B. *J. Stat. Phys.*, 54, 1091 (1989).
[91] Meakin P. *Phys. Rev. A*, 29, 997 (1984).
[92] Beloshenko V.A., Kozlov G.V., Varyukhin V.N., Slobodina V.G. *Acta Polymerica*, 48, 181 (1997).
[93] Chmutin I.A., Letyagin S.V., Shevchenko V.G., Ponomarenko A.T. *Vysokomolek. Soed. A,* 36, 699 (1994).

[94] Botet R., Jullien R. *J. Phys. A,* 17, 2517 (1984).
[95] Shiyan A.A. *Vysokomolek. Soed. B*, 37, 1578 (1995).
[96] Kozlov G.V., Mirzoev R.S., Lipatov Yu.S. *Mechanika Kompozith. Mater.*, 38, 253 (2002).
[97] Ahmed S., Jones F.R. *Composites*, 19, 277 (1988).
[98] Cates M.E., Witten T.A. *Phys. Rev. A*, 35, 1809 (1987).
[99] Kozlov G.V., Abaev A.M. *Poverchnost* (2003), in press.
[100] Belousov V.N., Kozlov G.V., Mikitaev A.K., Lipatov Yu.S. *Dokl. AN SSSR*, 313, 690 (1990).
[101] Kozlov G.V., Beloshenko V.A., Varyukhin V.N., Lipatov Yu.S. *Polymer*, 40, 1045 (1999).
[102] Kozlov G.V., Novikov V.U., Gazaev M.A., Mikitaev A.K. *Inzhenerno-Fizich. Zhurn.*, 71, 241 (1998).
[103] Budtov V.P. *The Physical Chemistru of Polymer Solutions*. Sanct-Peterburg, Khimia, 1992.
[104] Kozlov G.V., Abaev A.M., Serdyuk V. D. *a.a. Plast. Massy*, (11), 27 (1999).
[105] Chow T.S. *Polymer*, 32, 29 (1991).
[106] Vilgis T.A. *Physica A*, 153, 341 (1988).
[107] Alexander S., Orbach R. *J. Phys. Lett.* (Paris), 43, L625 (1982).
[108] Kozlov G.V., Temiraev K.B., Shustov G.B., Mashukov N.I. *J. Appl. Polymer Sci.*, 85, 1137 (2002).
[109] Novikov V.U., Kozlov G.V., Mikitaev A.K. *Materialovedenie*, (7), 2(1998).
[110] Lhuillier D. *J. Phys.* France, 49, 705 (1988).
[111] Rammal R., Toulouse G., Vannimenus J. *J. Phys.* France, 45, 389 (1984).
[112] Shklowskii B.I., Efros A.L. *Uspekhi Fizich. Nauk*, 117, 401 (1975).
[113] Family F. *J. Stat. Phys.*, 36, 881 (1984).
[114] Kozlov G.V., Temiraev K.B., Shetov R.A., Mikitaev A.K. *Materialovedenie*, (2), 34 (1999).
[115] Theocaris P.S. *Colloid Polymer Sci.*, 268, 1118 (1990).
[116] Novikov V.U., Tkalenko P.A. *Mechanika Kompozitn. Mater.*, 36, 467 (1996).
[117] Hentschel H.G.E., Deutch J.M. *Phys. Rev. A,* 29, 1609 (1984).
[118] Novikov V.U., Kozlov G.V., Bur'yan O.Yu. *Mechanika Kompozith. Mater*, 36, 3 (2000).
[119] Avnir D., Farin D., Pfeifer P. *Nature*, 308, 261 (1984).
[120] Wu S. *J. Polymer Sci.: Part. B: Polymer Phys.*, 27, 723 (1989).
[121] Yakubov T.S. *Dokl. AN SSSR*, 303, 425 (1988).
[122] Pfeifer P. *Appl. Surf. J.,* 18, 146 (1984).
[123] Pfeifer P. In book: "*Fractals in Physics*". Ed. Pietronero L., Tosatti E. Amsterdam-Oxford-New York-Tokyo, North-Holland, 1986, p. 72.
[124] Ivanova V.S., Balankin A.S., Bunin I.Zh., Oksogoev A.A. *Synergetics and Fractals in Science of Materials.* Moscow, Nauka, 1994.
[125] Kubat J., Rigdahl M., Welander M. *J. Appl. Polymer Sci.,* 39, 1527 (1990).
[126] Beloshenko V.A., Kozlov G.V., Lipatov Yu.S. *Fizika Tverd. Tela*, 36, 2903 (1994).
[127] Vysostkii V.V., Roldugin V.I., Pryamova T.D., Shamurina M.V. *Kolloid. Zhurn.*, 57, 299 (1995).

[128] Stanley H.E. In book: "*Fractals in Physics*". Ed. Pietronero L., Tosatti E. Amsterdam-Oxford-New York-Tokyo, North-Holland, p. 436.
[129] Kozlov G.V., Kolodei V.S., Lipatov Yu.S. *Materialovedenie*, (11), 34 (2002).
[130] Flory P.Y. *Pure Appl. Chem.*, 56, 305 (1984).
[131] Novikov V.U., Kozlov G.V. *Materialovedenie*, (12), 8 (1999).
[132] Zhenyi M., Langford S.C., Dickinson J.T., Engelhard M.H., Baer D.R. *J. Mater. Res.*, 6, 183 (1991).
[133] Kalinchev E.L., Sakovtseva M.B. *Properties and Processing of Thermoplasts*. Leningrad, Khimia, 1983.
[134] Burya A.I., Shogenov V.N., Kozlov G.V., Cholodilov O.V. *Materials, technologies, instruments*, 4, 39 (1999).
[135] Kozlov G.V., Shogenov V.N., Mikitaev A.K. *Inzhenerno-Fizich. Zhurn.*, 71, 1012 (1998).
[136] Kozlov G.V., Beloshenko V.A., Varyukhin V.N. *Ukrainian Fizich. Zhurn.*, 43, 322 (1998).
[137] Meakin P. *Phys. Rev. A*, 27, 2616 (1983).
[138] Meakin P. *Phys. Rev. B*, 30, 4207 (1984).
[139] *Ultra-high Modulus Polymers*. Ed. Ciferri A., Ward I.M. London, Applied Science Publishers, 1981.
[140] Aloev V.Z., Kozlov G.V. The Physics of orientational Phenomena in Polymer Materials. Nalchik, "*Polygraphservice and T*", 2002.
[141] Sokolov G.V., *Uspekhi Fizich. Nauk*, 150, 221 (1986).
[142] Kozlov G.V., Gazaev M.A., Beloshenko V.A. *a.a. Ukrainian Fizich. Zhurn.*, 40, 883 (1995).
[143] Havlin S., Ben-Avraham D. *Phys. Rev. A*, 26, 1728 (1982).
[144] Bartenev G.M., Frenkel S.Ya. *The Physics of Polymers*. Leningrad, Khimia, 1990.
[145] Balankin A.S. *Pisma v ZhTF*, 16, 14 (1990).
[146] Beloshenko V.A., Kozlov G.V., Slobodina V.G., Prut E.V., Grinev V.G. *Vysokomolek. Soed. B*, 37, 1089 (1995).
[147] Plummer C.J., Donald A.M. *Macromolecules*, 23, 3929 (1990).
[148] Beloshenko V.A., Grinev V.G., Kuznetsov E.N. *a.a. Fizika i Technika Vysok. Davl.*, 4, 91 (1994).
[149] Kramer E. *J. Polymer Engng. Sci.*, 24, 761 (1984).
[150] Kozlov G.V., Abaev A.M., Komalov A.S. *a.a. Plast. Massy*, (6), 28 (1995).
[151] Kozlov G.V., Beloshenko V.A. *Plast. Massy*, (7), 14 (2000).
[152] Ivanova V.S., Balankin A.S., Bannych O.A. *Metally*, (2), 11 (1992).
[153] Krisyuk B.E., Sandakov G.I. *Vysokomolek. Soed. A*, 37, 615 (1995).
[154] Mashukov N.I., Gladyshev G.P., Kozlov G.V. *Vysokomolek. Soed. A*, 33, 2538 (1991).
[155] Belousov V.N., Kozlov G.V., Mashukov N.I., Lipatov Yu.S. *Dokl. RAN*, 328, 706 (1993).
[156] Kozlov G.V., Beloshenko V.A., Varyukhin V.N., Novikov V.U. *Zhurn. Fizich. Issledov.*, 1, 204 (1997).
[157] Aloev V.Z., Kozlov G.V., Beloshenko V.A. *Izvestia KBNC RAN*, (1), 208 (2000).
[158] Mandelkern L. *Polymer J.*, 17, 337 (1985).
[159] Kozlov G.V., Novikov V.U. *Materialovedenie*, (8-9), 3 (1997).
[160] Zhurkov S.N. *Fizika Tverd. Tela*, 25, 3119 (1983).

[161] Vettegren V.I. *Fizika Tverd. Tela*, 26, 1699 (1984).
[162] Kozlov G.V., Sanditov D.S. *Anharmonic Effects and Physico-mechanical Properties of Polymers*, Novosibirsk, Nauka, 1994.
[163] Kozlov G.V., Mikitaev A.K. *Vysokomolek. Soed. B*, 30, 520 (1988).
[164] Shogenov V.N., Kozlov G.V., Gazaev M.A. *a.a. Plast. Massy*, (8), 32 (1986).
[165] Kausch H.H. *Polymer Fracture*. Berlin, Heidelberg, New York, Springer-Verlag, 1978.
[166] Wu S. *J. Appl Polymer Sci.,* 46, 619 (1992).
[167] Kozlov G.V., Beloshenko V.A., Slobodina V.G. *Plast. Massy*, (3) 14 (1996).
[168] Balankin A.S. *Dokl. AN SSSR*, 319, 1098 (1991).
[169] Kozlov G.V., Beloshenko V.A., Varyukhin V.N. *Prikl. Mechanica i Techn. Fizika*, 37, 115 (1996).
[170] Ball R.C. *Physica D.*, 38, 11 (19890).
[171] Abaev A.M., Beloshenko V.A., Kozlov G.V., Mikitaev A.K. *Fizika i Technika Vysok. Davl.,* 8, 102 (1998).
[172] Brown S.K. *Brit. Polymer J.,* 14, 1 (1982).
[173] Kozlov G.V., Novikov V.U. *Prikl. Fizika*, (1), 94 (1997).
[174] Novikov V.U., Kozlov G.V. *Materialovedenie*, (6-7), 42 (1997).
[175] Balankin A.S., Ivanova V.S., Breusov V.P. *Dokl. RAN*, 332, 1080 (1992).
[176] Isotov A.D., Balankin A.S., Lasarev V.B. *Neorganich. Mater.*, 29, 883 (1993).
[177] Balankin A.S., Bugrimov A.L. *Vysokomolek. Soed. A*, 34, 135 (1992).
[178] Balankin A.S., Bugrimov A.L., Kozlov G.V. *Dokl. RAN*, 326, 463 (1992).
[179] Kozlov G.V., Serdyuk V.D., Beloshenko V.A. *Mechanika Kompozith. Mater.*, 30, 691 (1994).
[180] Kozlov G.V., Novikov V.U. *Prikl. Fizika*, (1), 77 (1997).
[181] Kozlov G.V., Mil'man L.D., Novikov V.U., Mikitaev A.K. *Probl. Mashinostr. I Avtomatiz.,* (3-4), 54 (1997).
[182] Kozlov G.V., Novikov V.U., Zaikov G.E. *Plast. Massy*, (5), 21 (1998).
[183] Kozlov G.V., Yanovskii Yu.G., Lipatov Yu.S. *Mechanika Kompozit. Mater. i Konstr.*, 8, 111 (2002).
[184] Wu S. *Polymer Interface and Adhesion*. New York, Marcel Dekker, 1982.
[185] Kozlov G.V., Beloshenko V.A., Mikitaev A.K. *Fiziko-Khimich. Mekhanika Mater.*, 35, 116 (1999).
[186] Kozlov G.V., Novikov V.U., Bur'yan O.Yu. *Materialovedenie,* (11), 13 (1999).
[187] Ishikawa K. *J. Mater. Sci. Lett.,* 9, 400 (1990).
[188] Hansen J.P., Skjeitorp A.T. *Phys. Rev. B,* 38, 2635 (1988).
[189] Farin D., Peleg S., Yavin D., *Avnir D. Langmuir*, 1, 399 (1985).
[190] Pfeifer P., Avnir D., Farin D. *J. Stat. Phys*, 36, 699 (1984).
[191] Kozlov G.V., Ozden S., Dolbin I.V. In book: "*Fractals and Local Order in Polymeric Materials*". Ed. Kozlov G., Zaikov G. New York, Nova Science Publisher. Inc., 2001, p. 89.
[192] Thallis K. In book: "*Fractals in Physics*". Ed. Pietronero L., Tosatti E. Amsterdam-Oxford-New York-Tokyo, North-Holland, p. 98.
[193] Kozlov G.V., Novikov V.U. *Materialovedenie*, (7), 22 (1999).
[194] Kozlov G.V., Beloshenko V.A., Gazaev M.A., Novikov V.U. *Mekhanika Kompozitn. Mater.,* 32, 270 (1996).

[195] Novikov V.U., Kozlov G.V. *The Analysis of Polymers Fracture within the Framework of Fractal Conceptions*. Moscow, Publ. MSOU, 2001.
[196] Novikov V.U., Kozitskii D.V., Deev I.S., Kobets L.P. *Materialovedenie*, (11), 2 (2001).
[197] Novikov V.U. *a.a. Materialovedenie* (2002, in press).

In: Homolytic and Heterolytic Reactions: Problems and Solutions ISBN 1-59033-980-0
Editors: G.E. Zaikov, et al., pp. 91-119

Chapter 3

THE USAGE OF POLY- N,N- DIALLYL- N,N- DIMETHYL AMMONIUM CHLORIDE FOR SOLUTION OF ECOLOGICAL PROBLEMS

G. V. Kozlov, Yu. A. Malkanduev and G. E. Zaikov*

Kabardino- Balkarian State University, 360004, Nal`chik, Chernishevskaya st., 173, Russian Federation

* Institute of Biochemical physics, Russian Academy of Sciences. 119991, Moscow, Kosygin st., 4, Russian Federation

ABSTRACT

The main principles of synthesis of cationic polyelectrolyte poly-N, N- diallyl- N, N- dimethyl ammonium chloride (PDADMACh) are briefly considered. The basic fields of its application for the solution of ecological problems are discussed, particularly, for purification of waste water, oils and selective removal from oils and fates free fatty acids. The fractal model of impurities flocculation with the help of PDADMACh is presented. The methods of control of polymer molecular weight characteristics used representations of irreversible aggregation models and fractal analysis are considered.

Keywords: Radical polymerization, cationic polyelectrolyte, ecological problems, flocculation of impurities, irreversible aggregation models, fractal analysis, molecular weight characteristics.

1. PRODUCTION OF CATIONIC POLYELECTROLYTE

As it is known, a synthesis process of water- soluble cationic polyelectrolyte, particularly, homopolymer poly- N,N- diallyl- N,N- dimethyl ammonium chloride (PDADMACh) with application of chloroallyl, dimethylamine and NaOH is described by the equations:

$$(CH_3)_2NH + ClCH_2 - CH{=}CH_2 + NaOH \longrightarrow (CH_3)_2NCH_2CH{=}CH_2 + NaCl + H_2O \qquad (1)$$

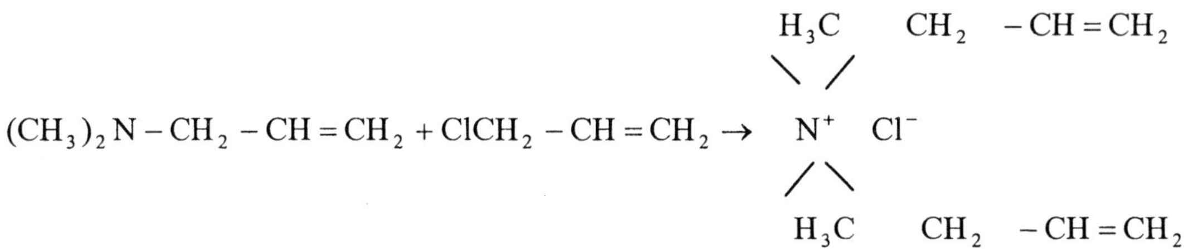

(2)

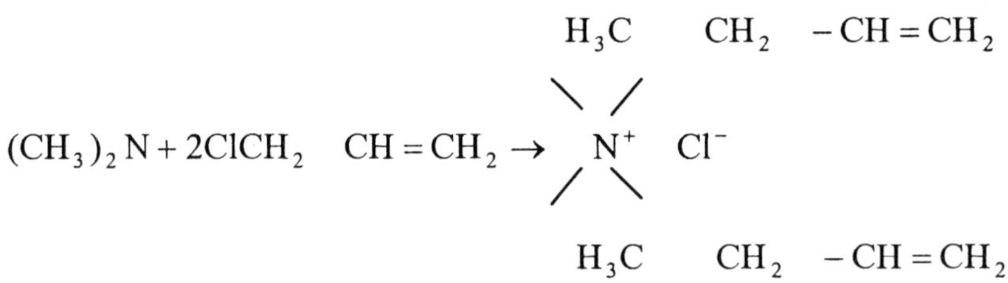

(3)

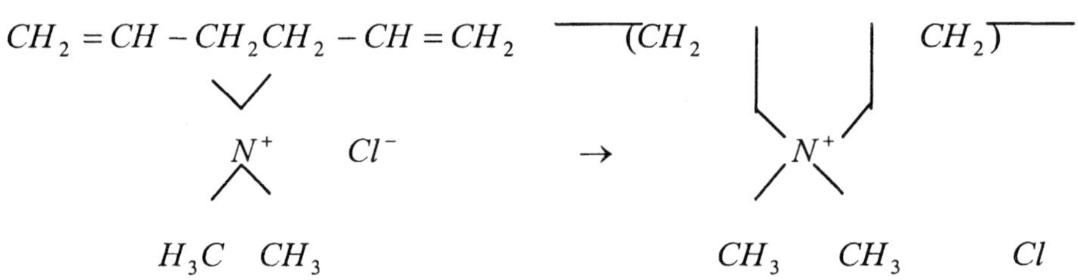

(4)

As follows from this scheme, PDADMACh synthesis can be carried out in one stage, i.e., without intermediate production of trimeric amine- ~~di~~methylallylamine (DMAA) according to equation (3) or in two stages with intermediate production of amine with accordance to equations (1) and (2).

One-stage methods of PDADMACh are cheaper and technological than two-stage methods. However one- stage synthesizes lead, according to equation (3), to final product with the production of some sodium chloride, whose separation from the final product is a work-consuming and technologically difficult operation.

The analysis of the literature data confirms that most often PDADMACh polymerization is performed in aqueous solution with the action of radical initiators of peroxide type. As initiator, ammonium persulfate and other non-organic peroxide compounds are usually utilized. More rarely organic peroxides and diazocompounds are used.

Besides water, alcohols and combinations of several organic compounds can be used as solvents for the polymerization of PDADMACh dimethylsulfoxide, N, N-dimethylformamide. Production of polymers based on DMDMACh is usually carried out at warm temperatures (30÷ 90°C) and atmospheric pressure though in principle the process can be performed in vacuum adding water to the reaction mixture. Photoinitiation methods are known as well as methods of radiation initiation for PDADMACh polymerization. It is known that both photo- and radiation initiated polymerization is inhibited by hydroquinone that points out to a radical mechanism. From literature data several possible variants of technological methods of PDADMACh polymerization are usual, mainly periodic polymerization in adiabatic reactor with stirring.

Methods of continuous polymerization for PDADMACh are also used. This process takes place in piping reactors, cascade of reactors or combined apparatus. In this case the process temperature should be raised gradually from 40 up to 90°C. In these cases for the repouring of providing reaction mass initial solutions of PDADMACh with low concentration (30÷45 %) are used.

Methods of PDADMACh polymerization in emulsion were also described. An emulsion can be stable or reversed depending on the hydrophilic- hydrophobic balance of the system. The polymerization method of PDADMACh in a three- phase emulsive system was also worded out. It is necessary to mention that the difficulty of purification of the final polymeric product and the comparatively large amount of waste make application of the mentioned above methods practically meaningless.

The production of PDADMACh in aqueous solution with usage of periodic action reactor is probably the simplest method of PDADMACh production with characteristics suitable for customer's requirements. At the same time, the viscosity of reactional mass increase in such processes of polymerization is an important factor preventing the usage in these processes of modern reactors with comparatively large volumes, as in these cases a possible appearance of local overheats that naturally leads to a molecular weight decrease.

These lacks are limited by using polymerization of PDADMACh in small volumes – either in thin enough layers or by "granular" polymerization. In these systems PDADMACh solutions with high concentration (80 – 97%) can be used to produce a final polymeric product in solid state. Apparently, polymerization in small volume gives good conditions for heat flow out helping the production of a polymer with substantially larger molecular weight than for polymerization of 50÷ 60 % aqueous solutions of PDADMACh in reactors of periodic action. Besides in this case the productiveness of the process increase its perspective [1].

2. The Solution of Ecological Problems with Usage of Poly- N,N- Diallyl- N,N- Dimethyl Ammonium Chloride

The good properties of this polymer (high and practically universal flocculating ability, comparatively high values of conductivity, heat and light stability, good solubility in water together with satisfactory sanitary and toxical characteristics allows a wide and effective use of PDADMACh in various fields of industry and agriculture. Some examples of practical application of polymer for ecological problems solution will be shown below.

2.1. Application of Polyelectrolytes for Purification of Waste Water at Production of Wood-Fibre Slabs.

It is known that the massive usage in timber slabs production of low quality wood from leaved trees processed by the wet method produces a large amount of wastes of wood with a very negative effect on the timber slabs quality. During the technological process and as a result of different actions, water waste will be muddy by a large amount of degradation products. Existing methods of physical and chemical purification of water waste from wood-fibre slabs production by hydrolysable coagulants provide a complete removal of suspend substance at values as low as 2,0÷ 3,0 g/l. However, difficulties in utilization of massive sediment and clarifying water make this method non-satisfactory for usage in a system of water supply and in machines of wood- fibre slabs production.

The problem of water waste solution should be connected with the necessity of keeping the required quality level of wood- fibre slabs at the obligatory usage of sediment and clarifying water in production process.

One solution to this problem is the application of the technological process of water-soluble cationic polyelectrolytes, which arc capable to dissociate in aqueous medium with polyvalent cation formation. However, these polyelectrolytes and reagents are very deficient and not good to guarantee a complete removal of cations. Therefore, cationic polyelectrolytes based on DADMACh were tested.

PDADMACh was used as the aqueous solution with concentration 1÷4 %. The studies were made on a water waste with dry rest 6450 mg/l, which contains 83 % in weight of substances defined as lignin and carbohydrates suspension substances, 72 % consistent on lignin. The raw material composition (in %) is as follows: wood of leave trees 80, coniferous trees 10, bark about 7, putridity about 2. The volume of water waste is 15÷ 18 m^3 per ton of wood- fibre slabs.

This water waste was separated in 3 different portions by using filters with various pore sizes. The first fraction is constituted by fibrous particles with length higher than 100÷ 200 μm in amount 65÷ 70%, length 250÷600 μm - 5÷12 %, length 600 μm and more – 5%. The second fraction mainly consisted of particles 60÷120 μm and consists of lignin 70%. The third fraction is characterized by the existence of carbohydrates (69%) and lignin (22÷23 %) as high disperse suspension and solutes.

The incorporation of PDADMACh to water waste at certain produces flocculation, aggregation and sedimentation. These phenomena are the result of the stability disturbation of a colloidal system and its coagulation. The main effect on the intensity of processes is made by the dosage of PDADMACh.

A flocculation process at pH= 3,5 ÷ 5,5 and the incorporation of PDADMACh in amount 100÷ 250 mg/l proceeds during 4÷30s. The acidity increases time of flocculation. At small amounts of polyelectrolyte the flocculation practically is not observed.

A massive formation of large flocks and their sedimentation begins in 60÷130s and ends in 8÷30 min. At large dosages of PDADMACh (more than 500 mg/l) flocculation and flocks sedimentation during two and more hours are observed. Volume of sediment depends on polyelectrolyte dosage is the range 7÷12 % in volume of clarified water.

At PDADMACh concentration higher than 500 mg/l and pH higher than 5.5, a sediment does not form and large volume and sharp boundary of phases is not observed.

The color of the analyzed water depends on pH and PDADMACh dosage and can range from brown up to light-yellow. At values of pH higher than 5.5 and large dosages of polyelectrolyte the color of clarified water becomes light brown.

The colloidal- chemical conversions in a system with the incorporation of PDADMACh were estimated by ξ- potential change for suspended particles and on the turbidity index depending on values of medium acidity and PDADMACh dosage. The increase of pH leads to the displacement of potential curves in direction to the polyelectrolyte large dosages and raising of turbidity, which can be also observed at small PDADMACh dosage.

It is established experimentally that the polyelectrolyte reacts chemically with products of the hydrothermal degradation of wood carriers or functional groups of acidic character, mainly with products as lignin. In the region of pH= 5,5÷ 7,5 the purification efficiency of this polymer is small. At pH= 7,5÷9,0 and PDADMACh dosage up to 250 mg/l a clarification efficiency is raised from 37 % up to 82 % at pH= 3,5÷ 4,5 it makes up 63÷ 85 %.

The decrease of carbohydrates contents about 20÷ 23% is observed only in alkali mediums at polyelectrolyte dosages 100÷ 250 mg/l. This can be explained by the ionization of their hydroxylic groups that leads to a chemical interaction with PDADMACh.

It is also established that polyelectrolyte in small degree decreases the contents of fractions of carbohydrates and removes low- molecular weight fraction of substances as lignin. It was established that the PDADMACh usage provides an efficient removal of compounds of water waste- phenols and carbonyl containing compounds (aldehydes, ketones etc).

The phenols contents in water waste is decreased in 1,15÷ 16,5 times, carbonyl compounds in 2.5÷ 5.0 times. The reduction of phenols contents is observed for a wide interval of pH and in the greatest degree in weakly acidic and neutral mediums, carbonyl compounds in acidic medium. The largest efficiency of purification is observed in acidic and weakly acidic medium. The optimal PDADMACh dosage is in limits 150÷ 250mg/l.The increase of a polymer expense does not lead to raising the purification efficiency. The molecular weight of polyelectrolyte does not influence substantially in purification.

Laboratory studies and industrial testing showed that the use of cationic polyelectrolyte leads to an effective purification of water waste formed in the production of wood-fibre slabs from different chemical and fractional compounds and can be recommended for wide usage in this field [2].

2.2. PDADMACh Application for Purification of Vegetable Oils

In vegetable and animal fats different impurities are contained differing in the amount, type of compound and properties. Some of these substances decrease the quality of the product, hamper the technological working and decrease the biological processing of a fatty raw.

A larger part of vegetable oils, obtained in seeds production process, cannot be used directly as a food product without a foregoing purification and elimination of undesirable substances. Nowadays in vegetable oils technology there is a large number of methods of removal of such substances. Sometimes the simple raising of efficiency of these methods do not provide enough degree of removal, leading to substantial losses and to a number of non-wishing sequences that forces to look for new methods of vegetable oils purification.

Vegetable oils used for industrial food production and technical products, as a rule, are subjected to a foregoing purification as the result of which, impurities preventing proceeding of technological process and hampering the quality of production are removed. Among these impurities we should indicate phosphatides which despite of raising the quality of vegetable oils, but decrease the quality of production by- products.

A traditional method of phosphatides removal from oil is a hydration resulting in a loss in their solubility and further sedimentation. However, when performing the hydration process only with water, the full removal of phosphatides from oil is not achieved. Non-hydrated phosphatides make up a substantial part of molecules and create serious difficulties on the following production stages.

Methods of oil purification by the action of strong mineral acids or anhydrides (H_3PO_4, HCl, $(COOH)_2$), tartacil and citric acids are considered. However, these methods have a number of faults. In case of ortophosphoric acid there is a side reaction of this acid with oils producing some oxidation products and resulting in strong corrosive action. Citric acid produces the separation of the sediment presenting a difficult- technological problem.

For the solution of vegetable oils and fats purification problems the cationic polyelectrolyte PDADMACh was used. The process of phospatides removal from vegetable oils with the help of PDADMACh was studied on phase boundary oil- water by means of an intensive stirring of aqueous polymer solutions with processing vegetable and soybean oils. The foregoing hydration of the oil according to the standard technique was carried out. The phosphatides content in oil were determined by the calorimetric method. The oil with aqueous polymer solution in wide concentrations was processed.

The study of non-hydrated phosphatides removal from soybean oil with a polymeric reagent was established and it was concluded that the polymeric reagents are selective only with phosphatides. As a result of the special studies, the optimal doses of polymeric reagents were determined. This allows defining the conditions for a practical full removal of non-hydrated phospatides from oil (below 90 %). For example, in the case of usage of PDADMACh the optimal concentration is 40 mg/l.

Studies of the effect of temperature conditions on the processing of the oil with a special technique earlier described, lead to know the time end of phases contact. It is found that the temperature raising up to 60-80^{0}C in case of PDADMACh usage does not lead to a substantial reduction of process efficiency.

It is necessary to emphasize that PDADMACh, as was shown earlier, is thermally stable until comparatively high temperatures (140^{0}C), which makes it possible to be used at high temperatures.

2.3. Selective Removal of Free Fatty Acids from Oils and Fats

One of the important problems of the process of refining is the removal of free fatty acids from oils and fats. They are formed as the result of chemical conversions in seeds and fats at keeping and processing. The widest spreading method of vegetable oils and fats purification from free fatty acids was the alkali refluxing by way of fats processing in alkaline aqueous solution. The indicated purification method consists of neutralization of free fatty acids by the alkali and proceeds in two stages: interaction of the alkali with free fatty acids with formation of a soap and neutral fats removal from the soap. The process of fats alkali refluxing has a number of faults: saponification of neutral fats by soapstock; removal of neutral fats by soapstock; non-fuel removal of free fatty acids from the oil; the necessity of careful washing of oil after the process; the use of aqueous solutions for refluxing electrolytes.

Several approaches to get a selective removal of free fatty acids from fats are used. They are based on the usage of aqueous solutions of alkali reagents that allows a total removing. With this purpose PDADMACh was used, as it can be used as stationary layer of adsorbent.

The usage of PDADMACh as a chemical reagent instead of traditional alkali chemical reagents gives the possibility to simplify a multistage and work-consuming technology of vegetable oils and fats purification by the following reasons:

- saponification of native fats;
- soap formation;
- soapstocks formation and characteristic for this stage losses of native fats;
- drying process of oil.

A process of adsorptive purification from free fatty acids of various samples of raw fats in a wide range of temperatures (15÷ 90^{0}C) was studied. It was show that the usage of PDADMACh allows to hold the process at lower temperatures and to obtain a refined fat corresponding to the requirements of the standard. Data show the full absence of polymer reagents or polymer fragments in the raw fat.

A regeneration of PDADMACh stationary layer is realized by solvent (petrol, hexane, diethylether) with a subsequent processing of the sorbent by a solution of alkali (1N). The acid number obtained in after the process of washing with a chemical reagent, after vaporization of the solvent makes 60÷80 mg KOH. These obtained “acidic oils” can be rationally used in the production of natural drying oils and alkyl resins [3-4].

3. The Fractal Analysis of Flocculating Ability of Poly-N,N-Diallyl-N,N-Dimethyl Ammonium Chloride

It is well known that both, macromolecular coils [5] and portions of chains [6] in polymers are fractals. This means that their properties (including diffusion [7]) are substantially different to those assumed in classical Euclidean space and their description within the framework of the Euclidean geometry can be only an approximation, whose correctness degree is defined by the degree of corresponding static geometrical exponents (dimensions) of fractal and Euclidean objects [8].The most important achievement of the fractal analysis is the possibility of quantitative description of an object geometry with the help of its fractal dimension D. As it is known [9], D characterizes the degree of “openness” of the object – the lower D at a fixed value of surrounded Euclidean space dimension, d, the less “compact” is the object. The degree of “looseness” of the object can be more precisely expressed by its density ρ determined as follows [9]:

$$\rho \sim \rho_0 R^{D-d} \tag{1}$$

where ρ_0 is density of a three-dimensional Euclidean object consisting of molecules of PDADMACh, R is the radius of the fractal object.

For a macromolecular coil, R corresponds to its gyration radius R_g connected with the number of monomer links (polymerization degree), N of the coil by the relationship [10]:

$$R_g^D \sim N \tag{2}$$

The value of N can be obtained by dividing the molecular weight of the polymer, M by the molecular weight of the monomer link, m_0 (for PDADMACh m_0 is 176 g/mol) [1] and finally obtain [11]:

$$\rho \sim \left(\frac{M}{m_0}\right)^{-(d-D)/D} \tag{3}$$

where d in the considered case is apparently equal to 3.

The fractal dimension of a macromolecular coil, D is determined from the known exponent α in Mark-Houwink-Sakurawa equation according to the following relationship [12]:

$$D = \frac{3}{1+\alpha} \tag{4}$$

For PDADMACh, the Mark-Houwink-Sakurawa equation has the following form [1]:

$$[\eta] = 1{,}12x10^{-4} M^{0{,}82} \tag{5}$$

where [η] is the intrinsic viscosity.

By application of equations (4) and (5) the following results for PDADMACh were obtained: in aqueous solution D = 1.44 and in NaCl solution D = 1.65. The indicated values are defined as a macromolecular coil configuration for linear polymers [5]. The first of these values is relevant to the fractal dimension of the so-called "transparent" coil, the second is the value D for a macromolecular coil in a good solvent. The decrease in D means a more open configuration of the polymer chain (D =1 corresponds to completely extended chain and a transition to non-fractal behavior [13].

Then, one of the actions on a polymeric macromolecule is the change of its configuration (and therefore, D) with a variation in the solvent quality.

As follows from relationship (3), for a compact object (D=d) it is obtained ρ=1 (in relative units).One of the most important properties of fractal objects is the reduction on density (loosening) with the increase in R (or R_g or M) at a constant value of D. Apparently, the flocculation degree will be a function not only of active centres number, but of their accessibility degree. In terms of the fractal analysis the last factor can be characterized by macromolecular coil density ρ- the lower ρ the easier trapping of an adsorbed substance (in the considered case- phosphatides [4] on all the coil bulk. In essence, an analogue explanation of the effect observed in [4] can be used, where the decrease of the flocculent (PDADMACh) concentration, c with the increase in [η] is also connected to geometrical features of a macromolecular coil, though only on the qualitative level. In Fig.1, the dependence ρ(M) for PDADMACh in NaCl solution (D= 1.65) is shown. This fact demonstrates two important points for fractal objects. Firstly, this plot demonstrates how the density ρ of the fractal object with D= 1.65 corresponds to the value of a compact object (D=d=3). Secondly, this plot shows a very strong dependence ρ (M) that explains the strong increase of the accessibility degree of a macromolecular coil in relation to the penetration into its internal regions and, hence, a strong dependence of optimal concentration of a flocculent C_f on M [4]. In Fig. 2 the relationship C_f (M^{-1}) in double log-log coordinates plotted according to the data of [4] is shown. As can be seen, this relationship can be expressed by the following scaling expression [11]:

$$C_f \sim M^{-n} \tag{6}$$

where n is ~ 0,80, that is close to its absolute value. The exponent (d-D)/D in relationship (3), which for D= 1.65 is equal to ~ 0.818.

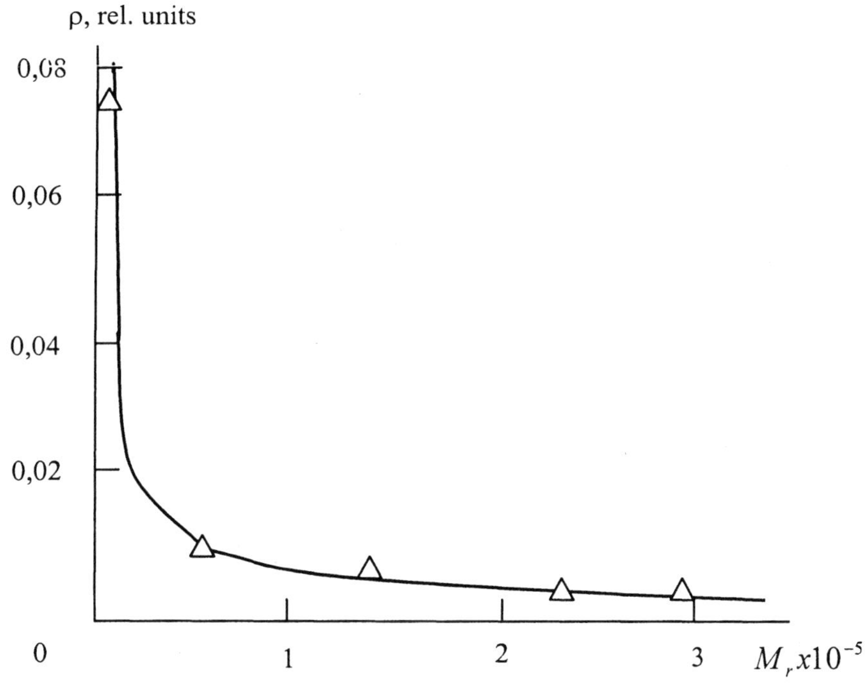

Figure 1. Dependence of the macromolecular coil density ρ (in relative units) on the average- viscosity molecular weight M for PDADMACh (D= 1,65) [11].

The physical sense of equation (6) can be easily understood within the modern representations of fractal clusters [14,15]. The depth of penetration of the particle in cluster Δr is determined as follows [14]:

$$\Delta\eta \sim N^{q} \tag{7}$$

The exponents ratio q/D for three dimensional Euclidean space is approximately 0.8 [14]. For D= 1.65 and with allowance of the condition $q \sim n^{-1}$ will be obtained n~ 0.76 that is close to the value of n estimated from Fig.2. Then, for higher phospatides penetration in the macromolecular coil of PDADMACh, it will result in the optimal concentration of flocculent.

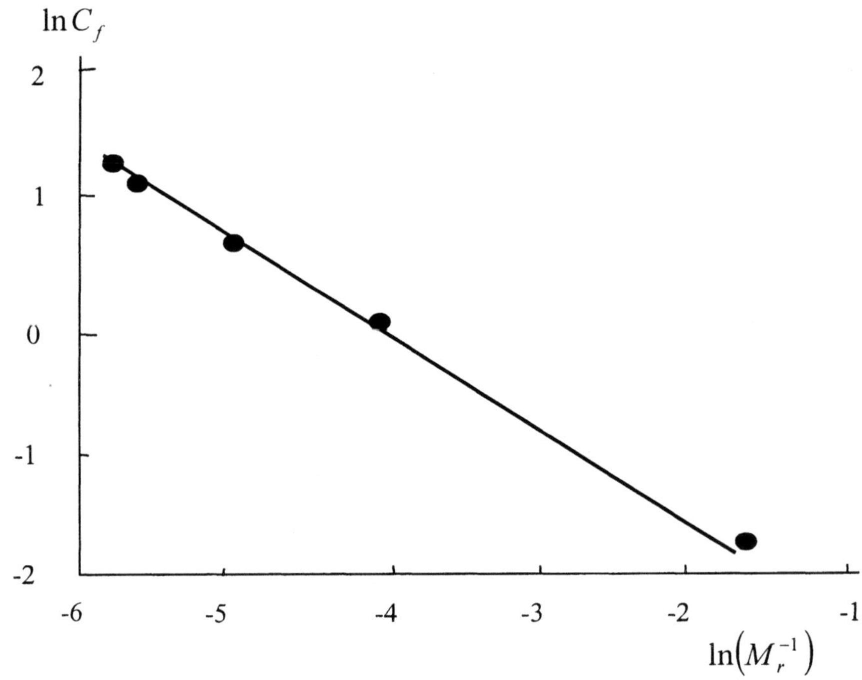

Figure 2. Scaling relationship between a concentration of PDADMACH C_f and its average- viscosity molecular weight M in double log- log coordinates [11].

Apparently, the main factor of the flocculation efficiency will be the fractal dimension, D of the macromolecular coil, which can be changed, for example, by solvent variation. Then, from relationship (6) by changing D to preserve the value of C_f on a previous level it is possible to change M. Authors [11] compared this possibility for PDADMACh in two solvents: water and NaCl aqueous solution (D~ 1.44 and 1.65, respectively) and obtained the coefficient K_{cl} which shows how many times it is necessary to decrease M of polymer at the transition from D= 1.65 to D= 1.44 to preserve the previous value of C_f. The dependence K_c (M) is shown in Fig.3, where a strong dependence of C_f on fractal dimension of a macromolecular coil or on the degree of coil accessibility for particles penetration. Then, the decrease of D from 1.65 to 1.44 for M= 2.99·x 10^5 at preservation of the previous value of C_f it is possible to decrease M in one order [11].

Then, these data show that between factors influencing the flocculation process efficiency by the addition of PDADMACh are included the molecular weight, fractal dimension of the macromolecular coil and medium in which the flocculation takes place. The effect of the medium on the flocculation process proceeds in by two ways- by change of the macromolecular coil fractal dimension and viscosity variation. The last factor can influence the intensity of diffusive processes. The only factor which will influence in equal degree properties of fractal and compact objects is the variation of medium viscosity and the influence of the three remaining factors is defined only by the fractal nature of the macromolecular coil of the polymeric flocculent.

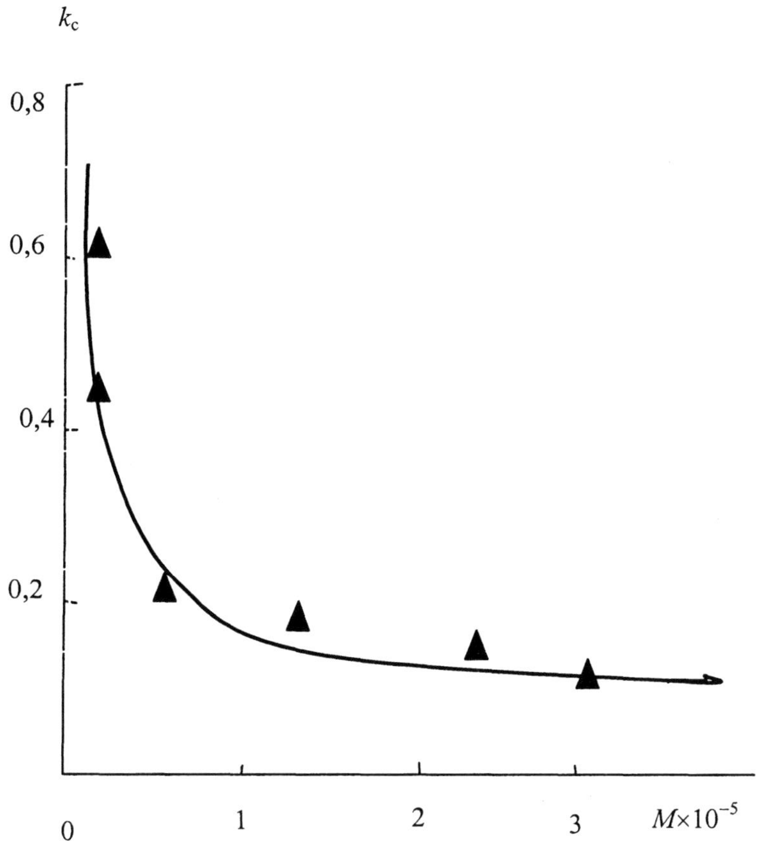

Figure 3. Dependence of the coefficient k_c of average- viscosity molecular weight reduction at the transition from D= 1.65 to D= 1.44 for the molecular weight M for PDADMACh [11].

Another interesting dependence was the change of phosphatides removal degree as function of PDADMACh concentration for each molecular weight [4]. Because of its applied and theoretical importance this problem requires a special examination. In [16] it was given a theoretical description of this effect for PDADMACh within the framework of the fractal analysis.

The increase of phosphatides removal degree, Q, up to some polymer concentration C_{max}, at which a maximal value (Q_{max}) is achieved, is due to the simple increase of "active centres" [4] for flocculation as the result of the increase of the macromolecular coils number (polymer concentration) in solution. At a concentration C_{max} the touching of macromolecular coils correspond to Q_{max}. The interpenetration of coils is realized and a scale of mentioned transition r_c is defined by the following criterion [17]:

$$\eta_c \sim C^{-1/(d-D)} \quad (8)$$

The value of r_c on the condition of coil touching is accepted to be $2R_g$ [16]. In Fig. 4 the comparison of values calculated according to relationship (8) theoretical values (C_{max}) and experimental magnitudes of this parameter ($C^e{}_{max}$) [4] is shown. For all molecular weights, excepting the smallest, ([η]=0.1 dl/g or M~ 4×10^3) a good correspondence between theory and experiment proves that the assumption about the physical sense of C_{max}.was correct. As for PDADMACh with M~ 4×10^3, C_{max}, i.e., efficiency of low-molecular flocculent is found much higher than the expected. This important question deserves special consideration.

The molecular weight of PDADMACh with M 4×10^3 is closer to olygomer than to polymer. Within the framework of an irreversible aggregation model, it was shown [14] that at low N small rod- like aggregates are formed, assuming a smaller value for D than that obtained from equation (4) at α= 0.82 for a high- molecular polymer [18]. Besides, it is known [19] that D is a monotonously raised function of N. Then, for low- molecular weight (M~ $4\cdot10^3$) PDADMACh, D will be much lower than 1.65, obtained for high-molecular polymers. From the condition $C^T_{max} = C^l_{max}$ and using relationships (2), (4) and (8), D for low- molecular PDADMACh was estimated ~ 1.26, that completely agree with the above assumptions and previous results [18,19]. This example demonstrates the very strong effect of the spatial geometrical structure of a macromolecule characterized by a fractal (Hausdorff) dimension, D, which controls impurities (in our case- phosphatides) into internal regions of flocculent, during the flocculation process. As mentioned above, quantitatively this factor can be calculated with the help of the fractal density ρ determined according to equation (1).

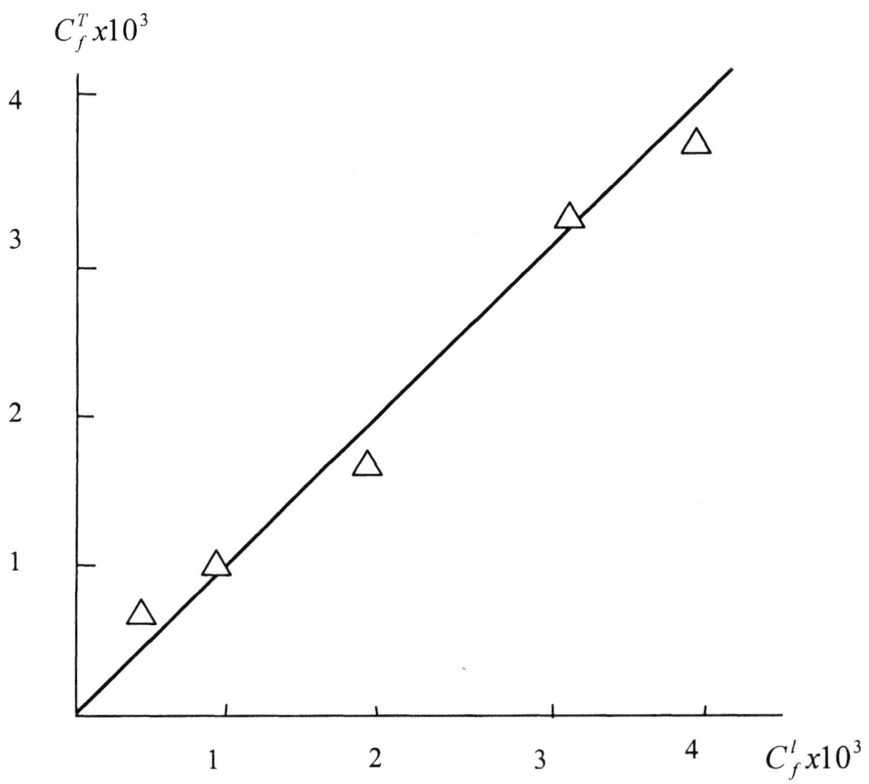

Figure 4. Relationship between concentrations of PDADMACh, calculated according to equation (8) C^T_f and experimental C^e_f at which the maximal degree of phosphatides removal is achieved [16].

The power dependence of ρ with D defines the strong dependence Q (D). In order to increase Q two times for PDADMACh with $M=3\times10^5$ it is necessary to reduce D from 1.65 to 1.50 at a constant concentration of flocculent. As it is known [20], the value of the exponent α in the Mark- Houwink-Sakurawa equation depends on the type of solvent used in measurements. Therefore, by the selection of conditions the configuration of a macromolecular coil can be changed and this helps to control the ability to flocculate impurities. The control of this ability can be carried out by the measurement of α, as follows from equation (4). The increase of α means the decrease of D.

As follows from the mentioned above assumptions, the value of Q showed a dependence as a minimum, on two parameters [6]:

$$Q = K_0\left(\frac{C}{\rho}\right) \tag{9}$$

where k_0 is a constant, ρ is the density determined according to equation (1).

For C C_{max} coils do not touch each other, ρ for them will be constant (at M= const) and, in essence, Q is a function only of c. For $C > C_{max}$ the interpenetration of macromolecular coils on their external regions, i. e., as if there were flocculated each other, reduces their ability to flocculate the impurities from solution. The fractal aggregates have one common feature, for large N joining particles (or small clusters of particles), that aggregate can be realized only on narrow external "active zones" and internal regions are shielded by the mentioned zone [21]. Therefore, between effective (non-shielded) radius of a macromolecular coil R_{ef} and polymer concentration c there is a relationship [21]:

$$C \sim R_{ef}^{D-d} \tag{10}$$

from which follows a reduction of R_{ef} at $C> C_{max}$. Using values obtained by that way, the effective density of coil ρ_{ef} can be estimated according to relationship (1) and then calculating the constant k_0 by equation (9) from the condition of equality of theoretical and experimental values Q in the maximum. In order to estimate theoretically the dependence Q(C) for PDADMACh with different M some calculations were carried out. In Fig.5 the comparison of theoretical (curves) and experimental (points) for the dependences Q (C) for PDADMACH with viscosity [η]= 0.9; 1.8 and 3.45 de/g is shown. As can be seen, this technique expresses precisely the qualitative change Q with c though quantitative correspondence. Authors [16] assumed that this non-correspondence is not only due to inexactitudes of the theoretical calculation but its simplicity gives certain possibilities of improvement. Then, it should be expected the obvious extrapolation Q=0 at C=0 though experimental data do not always assume it (for example, for [η]= 1.8 de/r [4]). Equations assume that the aggregate (macromolecular coils) consists of zero- dimensional objects (points). Apparently, the real polymeric coil consists of monomer links with finite sizes (for example, of length a) and in this case it is necessary to incorporate sized characteristics (scale) to the corresponding relationships. For example, relationship (2) looks like [22]:

$$\left(\frac{R}{a}\right)^{D} \sim N \tag{11}$$

also apparently, the incorporation of a linear scale is specially important at the comparison of the flocculating ability of various polymers. However, authors [16] did not attempt to achieve a full quantitative correspondence of theory and experiment, but wanted to demonstrate the principal possibility of the description of such complicated phenomena as flocculation within the framework of the irreversible aggregation models and fractal analysis.

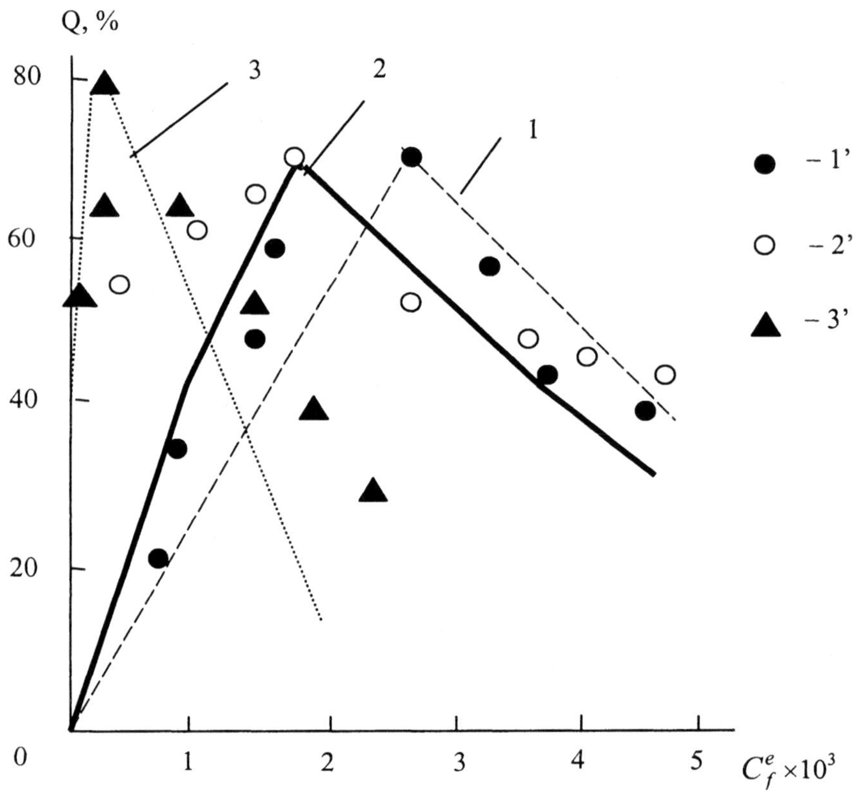

Figure 5. Dependence of the degree of phosphatides removal Q on flocculant concentration C_f^e C^{l}_{f} for PDADMACh with molecular weight: 5,8 x·10^4 (1,1), 13,5 x·10^4 (2,2) and 30,0·x 10^4 (3,3) kg/mol calculated according to equation (9) (1,2,3) and experimentally obtained (1 ,2 .3) [16].

4. Methods of the Control of Molecular Weight Characteristics PDADMACh

As mentioned above one of the main factors affecting the flocculation process is the molecular weight of flocculent. Therefore, methods of molecular weight characterization of PDADMACh based in representations of the fractal analysis will be considered.

The dependence of M on monomer concentration, C_m for PDADMACh (a_n experimental data are shown by solid line) is shown in Fig. 6. As can be seen, the dependence M (C_m) presents a maximum at C_m 4 mol/l and after the variation range is established at C_m (4,5÷5,5 mol/l), a fast decrease of M (approximately in 2 times) is observed. It is necessary to explain such dependence M(C_m) by considering the most important features of the irreversible aggregation model [23].

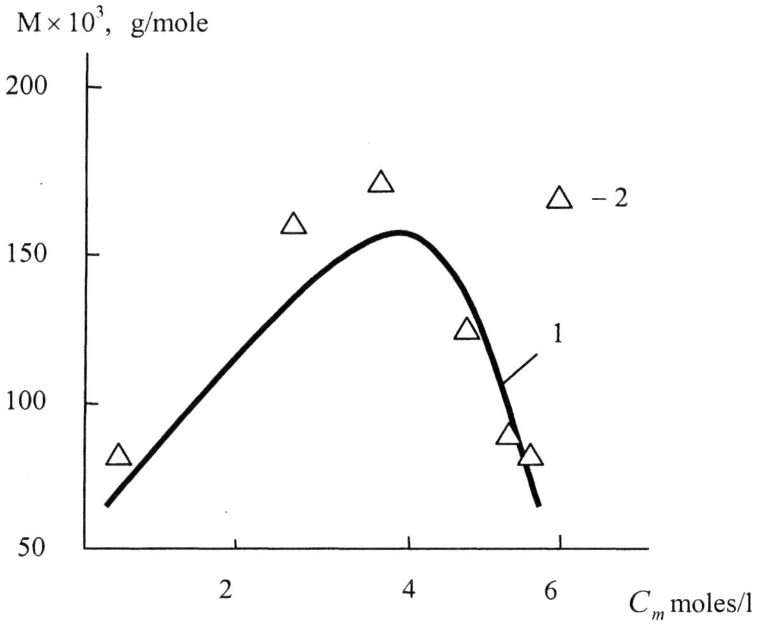

Figure 6. Experimental (1) and theoretical (2) dependence of the average- viscosity molecular weight M on initial concentration of monomer Cm for PDADMACh [23].

In this case D 1.65. This means that the process of formation of PDADMACh should be prescribed to the class of cluster- cluster aggregation process controlled by diffusion (D = 1.70÷2.0) [17]. The reasons for the low value for D in the considered polymer will be discussed below. In this case, the dependence M(C_m) can be expressed with a simple relationship [24]:

$$R \sim \left(\frac{4C_m KT}{3\eta_0 m_0} \right)^{1/D} t^{1/D} \tag{12}$$

where R is the aggregate gyration radius (R_g of a macromolecular coil), k is the Boltzmann constant, T is the temperature, t is the reaction time, η_0 is the initial solution viscosity and m_0 is the mass of particles (monomer link). Taking info account that the values of M are found for polymers obtained after certain synthesis times (t~ 160 min) and by using relationships (2) and (3) from the relationship (12) we obtain [23]:

$$M \sim C_m / \eta_0 \tag{13}$$

In Fig. 7 the dependence η_0 (C_m) is shown. At low C_m (up to ~ 4.0 mol/l) a weak increase of η_0 is observed at raising C_m and then in the range C_m 4.5÷5.5 mol/l η_0 increases (approximately 3 times). Therefore the ratio C_m/η_0 goes through a maximum corresponding to axis C_m to a maximum M. In Fig.6 the comparison of experimental and calculated data according to (12) is shown, which demonstrates both qualitative and quantitative correspondence of an irreversible cluster- cluster aggregation model and experimental data. A proportionality coefficient is determined by a fitting method. Hence, the experimentally observed M of PDADMACh in monomer concentration range c_m~ 4,5÷5,5 mol/l is due to a sharp increase of the monomer solution viscosity η_0 in this range C_m [23].

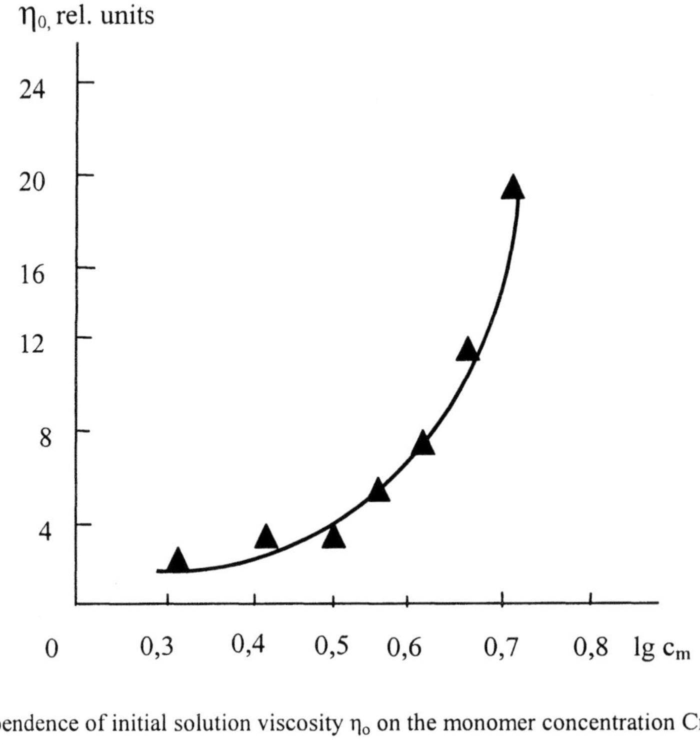

Figure 7. Dependence of initial solution viscosity η_o on the monomer concentration Cm for PDADMACh [1]

The second variant of description of the dependence R(t) for an irreversible cluster-cluster aggregation model is shown the scaling relationship [25]:

$$R \sim t^{1/z} \tag{14}$$

where z is the scaling exponent (index) connected to the fractal dimension of the aggregate D [25]:

$$Z = D(1-\alpha) - (d-2) \tag{15}$$

where α is exponent for a rate ν of diffusible particle or cluster:

$$\nu \approx (Nm_0)^{\alpha} \tag{16}$$

The estimations according to relationships (14)÷(16) showed that the α, characterizing the diffusive properties of the polymer- solvent system, is changed related to M and goes also through maximum at C_m~4,5 mol/l. It is natural to expect the dependence of ν on C_m and η_o. However, the two last parameters do not present a maximum (in the difference from ν) and therefore authors [23] obtained the dependences ν on combination of parameters C_m and η_o in two variants: as their product and ratio C_m/η_o. The dependence of δ on (C_m/η_o), shown in Fig.8 for PDADMACh, is found linear and passing through origin. It is seen that the increase of the initial reaction solution viscosity showed a decrease of mobility of diffusible particles that expresses the dependence on Fig. 8. However, this dependence assumes also its increase at raising C_m that means the existence of an enough strong attraction between clusters of PDADMACh [23].

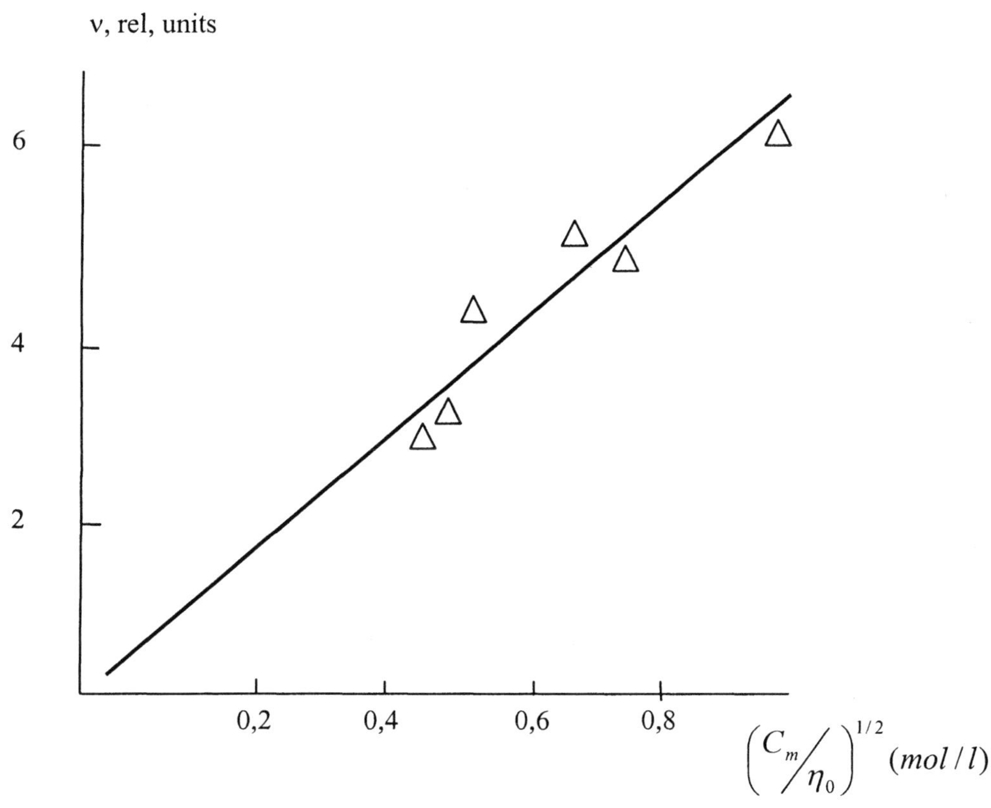

Figure 8. Dependence of the motion speed of diffusible clusters ν (in relative units) with $(Cm/\eta_o)^{1/2}$ for PDADMACh [23].

In Fig. 9 the dependence of ν with $C_m\,\eta_o$ is shown. On the first part of the curve (corresponding to C_m 4,5 mol/l) the value of δ increases with η_o because of the raising C_m.

At $C_m > 4{,}5$ mol/l the sharp increase of η_o (Fig. 7) leads to the essential reduction of diffusible clusters mobility characterized by the exponent α [23].

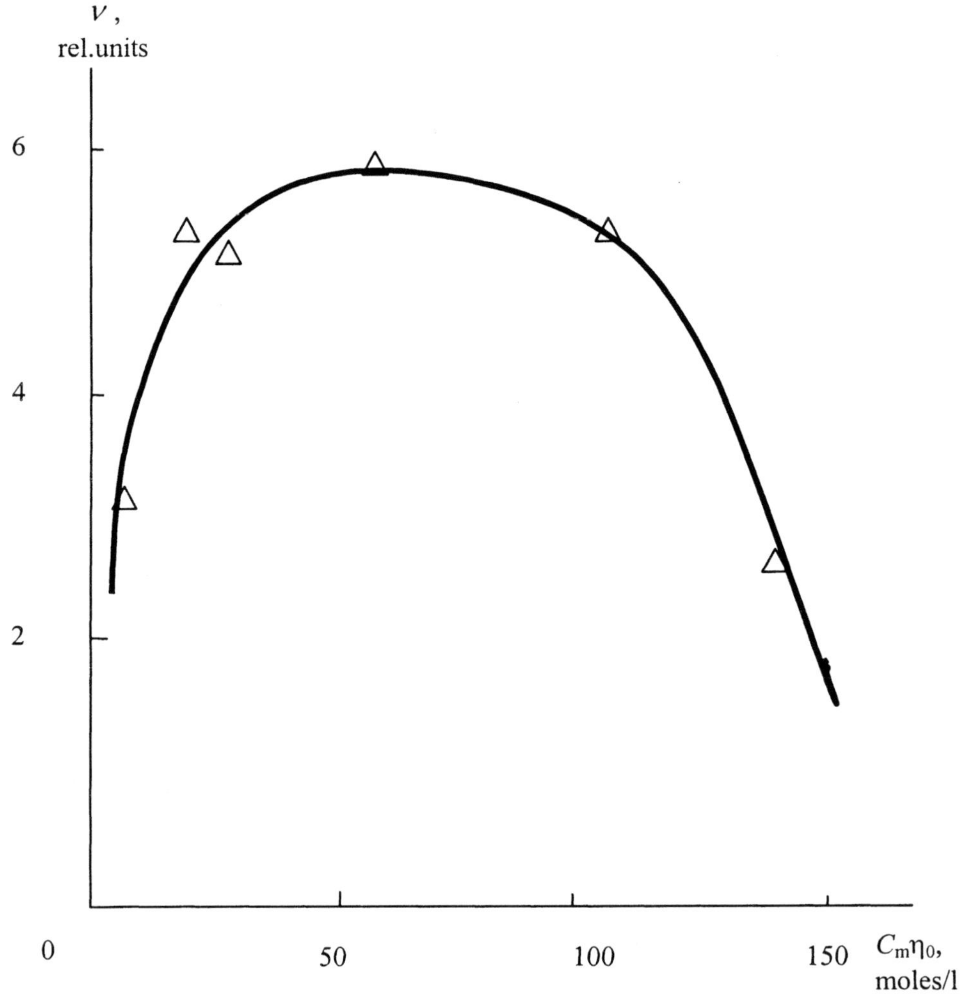

Figure 9. Dependence of the motion speed of diffusible clusters v (in relative units) on the value of parameter (Cm η_o) for PDADMACh [23].

Let us return to the value of fractal dimension D of PDADMACh macromolecular coils, which is ~ 1.65. Firstly, this value corresponds exactly to the fractal dimension of a linear polymer [26], which is PDADMACh. Secondly, this dimension also corresponds to a coil dimension in a good solvent, which is 5/3 [5,10]. The minimal value of D assumes that in the radical polymerization process of PDADMACh, simulated here by a irreversible aggregation cluster-cluster, the following conditions should be carried out:

1) Probability of particles (clusters) reaction at their first contact is very high and close to one [27].
2) The dominating factor of particles interaction are the attraction forces between them.

3) The existence of Brownian trajectory of diffusible particles motion reaction process [29].
4) The absence of disaggregation and restructurization in a reaction course [30].

Hence, within the frameworks of this model, a decrease of M at $C_m > 4.0$ mol/l for PDADMACh is explained by the sharp raising of initial viscosity in the reactionary medium η_o [23].

For high-molecular substances the concepts of molecule and molecular weight have the features connected with the qualitative difference of polymers from low-molecular weight substances [31]. This difference is associated with the mixture of macromolecules with different M (mixture of polymer homologues). The value of M found depends on the polydispersity degree, on the type of the molecular weight distribution (MWD) function and on the method of experimental M definition [20]. Therefore, a complete description of the molecular weight characteristics of the polymer requires the knowledge of its MWD.

As mentioned above, the macromolecular coils in solution are fractals, whose structure or more precisely, the spatial distribution of coil elements is characterized by its fractal dimension D. However, despite of its doubtless importance, the value of D gives only limited information about the aggregation (polymerization) process. At first, it is a static value and does not describe the dynamics of an aggregation process. Secondly, D characterizes the geometric properties only of one cluster (macromolecular coil) and cannot be utilized for the description of a set of clusters [32].Thus, both classic and fractal approaches, indicate the necessity of MWD analysis for entirety of the characterization of both, polymers and a polymerization process.

The range of values D for macromolecular coils in solution [5] supposes that the polymerization process proceeds according to the mechanism of an irreversible a cluster-cluster aggregation. The distribution functions for the indicated mechanism are investigated in some papers [32-34].

The theoretical description of functions MWD within the framework of theoretical treatment [34] and determination of the factors influencing on the shape of these functions will be given below for PDADMACh.

The theoretical treatment of an aggregation cluster-cluster takes into account the existence in actual polymerization processes the join of a particle or cluster (monomer or macromolecular coil) to a cluster and their disconnection (destruction). In dilute polymeric solution, macromolecules are in random environment influencing processes or an aggregation, or destruction that is described by a stochastic equation [34]:

$$N = \lambda N^{\alpha} - N^{b}\xi_{t}N^{a} 0 \prec a \prec b \tag{17}$$

where N is the number of particles in the aggregate (polymerization degree), a and b are exponents describing aggregation and destruction processes, respectively, $\xi_t = C_t/m$, where C_t – stochastic contribution to intensity of an aggregation process because of the influence of environment and <C> is its average value, m is coefficient.

The value λ is determined as follows [34]:

$$\lambda = \langle C \rangle / m \tag{18}$$

Following Shiyan [34], we believe that the reference time of random effects for a fractal aggregation process of macromolecules are much lower than reference times of the aggregation itself and consequently ξ_t It is possible to present as a white noise of intensity $\langle \xi_t^2 \rangle = \delta^2$.

The exponent in case of a cluster-cluster aggregation is connected to the fractal dimension D of a macromolecular coil by the following relationship [34]:

$$a = \frac{2D - d}{D} \tag{19}$$

Equation (17) allows to calculate the density of probability $P_s(N)$, the stationary solution a 1 [34].

The value of λ has no effect distribution $P_s(N)$, these relationships suppose three basic parameters effecting on the distribution $P_s(N)$: a, b and σ^2. Each of the indicated parameters characterizes the polymerization process. So, the exponent a is essentially determined by the macromolecular coil structure, that directly is calculated from equation (19). The value of b characterizes the type and intensity of the destruction process. Parameter σ^2 is determined by the stochastic contribution to the polymerization process and it is possible to assume a dependence σ^2 on C_m as the initial concentration of the monomer, the larger probability of their random collisions. All experimental MWD curves have unimodal shape that supposes a low mobility of coils in solution or $\sigma^2 < 2/3$ [34].

First of all we shall consider the general aspects of the influence of the three indicated parameters on the shape of MWD curves. For this purpose we shall plot the theoretical dependences P_s (N) when only one of indicated parameters is varied while the other two are constant. In Fig.10 the curves P_s (N) are shown for the fractal dimension of a coil. D or a is variable while σ^2= const, b= const. In Fig.10-12 the normalization constant A was chosen so that the maximal magnitude Ps was ~ 0,4 for all curves Ps(N). As follows from the data of Fig.10, the increase in D results in a displacement of the distribution maximum to the higher N. This tendency is also observed for D=2 [5]. For experimental MWD curves the greatest value of N, corresponding to a maximum of MWD distribution, is obtained for C_m = 4,0 mol/l and is N= 550. As follows from Ps(N) curves shown in Fig.10, the indicated value for N corresponds to D= 1.65, that completely agrees with the value of D calculated from equation (4). This result demonstrated that the contraction of a coil up to θ – conditions at high enough C_m is not observed in practice [35].

In Fig. 11 the theoretical Ps (N) curves are shown when σ^2 is variable and D= const, b= const. As follows from the data on this figure, σ^2 renders the essential effect on width of MWD. The strictly monodisperse distribution can be obtained only at σ^2=0. The increase of the stochastic contribution in a polymerization intensity results in a symmetrical broadening of MWD relative to its maximum.

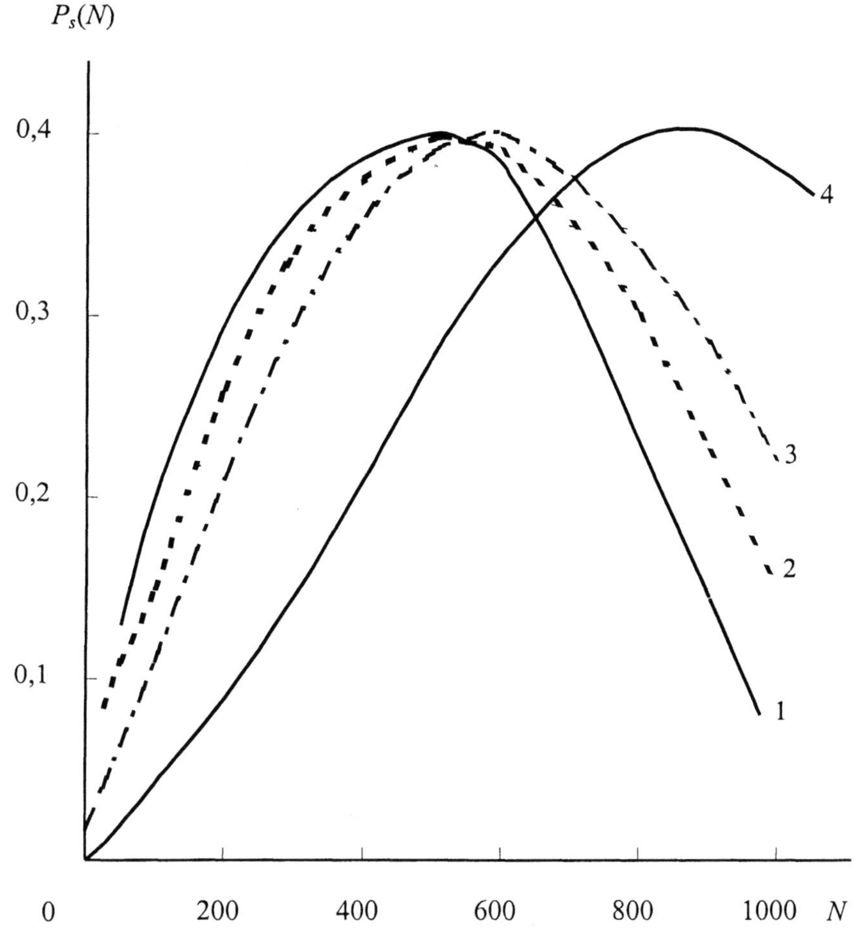

Figure 10.Simulation of MWD curves according to the equation (19) for D= 1.50 (1), 1.65 (2), 1.80 (3) and 2.0 (4). B= 1; σ^2 = 0,25.

The theoretical curves P_s (N) are shown in Fig. 12 when b is variable and D=const, σ^2=const. The value b=1 means the availability of the channel disintegration for each bond of a cluster. When the large part of a bond is fixed (b=0.2), the maximum in an investigated interval N= 0÷1000 is not achieved in general. At b= 0.5 (half of bonds is fixed), Ps(N) curve has a maximum but with obvious asymmetry at large N. The further growth of b means, as it was expected, a decreasing of a fraction of clusters with large N (high- molecular fraction).

The comparison of experimental and theoretical MWD curves has shown that these curves for PDADMACh, synthesized at C_m= 4.0 and 5.0 mol/l, are simulated directly.

Parameters for the Ps(N) curve: D= 1.65 (a~ 0.182), σ^2= 0.25 and b= 1. Such simulation for C_m= 4 mol/l is shown in Fig.13 (curve 3), showing a good correspondence between theory and experimental values. At C_m= 1.0 and 2.5 mol/l for MWD curves such direct simulation fails because the position of a maximum on a MWD curve correspond to N_{max}= 175 and 375, while in theoretical curves such low values of N_{max} are not achieved (Fig.10÷12). Nevertheless, correspondence of the theory and experiment with the help of renormalization is possible for these curves. It is due to auto-modeling of Ps (N) distribution on a variable Ñ =

N/N_o [34]. Simultaneously, it is necessary to execute the renormalization of white noise of intensity σ^2 as follows [34]:

$$\sigma^2 \rightarrow \sigma_0^2 = \sigma^2 N_0^{2a-1-b} \tag{20}$$

The indicated renormalization is made by definition of N_o under condition of equaling $\tilde{N}$ and the theoretical value N_{max}, with experimental values of this parameter. As shown in Fig. 13, an excellent correspondence of experimental and theoretical MWD curves of PDADMACh, synthesized at C_m=1.0 and 2.5 mol/l prove a correctness of renormalization. In its turn, this renormalization shows one of the basic properties of fractals- their automodelity [36].

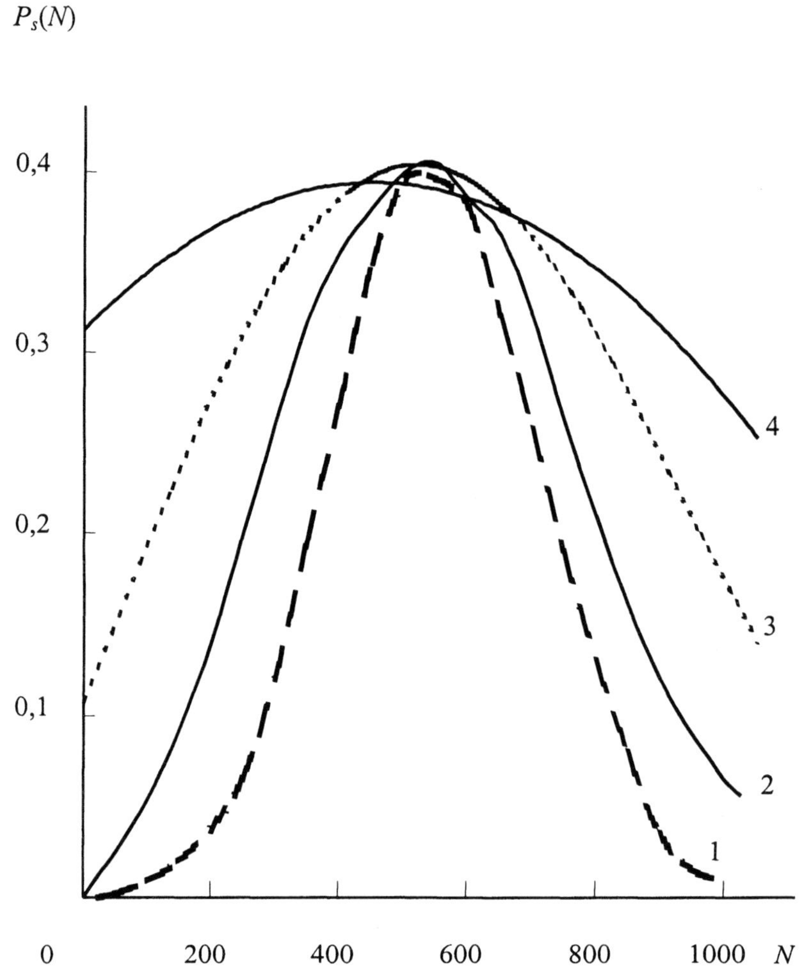

Figure 11. Simulation of MWD curves according to equation (19) for σ^2= 0.05 (1), 0.10 (2), 0.25 (3) and 0.60 (4), b= 1, D= 1.65.

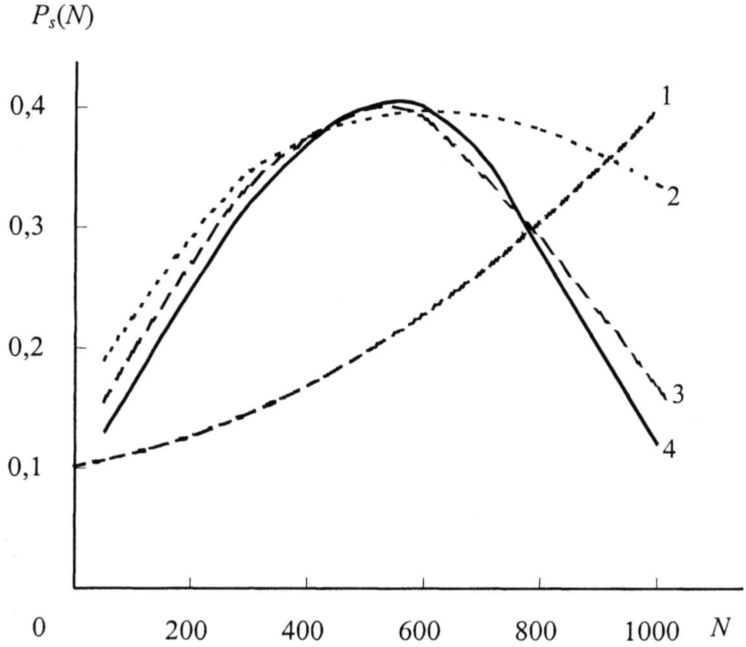

Figure 12. Simulation of MWD curves according to equation (19) for b= 0.2 (1), 0.5 (2), 1.0 (3) and 2.0 (4). D= 1.65, σ^2= 0.25.

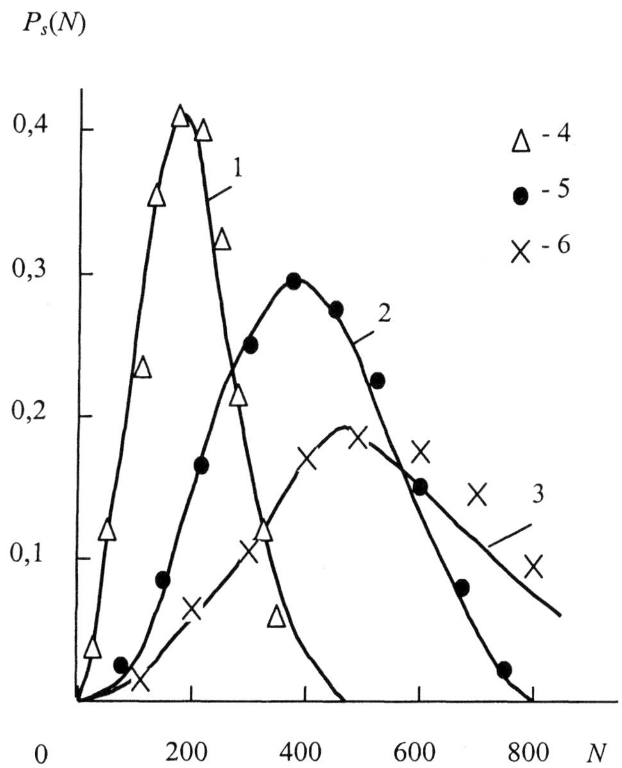

Figure 13. Comparison of experimental (1-3) and calculated according to equation (19) (4-6) MWD curves for PDADMACh at C_m= 1.0 (1.4), 2.5 (2.5) and 4.0 (3,6) mol/l.

As it is known [33], the MWD curve for a cluster- cluster aggregation depends on the diffusive characteristics of a system in many respects, namely on mobility of clusters expressed by their speed v, which can be expressed by the following simple equation [33]:

$$v = M_{cl}^{\beta} \tag{21}$$

where m is the mass of cluster.

The value of exponent β (or α in equation (16)) determines the position of the maximum of a MWD curve [33]:

$$N_{max} = \frac{-\beta}{1-\beta} \tag{22}$$

One should expect that the mobility of clusters v will be as high as the lower is the viscosity of the initial solution of monomer η_0. This supposition confirms Fig. 8 data.

As it was mentioned above, one should expect an increase of the stochastic contribution in the polymerization intensity or white noise, δ^2 in the process of growth of monomer initial concentration C_m. This supposition confirms the relationship δ^2 ($C_m^{1/2}$) given in Fig. 14, which is linear and passes through the origin. The data on Fig. 8 and 14 demonstrate that the parameters of equation (19) can be expressed with the help of the technical characteristics of a polymerization process, for example, C_m and η_0.

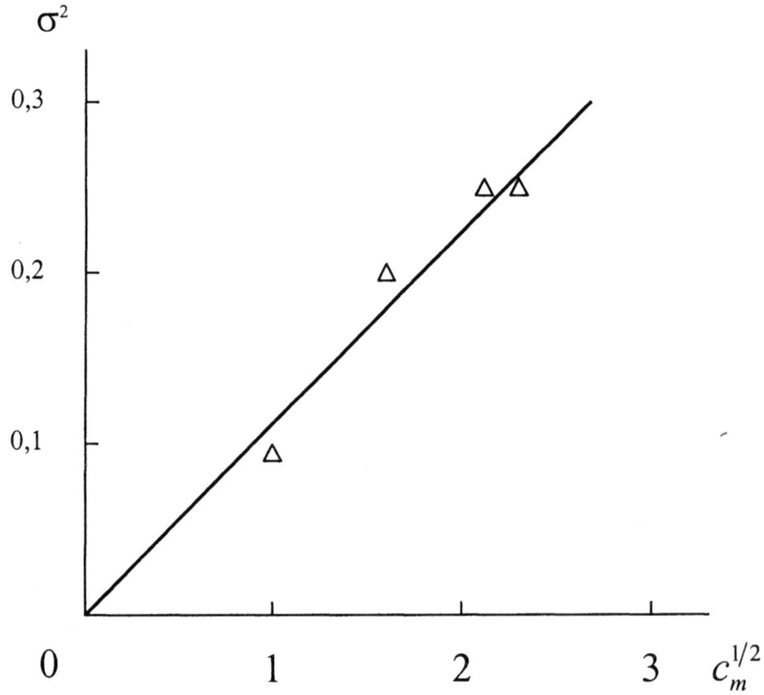

Figure 14. Relationship between white noise of a polymerization intensity σ^2 and the initial concentration of the monomer C_m for PDADMACh.

Thus, these results show that MWD of PDADMACh can be simulated and predicted within the framework of the model of an irreversible cluster-cluster aggregation. Other variant of MWD description in the terms of same model has been described [32]. It is assumed that the examination of the dynamic distribution function of cluster sizes n_s (t) is the number of clusters consisting of S unities formed in time t.

The dynamic scaling description of the cluster size distribution in the diffusion-limited cluster-cluster aggregation model has been studied in some works [32,37-39]. This can be applied to describe the radical polymerization of PDADMACh as the value D=1.65 corresponds to a typical fractal dimension for aggregates formed in the mentioned process. On this basis, for the description of MWD of PDADMACh a dynamic scaling function can be used [32]:

$$n_s(t) \sim S^{-2} t^{-z} \tag{23}$$

where t is reaction time, which is accepted to be equal to the gelation time t_g, Z is an exponent estimated according to the equation (15).

Let us consider the methods for the estimation of parameters in equation (23). The values $n_s(t_g)$ are determined from the experimental curves MWD W_i (N)(where W_i is the fraction of the polymer having a polymerization degree N_i) (Fig.13) as follows. We assume that N=S and that the fraction of the polymer corresponding to S_i is the summary weight fraction of polymer W_i. Dividing W_i by S_i and multiplying by the maximal degree of conversion, Q can be obtained the value for $n_s(t_g)$ or n_i for S_i. In equation (16), α is an exponent in the relationship for diffusion constant D_s as function S ($D_s \sim S^{\alpha}$). The value of D_s can be calculated as follows[40]:

$$D_s = \frac{kT}{6\pi\eta_0 R_g \gamma} \tag{24}$$

where γ is a numerical coefficient defined by the boundary conditions of particle surface.

As it was mentioned above, the value of D_s within the framework of the irreversible aggregation models usually accepted is [25, 32]:

$$D_s \sim S^{\alpha} \tag{25}$$

From the comparison of relationships (24) and (25) it is easy to obtain [41]:

$$\alpha \sim -\ln \eta_0 \tag{26}$$

As it was pointed out [25,32], the value α defines a deviation from the distribution function. For $\alpha < -0{,}5$ the "bell- shaped" distribution curves having a maximum are received. For $\alpha > -0{,}5$ the monotonously decaying curves are typical. As follows from Fig.13, the experimental curves MWD present a maximum. On the basis of the absolute values η_0 we have assumed in (26) a sign of the equality and in this case values of α are within limits ~ 1÷3 and this interval completely meets the shape of experimental curves MWD (Fig. 13). Besides, as it was shown earlier, the position of the maximum of the MWD curve is determined by relationship (22). It is not difficult to see that the increase of C_m, giving the increase of η_o, is defined by raising the absolute value α and increase of N_{max}.

In Fig. 15 the dependences (S^2n_s) on (St^z) in double log- log coordinates for four polymers PDADMACh, synthesized at various C_m are shown. Each MWD curve is described by a unique curve. This result confirms the correctness of the application of the irreversible aggregation model for the description of the polymerization process.

Using the generalized curve shown in Fig. 15, it is possible to predict theoretically the kinetics of MWD changes as a function of time. For this purpose, at first, we set the values S= N and determined the value St^z at arbitrary t. Then, from the plot of Fig.15 the value S^2n_s,is found, and according to the described procedure we defined W_i. Then the same calculation is iterated for another S, etc. In Fig.16, as an example, the comparison of MWD curves for C_m= 4.0 mol/l is given at t= t_g= 108 min. and t= 53min. As is seen from the comparison of curves 1 and 2 in Fig.16, the decrease of t (t< t_g) gives the maximum MWD to lower the molecular weight values and narrow MWD. Besides, in Fig.16 the MWD curve for C_m= 1.0 mol/l is given at t= t_g (curve 3) and from the comparison of all three curves it follows that the decrease of t and C_m give a similar effect.

Thus, the correctness of this theoretical treatment is proved by the plotting of a generalized distribution curve and allows predicting the kinetics of MWD change as a function of the monomer initial concentration C_m and reaction duration t.

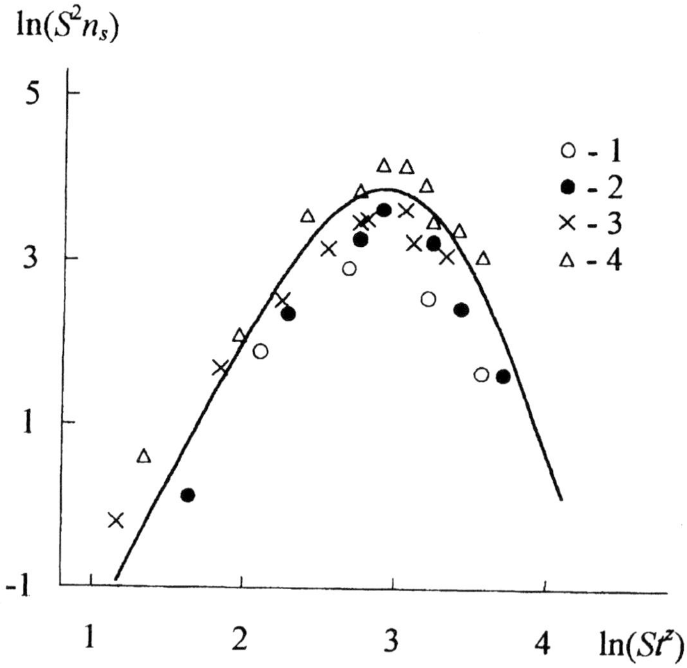

Figure 15. Generalized MWD curve in the form of functions s^2n_s (st^z) in double log-log coordinates for PDADMACh, synthesized at C_m: 1.0 (1), 2.5 (2), 4.5 (3), 4.5 (3) and 5.0 mol/l [41].

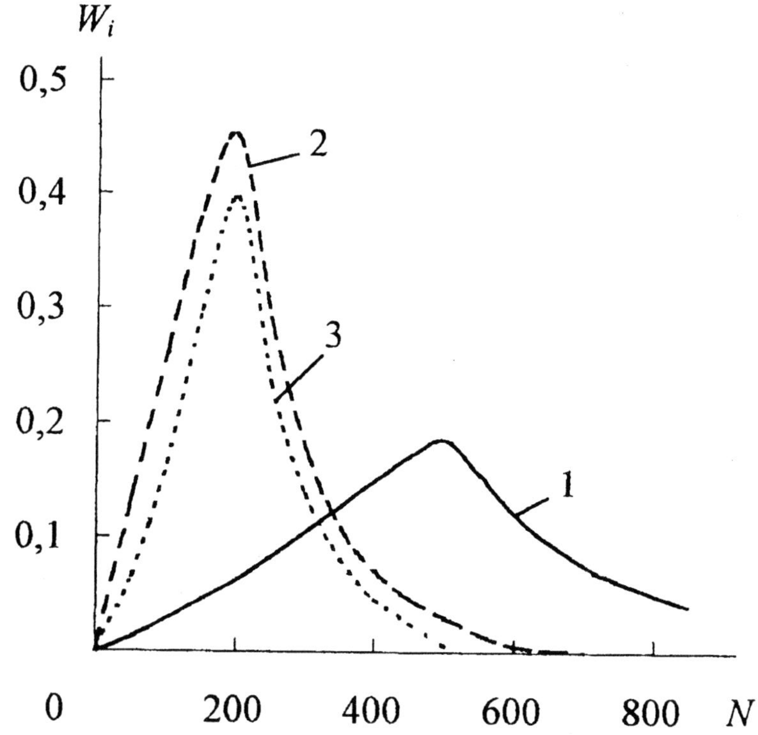

Figure 16. Experimental MWD curves at gelation time for PDADMACh, synthesized at C_m= 4.0 (1) and 1.0 (3) mol/l. Calculated MWD curve at t= 53 min. for PDADMACh, synthesized at C_m = 4.0 mol/l (2) [41].

CONCLUSIONS

The main principles of synthesis of cationic polyelectrolyte, poly-N, N- diallyl- N, N-dimethyl ammonium chloride (PDADMACh) are briefly considered. The basic fields of its application for solution of ecological problems are discussed, particularly for purification of waste water, oils and selective removal from oils and fates free fatty acids. The fractal model of an impurities flocculation with the help of PDADMACh is used. The methods of control of polymer molecular weight characteristics used representations of an irreversible aggregation models and fractal analysis are considered.

REFERENCES

[1] Topchiev D.A., Malkanduev Yu. *Cationic Polyelectrolites of Poly-N,N-dialkyl-N,N-diallylammonium Halohenides Set: a Features of Formation Processes, Properties and Application*. Nal chik, KBSU,1997,181p.

[2] Groshev I.M., Matsul V.N., Suchaya T.V. *Wood-working* (in Russian), Moscow, VNIPIEIlesprom,1989,194p.
[3] Vasil eva O.V., Davydov A.V., Kolganova I.V. *Dokl. AN SSSR*,1983,v.276,N6,p.621-625.
[4] Shnaider M.A., Kolganova I.V., Ter-Minasyan R.I., Topchiev D.A.*Maslozhirovaya promyshl.*,1990.N10,p.17-21.
[5] Baranov V.G., Frenkel S.Yu.,Brestkin Yu.V. *Dokl. AN SSSR*,1986,v.290,N2,p.369-372
[6] Havlip S., Ben-Avrahom D.*Phys. Rev.A.*, 1982,v.26, N3,p.1728-1734.
[7] Gefen Y., Aharony A.,Alexander S. *Phys. Rev.Lett.*, 1983,v.50, N1,p.77-80.
[8] Rammal R.,Toulouse G. Y.*Phys.Lett.*(Paris),1983,v.44,N1,p.L13-L22.
[9] Brady R.M.,Ball R.C. *Nature*,1984,v.309,N5965,p.225-229
[10] Vilgis T.A., *Physica A*,1988,v.153,N2,p.341-354.
[11] Esmurziev A.M., Malkanduev Yu.A., Kozlov G.V. *Vestnik KBSU, Khimich.nauki*,2001, N4 p.121-123.
[12] Karmanov A.P., Monakov Yu.B.*Vysokomol.Soed.B*,1995,v.37,N2,p.328-331.
[13] Kozlov G.V., Novikov V.U.*Materialovedenie*,1997,N8-9,p.3-6.
[14] Smirnov B.M. A *Physics of Fractal Clusters*.(in Russian). Moscow, Nauka,1991,136 p.
[15] Shogenov V.N. Kozlov G.V. *Fractal Clusters in Physics and Chemistry of Polymers* (in Russian).Nal chik, Polygraphservice and T., 2002,268 p.
[16] Kozlov G.V., Malkanduev Yu.A., Mirzoeva A.A. In *Mater.IY International Science-Practical Confer."The Economic of Usage and Preservation of Nature*". Penza, 2001,p.153-156.
[17] Kokorevich A.G., Gravitis Yu.A., Osol-Kalnin V.G. *Khimiya drevesiny*,1989,N1,p.3-24.
[18] Kolb M., Botet R., Jullien R. *Phys.Rev.Lett.*,1983,v.51, N13,p.1123-1126.
[19] Botet R., Jullien R., Kolb M. *J.Phys.A*, 1984, v.17, N2,p.L75-L79.
[20] Budtov V.P. *A Physical Chemistry of Polymeric Solutions*.Sankt-Petersburg, Khimiya,1992, 384p.
[21] Witten T.A., Meakin P.*Phys.Rev.*1983,v.28,N10,p.5632-5642
[22] Hentschel H.G.E., Deutch J.M., Meakin P.*J.Chem.Phys.*,1984,v.81,N5,p.2496-2502.
[23] Malkanduev Yu. A., Kozlov G.V., Hashirowa S.Yu. Izvestiya VYZov, Severo-*Kavkazck. region, estestv.nauki*, 2000,N1, p.87-90.
[24] Weitz D.A., Huang J.S.,Lin M.Y., Sung J.*Phys.Rev.Lett*,1984,v.53,N17,p.1657-1660.
[25] Kolb M. *Phys.Rev.Lett.*,1984,v.53,N17,p.1653-1656/
[26] Isaacson J.Lubensky T.S. *J.Phys. Lett.*(Paris),1980,v.41,N19,p.1469-1471.
[27] Kolb M., Jullien R.*J. Phys. Lett.*(Paris), 1984, v. 45, N 20, p. L 977- L981.
[28] Meakin P. *J. Chem. Phys.*, 1983, v. 79, N 5, p. 2426- 2429.
[29] Meakin P. *Phys. Rev. A*, 1984 v. 29, N2, p. 997- 999.
[30] Kolb M. *J. phys. A*, 1986, v. 19, N 3, p. L 263- L 268.
[31] Rafikov S. P., Pavlova S.A., Tverdokhlebova I.I. *A Methods of Molekular Weights and Polydispersity Determination of High- molecular Compounds*. (in Russian), Mosow, 1zd. AN SSSR, 1963, p.368.
[32] Meakin P., Vicsek T., *Family F. Phys. Rev.B*, 1984, v. 34, N1, p. 564-569.
[33] Botet R., Jullien R. *J. Phys. A*, 1984, v. 17, N12, p. 2517- 2530.
[34] Shiyan A.A. *Vysokomol. Soed. B*, 1995, v. 37, N9, p. 1578- 1580.

[35] Bityurin N.M., Genkin., Zubov V.P., Lachinov M.B. *Vysokomol. Soed. A*, 1981, v.23, N8, p. 1702- 1709.
[36] Feder F. *Fractals*. New York, Plenum Press, 1989, p. 247.
[37] Vicsek T., Family F. *Phys.Rev. Lett.,* 1984, v.52, N 19, p. 1669- 1672.
[38] Kolb M., Herrmann H.J. *J.Phys.A,* 1985, v.18, N 8, p. L435- L441.
[39] Kolb M. *Physica A,* 1986, v.140, N1- 2, p. 416- 420.
[40] Shamurina M.V., Roldugin V.I., Pryamova T.A., Vysotzki V.V. *Kolloidn. Zhurn.,* 1995, v.57, N4, p.580- 584.
[41] Kozlov G.V., Malkanduev Yu. A., Zaikov G.E. In book: *New Perseptives in Chemistry and Biochemistry*. Ed. Zaikov G. New York, Nova Science Publishers, Inc., 2002, p.35- 40.

In: Homolytic and Heterolytic Reactions: Problems and Solutions ISBN 1-59033-980-0
Editors: G.E. Zaikov, et al., pp. 121-136

Chapter 4

PECTIN AND POLYACRYLAMIDE COMPOSITE HYDROGELS: EFFECT OF PECTIN ON STRUCTURAL AND DYNAMIC MECHANICAL PROPERTIES*

Linshu Liu*†, *Peter H. Cooke, David R. Coffin, Marshall L. Fishman and Kevin B. Hicks

U.S. Department of Agriculture, ARS, Eastern Regional Research Center, 600 East Mermaid Lane, Wyndmoor, PA 19038, USA

ABSTRACT

Composite hydrogels of pectin and polyacrylamide were synthesized and evaluated by scanning electron microscopy, atomic force microscopy, light microscopy, and by dynamic mechanical analysis. The cross-linking polymerization of acrylamide in pectin solution resulted in a composite having a macroporous pectin domain with an interstitial polyacrylamide domain. This composite had improved mechanical properties compared to either polymer alone, and it absorbed and retained more water than cross-linked polyacrylamide alone. Furthermore, cross-linking polymerization of acrylamide in an existing pectinate scaffold resulted in a double network architecture, where filamentous polyacrylamide networks penetrated through pores of the pectin scaffold. It was found that pectins dictated the features of microstructure in the composites through regulating the coordination of phase separation of the two components and water partition between the two phases. Results from this study highlight potential new uses of pectins in protecting the physical structure of environmentally sensitive polymers from mechanical damage related to freezing, lyophilization, and other conditions experienced during their use in biomedical and industrial products.

Keywords: Pectin; polyacrylamide; composite hydrogels; microstructure

---

* Mention of Brand or firm name does not constitute an endorsement by the U.S. Department of Agriculture above others of a similar nature not mentioned.

† Correspondence to: L. Liu (lsliu@arserrc.gov), Tel. (215)233-6486.

INTRODUCTION

Pectin derived hydrogels swell in solutions at high pH and shrink at low pH, offering a great opportunity for use in controlled delivery of bioactive substances, [1] in the food industry, [2] and soil and water preservation [3]. Combining pectin with a second polymer into composites can create unique properties and extend practical applications for the pectin composite systems as compared to each polymer alone [4,5]. The formation of composite hydrogels involves a series of complicated and coordinated physico-chemical processes, such as changes in hydrodynamic properties of each polymer, phase separation, and water partition. Physical and chemical interactions between individual components determine the structure and properties of the composite hydrogel. Water partition within the hydrogel strongly influences the response of the hydrogel to external changes in temperature or electric field, to stimuli from solvent composition, to biological reactions, and to light irradiation [6-12]. Hydrogels have been applied to the study of separation processes [13,14]. Other areas of application in which hydrogels are important scientifically and economically are agriculture, pharmaceuticals, biotechnology, tissue engineering, and robotics [7–9,11,15,16]. Recently, hydrogels with specific architectures have been developed to respond to needs for high efficiency media and for materials with new functionality and lower cost [17-19]. Mostly, attention and resources have been focused on the efforts to regulate the microstructures of individual phases and on the entire architecture of composites. Studies of water partition occurring in composite hydrogels have increased the understanding of the relationship between the structure and physical properties of the composite. For practical reasons, polyacrylamide hydrogels are often chosen as a model study system.

In this study, the use of pectin to regulate water partition in composite hydrogels was studied. Two methodologies for preparing composite hydrogels from pectin polymers and acrylamide monomers were studied. The microstructure of composite hydrogels was evaluated by means of microscopy, the rheology by mechanical properties, and the capacity to absorb and retain water by water content. In this study, we focused particularly on the effect of the physical status of pectin on the microstructures of the polyacrylamide phase and on the entire architecture of the composites.

EXPERIMENTAL

Materials

Sodium pectinate (Grindsted®, MW 90,000; degree of esterification, DE, 60%) was obtained from Danisco (Danisco Cultor USA Inc., New Century, KS). Acrylamide, bis-methylene-acrylamide, and N, N, N, N'-tetra-methyl-ethylenediamine (TEMED) were purchased from Bio-Rad (Hercules, CA). Ammonium persulfate (APS), methylene blue, and calcium chloride were from Aldrich (Milwaukee, WI).

Preparation of Pectin and Polyacrylamide Gels

Polyacrylamide gels were prepared from the solution of acrylamide, 2 M, and bis-methylene-acrylamide, 32 mM. To polymerize acrylamide, the solution was degassed followed by the addition of APS, 2.2 mM and TEMED, 3.3 mM. The solution was poured into a Petri dish to form a layer of 4 mm in thickness. Gels thus prepared were lyophilized and labeled as P_1.

Pectin gels were cast in 96 well microtiter plates (Fisher Scientific, Pittsburg, PA). Each well contained 120 µl of pectin solution, 20 mg/ml in deionized water (D.I. water). The solution was degassed, incubated at 4°C for 2 h, frozen at –20°C for 4 h, and lyophilized to create a sponge-like, porous structure. The dry gels were immersed in 0.1 M $CaCl_2$ to insolubilize the pectin and to fix the three-dimensional features of the gel. Gels were washed with a large volume of D.I. water with several changes, lyophilized again, and labeled as P_2.

Pectin/polyacrylamide gels were prepared by polymerizing acrylamide and bis-methylene-acrylamide in pectin solution together in one step. One volume of pectin solution, 4%, w/v, was mixed with an equal volume of solution containing acrylamide, 4 M, and bis-methylene-acrylamide, 64 mM. The mixed solution was degassed followed by addition with APS, 4.4 mM, and TEMED, 6.6 mM. The solution was then quickly mixed and poured into a cylindrical polypropylene tube (diameter, 9 mm; Fisher Scientific, Pittsburg, PA), covered with parafilm at both ends, allowed to stand at ambient temperature for 2 h, then lyophilized. The gels were removed, immersed in 0.1 M $CaCl_2$ at ambient temperature for 1 h, washed with a large volume of D.I. water, and lyophilized again. Gels thus prepared are labeled as P_1P_2I.

Alternatively, pectin/polyacrylamide gels were prepared by a two-step method from the lyophilized pre-formed pectin gels, P_2, and the solution of 2 M acrylamide and 32 mM bis-methylene-acrylamide. The gels and the solution were de-gassed separately. APS and TEMED were added to the solution, mixed vigorously, and then, injected into pectin gels using a pipet, 120 µl for each. After polymerization, the gels were lyophilized, and labeled as P_1P_2II.

In another experiment, wet P_2 gels were prepared by incubation of dry P_2 gels in D.I. water for 2 h at ambient temperature, then removed from the water, placed on tissue papers and compressed gently to remove residual water in the pore spaces of the gels. The gels thus treated were injected with 80 µl of acrylamide solution with the same compositions as used for P_1P_2II preparation. After polymerization the gels were lyophilized, and labeled as P_1P_2III.

In still another experiment, acrylamide solution of the same compositions as used for P_1P_2II preparation was poured on the surfaces of a dry P_2 gel, polymerized at ambient temperature followed by lyophilization, and labeled as P_1P_2IV.

Scanning Electron Microscopy (SEM)

For SEM examination, samples were dehydrated by immersion in absolute ethanol and frozen in liquid nitrogen. After 5 minutes of freezing, samples were fractured manually with the edge of a cooled scalpel blade. Sample fragments were thawed in absolute ethanol and critical point dried from liquid carbon dioxide. Dry fragments were mounted on aluminum specimen stubs with colloidal silver adhesive (Electron Microscopy Sciences, Ft.

Washington, PA) and coated with a thin layer of gold by DC sputtering. Images of topographical features in fracture-faces were made using a model JSM 840A scanning electron microscope (JEOL USA, Peabody, MA) coupled to an Imix-1 digital image workstation (Princeton Gamma-Tech, Princeton, NJ).

Optical Microscopy

For correlative imaging with SEM, optical images of sample fragments were made (before sputter coating with gold) by reflected light from a model 190 fiber optic illuminator (Dolan-Jenner, Woburn, MA) and a model MZ FLIII stereomicroscope (Leica Microscopy Systems, Heerbrugg, Switzerland) equipped with a color CCD camera.

Atomic Force Microscopy (AFM)

Sample fragments, similar to those freeze-fractured and critical point dried for SEM, were cemented to metal disks and imaged in a model Nanoscope IIIa scanning probe microscope with TESP cantilevers (Veeco/Digital Instruments, Santa Barbara, CA) operated in the intermittent contact mode as an atomic force microscope.

Mechanical Test

Compressive mechanical testing of the samples was performed on a Rheometric Scientific RSA II Solids Analyzer (Rheometric Scientific; Piscataway, NJ). The test fixture consisted of two 25 mm parallel plates. Most of the samples tested had been prepared in the 96 well microtiter plate described above, and had nominal dimensions of 5.5 × 3.5 mm (d × h). For P_1P_2I the test specimen was cut from the cylindrical sample using a hack saw. The samples were placed on the lower plate and the upper plate was lowered onto the sample to give a slight compressive force. The upper plate was then locked in place. The samples were tested using a compressive strain of 0.25% to 1.0% depending on the sample. The samples were tested using a temperature ramp from -100°C to +200°C at a heating rate of 10°C/min. Storage modulus, loss modulus, and loss tangent were determined for the samples over this temperature range. The data were analyzed using Rheometric Scientific Orchestrator software, version 6.5.7.

Water Content and Retention

Swelling studies were carried out at ambient temperature using specimens of the same size as those applied for mechanical testing. Specimens of all samples were freeze-dried for 48 h, weighed (Wd) and transferred into large volume of D.I. water. At regular intervals, specimens were removed from water, wiped with tissue paper to remove the excess water adhering to the surface, weighed (Ww), and reimmersed in the water. This process was repeated until the specimens attained a constant weight. The water content was calculated as (Ww-Wd)/Ww [6].

To test water retention, specimens, 500 mg for each sample, were evenly seeded on Petri dishes (50 × 11 mm; Fisher Scientific, Pittsburgh, PA) and 10.0 g of D.I. water was added. The dishes were placed in an incubator and incubated at 25°C under the humidity of 18 – 21%. After 24 h, the weight loss of the contents in each Petri dish was recorded. Ignoring the influence of the elevation in Philadelphia on gravity, the rate of water evaporation (r) was calculated and expressed as r = mm/h. Plain Petri dishes containing water were used as control.

Experiments for water content and retention were carried out four times for each sample. Data are expressed as the mean ± standard deviation. Significance was determined with the use of a student's *t* test.

RESULTS

In the present study, acrylamide monomers were polymerized either in a solution of dissolved pectin or in an existing structure of pectin which was insolubilized by calcium. The morphology of the resulting composites was investigated by microscopy and dynamic mechanical testing. These methods allowed us to characterize such composite features as the domain size and shape of each component, the microstructure and continuity of each phase, and composite global structural and mechanical properties.

Electron Microscope Characterization of Composites

Micrographs of polyacrylamide (P_1) and pectin/polyacrylamide composite (P_1P_2I) are shown in Figure 1. SEM (Fig. 1A) and AFM (Fig. 1B) revealed that the frozen-fractured faces of freeze-dried polyacrylamide alone (P_1) were multi-faceted on a macroscopic scale (Fig. 1A and B). Facet widths ranged from less than 0.1 mm to over 2 millimeters. Figure 1A revealed that individual facets in the fracture-face were very smooth except for small circular depressions between 50 and 100 nm wide and deep. When circular depressions were absent, irregular clusters with dimensions around 200 nm were observed (data not shown). Fracture-faces of P_1P_2I composites have a very similar macroscopic structure to polyacrylamide alone (c.f., Fig. 1A and C); the frozen-fractured faces are multi-faceted on a macroscopic scale, but the facets are larger and separated only by discrete circular holes or discoidal clefts ranging from 10 to 100 micrometers wide. Areas around the borders of the holes and clefts were very smooth topographically, and regions between these open areas were identical to the clusters and circular depressions in the microstructure of polyacrylamide alone. P_1P_2I composites were made with the addition of methylene blue to identify the pectin component through correlative optical color imaging (Fig. 1 D) and SEM (Fig. 1 E). Comparison of these two figures indicates that the areas around the holes and clefts correlate with pectin which stains blue whereas intervening solid regions were colored white as expected for polyacrylamide which is not stained by methylene blue. The white color arises from the numerous small depressions or other light scattering surfaces. These results indicate that the P_1P_2I composite is a macroporous material with pectin lining hollow pores and polacrylamide filling the large interstices between pores.

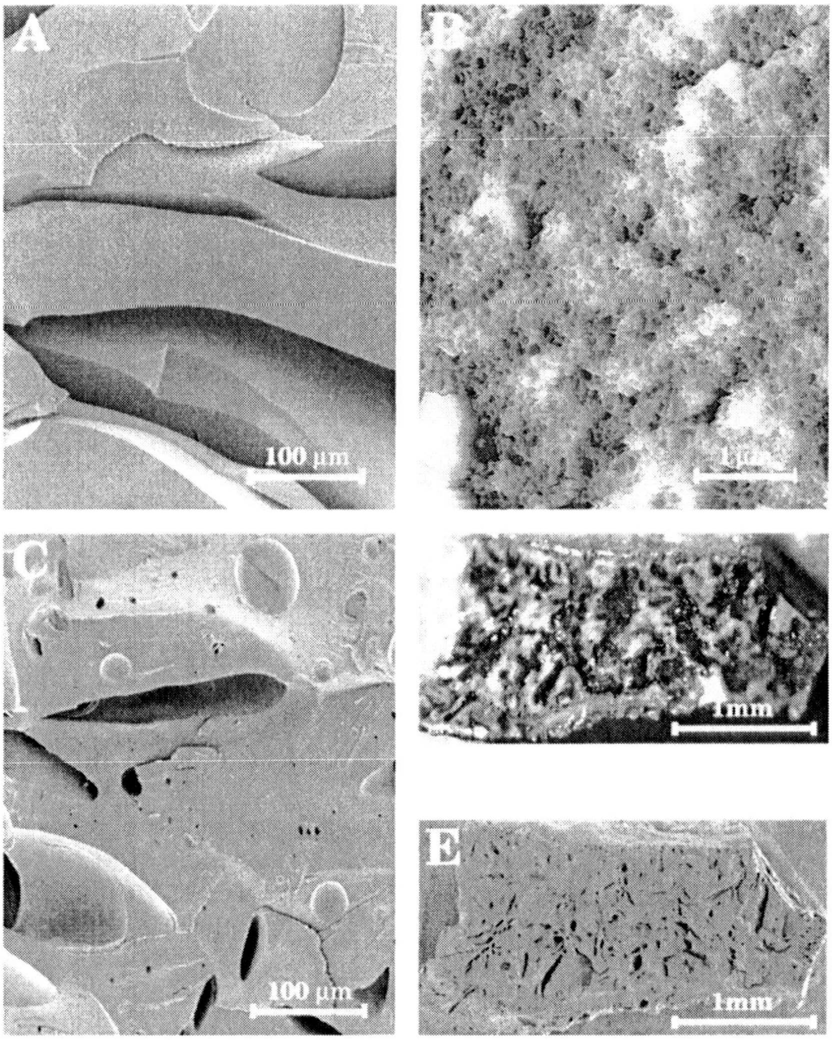

Figure 1. (A) SEM photograph of frozen-fractured polyacrylamide gels (P_1), showing facets of smooth surface embedded with circular depressions (50 - 100 nm in deep) and irregular clusters (200 nm in dimensions) (bar = 100 μm). (B) AFM on P_1 gels shows a close image of circular depressions in the smooth surface of a facet (bar = 1 μm). (C) SEM image of frozen-fractured pectin and polyacrylamide composite gels, P_1P_2I: Facets consist two typical areas: extensive smooth surfaces with small circular depressions and large irregular clusters, which are separated by discrete circular holes and discoidal clefts (bar = 100 mm). (D) Image of light microscope of P_1P_2I gels after staining with methylene blue. Areas around the holes and clefts are pectin aggregates staining with blue, the intervening solid regions are polyacrylamides (colored with white) with small depressions (bar = 1 mm). (E) SEM image of the correlative area shown in (D).

The organization and microstructures of sample P_2 and the combined components P_1P_2II are illustrated in Figure 2.

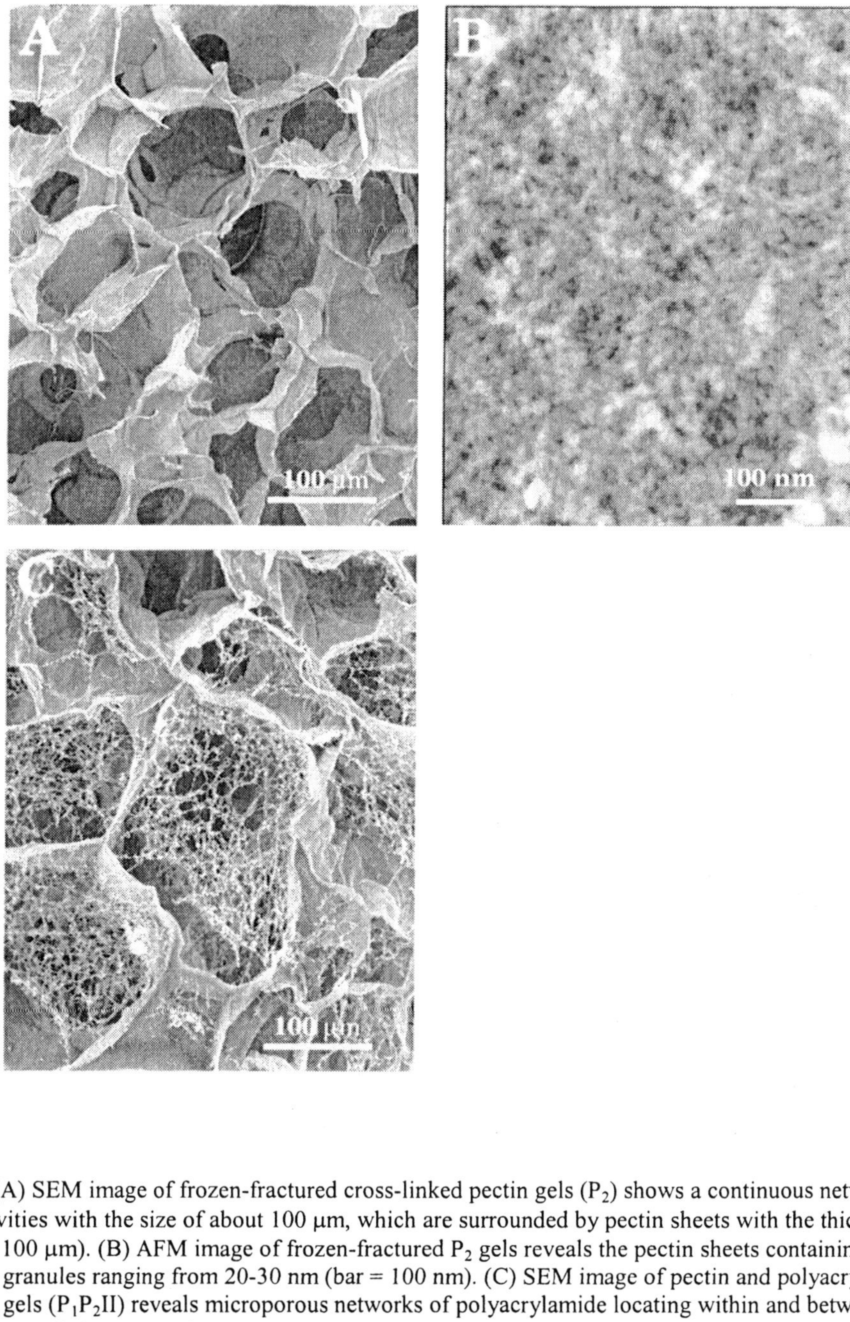

Figure 2. (A) SEM image of frozen-fractured cross-linked pectin gels (P_2) shows a continuous network of solvent cavities with the size of about 100 µm, which are surrounded by pectin sheets with the thickness of 1 µm (bar = 100 µm). (B) AFM image of frozen-fractured P_2 gels reveals the pectin sheets containing short fibrils and granules ranging from 20-30 nm (bar = 100 nm). (C) SEM image of pectin and polyacrylamide composite gels (P_1P_2II) reveals microporous networks of polyacrylamide locating within and between many of the pectinncellular spaces (bar = 100 µm).

Figure 2 A is an SEM micrograph showing a frozen-fractured faces of freeze-dried pectin gel alone, P_2 Fig. 2 A reveals a regular porous organization, resembling the natural tissue cell structure in plant organs, notably potato tubers and citrus fruits [20,21]. The pectin was arranged into a continuous and regular system of walls or sheet-like partitions containing open pores around 100 micrometers in diameter (Fig. 2A). The walls lining these cellular spaces were less than 1 micrometer thick and form numerous triangular junctions resembling the middle lamella of plant cell walls. Some cellular pores or spaces contain circular apertures or openings into adjacent spaces. The surface of cavity walls was further probed by AFM (Fig. 2B). AFM imaging revealed that the surface of the walls or sheet-like partitions were composed of a flat but complex arrangement of short fibrils and/or granules ranging from 20 to30 nm wide (Figure 2B). The AFM image may suggest complex aggregates of pectin molecules which are randomly arranged in the plane of the walls. When polyacrylamide was injected into the regular porous, cellular structure of pectin, loose, microporous networks of fine strands were located within and between many of the cellular spaces. These strands are composed of strings of small granules which are around nm scale in diameter (Fig. 2C).

The organization and microstructure of P_1P_2III and P_1P_2IV are illustrated in Figure 3. Polyacrylamide which was formed in a wet, porous pectin gel has a non-woven network structure, (Fig. 3A and B). In contrast to those formed in dry pectin structure, the acrylamide networks in the P_1P_2III composite consist of belt-like, flat strands with widths on a micrometer scale. The strands have very smooth surfaces, similar to the facets found in the fracture-face of gels containing only polyacrylamide. The pores created in the polyacrylamide structure in P_1P_2III composite are irregular in shape ranging from 1 to 2 micrometers in width. Polyacrylamide formed on the surface of dry pectinate gel displays a network structure similar to those observed in P_1P_2I composites (c.f. Fig. 2C with Fig. 3C).

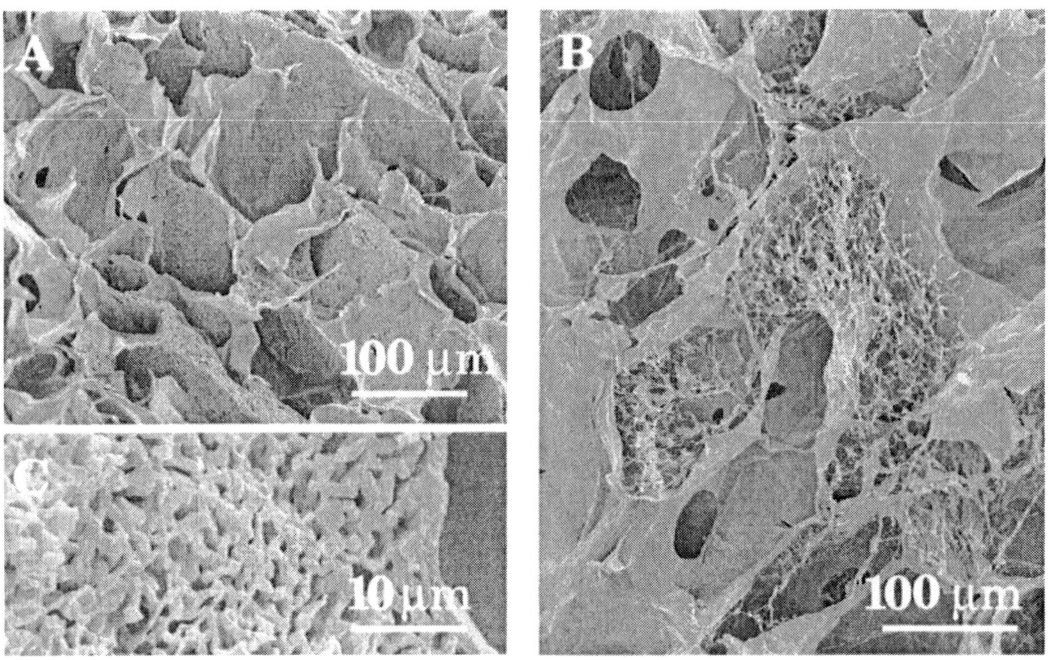

Figure 3. (A) SEM image of frozen-fractured pectin and polyacrylamide composite gels (P_1P_2III), which were formed by polymerizing acrylamides in a pre-wet pectin structure. The polyacrylamide shows a tightly packed network structure, resembling the combined morphologies of P_1P_2I and P_1P_2II gels (bar = 100 μm). (B) SEM image of frozen-fractured P_1P_2III gels in high magnification (bar = 10 μm). (C) SEM image of frozen-fractured pectin and polyacrylamide composite gels, P_1P_2IV, which was prepared by polymerizing acrylamides on the top of a dry cross-linked pectin gel. The P_1P_2IV gels show a similar morphology to P_1P_2II gels (bar = 100 μm).

Compression Test

Typical compressive storage modulus (E'), loss modulus (E"), and loss tangent (tan Δ) curves are compared for each sample in Figure 4. The polyacrylamide gel and two step pectin/polyacrylamide composite gel (P_1P_2II) had fairly similar curves for the storage modulus, and exhibited peaks at 113°C and 97°C respectively. The one step pectin/polyacrylamide gel (P_1P_2I), was somewhat similar, but had two noticeable differences. The initial modulus behavior from -95 to +75°C showed the same flat curve as the other two samples, although the value obtained was about 50% higher. A peak occurred at about 93°C, and the modulus dropped significantly below the other curves by 125°C. The curve for the pectin gel was relatively flat, with a broad minimum at about 13°C. This curve was well below those of the other three over most of the temperature range, however at about 135°C the curve for P_1P_2I dropped below it. By 200°C the other two curves had dropped to the approximate value of the pectin gel.

The loss modulus behavior was somewhat different (Fig. 4 B). The P_1P_2I and P_1P_2II gels gave roughly similar curves with large peaks at 105°C and 121°C respectively. The polyacrylamide gel gave a smaller peak at about 133°C. From -100°C to about 55°C all three samples had comparable modulus values. As in the case of the storage modulus, the loss modulus value for P_1P_2I dropped significantly after the peak. The pectin curve again had much lower modulus values, and showed two broad maxima at -51°C and +81°C, and one broad minimum at 13°C. By 200°C the value for P_1P_2I was down to that of the pectin.

The loss tangent behavior (Fig. 4C) was overall rather similar to that seen for the loss modulus. The peaks for the polyacrylamide gel, P_1P_2I, and P_1P_2II were at about 141°C, 133°C, and 129°C respectively. They also had the same relative sizes as they had in the loss modulus curves. The pectin curve had a broad maximum at about 21°C.

Overall, the dynamic mechanical behavior of the polyacrylamide gel and the two pectin/polyacrylamide gels were fairly similar. As a group they were very distinct from the pectin-only gel. The glass transition temperatures of the polyacrylamide containing gels, as measured by the peak in the loss tangent curves, are in the range of 129-141°C. These are comparable to the value of 165°C reported in the Polymer Handbook [22]. The presence of the pectin gel in the two samples probably accounts for their lower glass transition values. The P_1P_2I sample appears to be made so as to have a higher density than the other samples. This may account for the higher storage modulus values seen for it below the glass transition temperature.

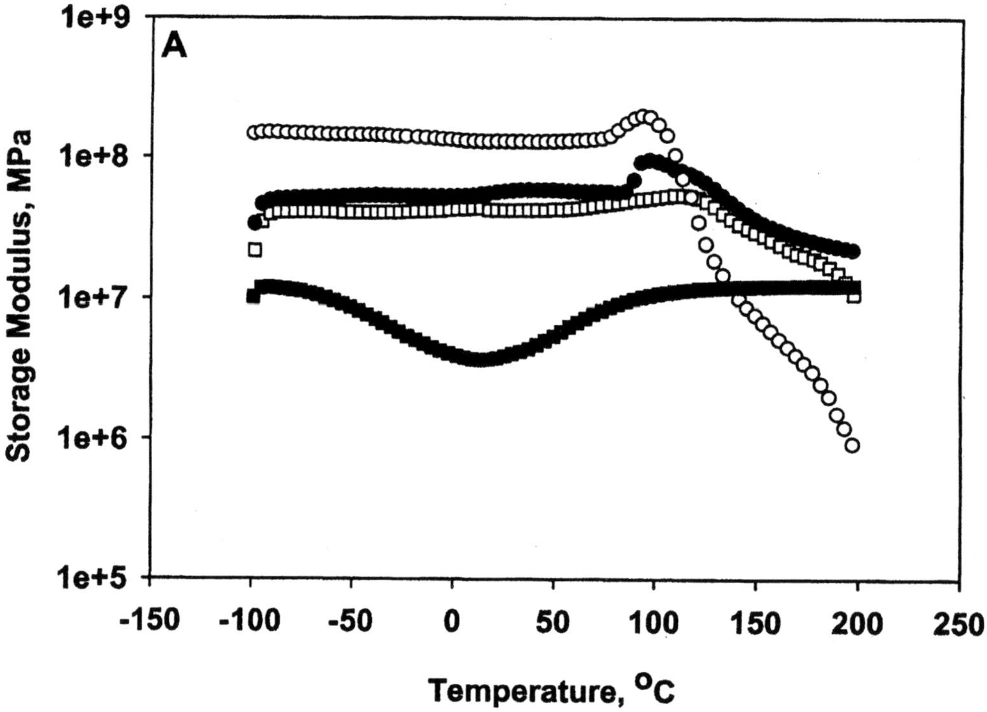
A
Storage Modulus, MPa
1e+9
1e+8
1e+7
1e+6
1e+5
-150
-100
-50
0
50
100
150
200
250
Temperature, °C

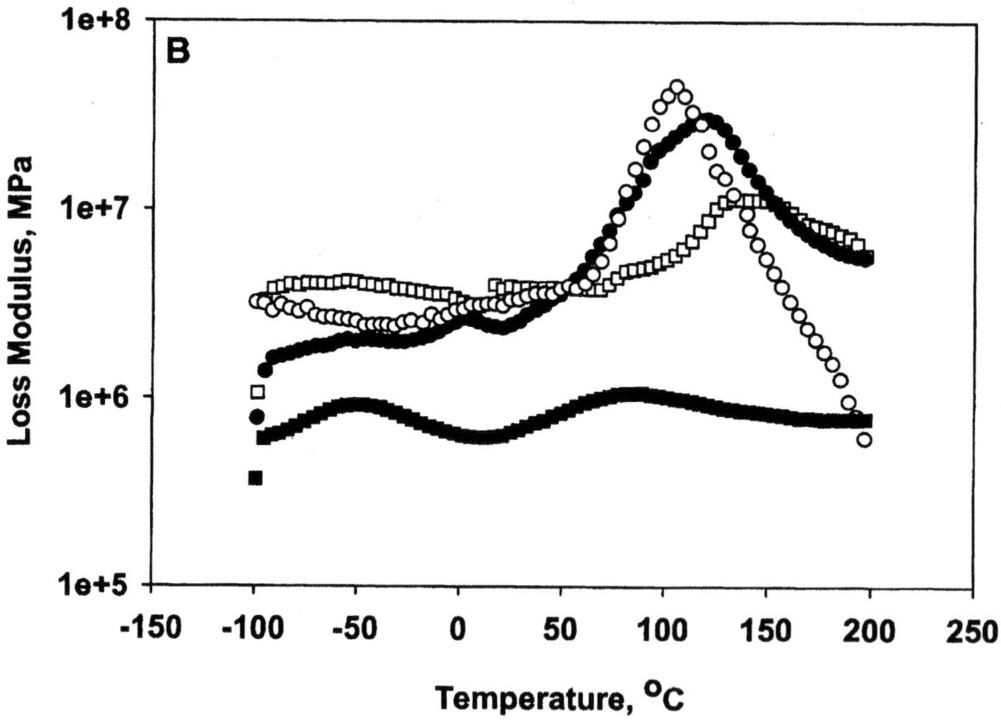
B
Loss Modulus, MPa
1e+8
1e+7
1e+6
1e+5
-150
-100
-50
0
50
100
150
200
250
Temperature, °C

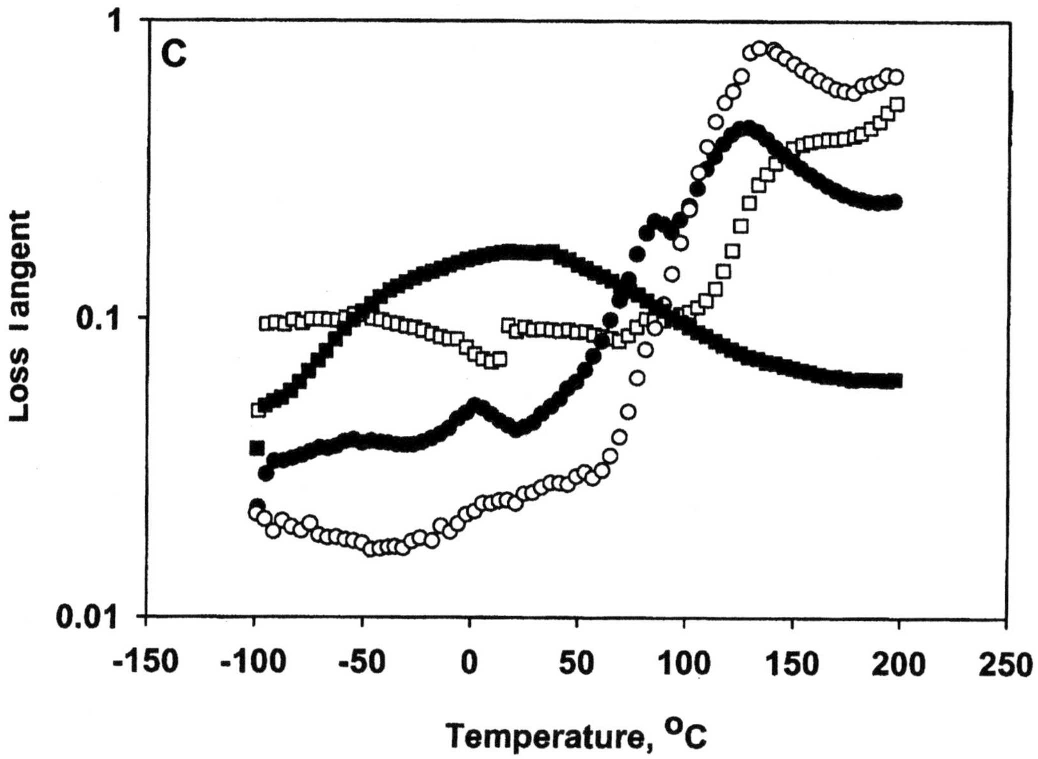

Figure 4. Typical plots of (A) storage modulus, (B) loss modulus, and (C) loss tangent as a function of temperature. The storage modulus of P_1P_2I gels ( ) has the highest value among the four samples at the temperature lower than 100 C, $P1P_2II$ gels ( ) and P_1 gels ( ) have the similar modulus, and P_2 gels ( ) has the lowest storage modulus. The loss modulus of P_1, P_1P_2I, and P_1P_2II gels all have high degree of similarity, except that the modulus value of P_1P_2I gels fell significantly more than the other two. The curve of P_2 gels has the lowest overall values. The loss tangent curves of P_1, P_1P_2I, and P_1P_2II gels are similar in form, with the sharpest peaks in the range of 125 – 145°C. The curve of P_2 gels had a maximum at about 40°C.

Table I. Characteristics of pectin based gels for water absorbing and desorbing

Samples ID	#Water content, %	Rate of water evaporation, mm/h
Control	NA*	0.203 ± 0.017
P_1	79 ± 3	0.173 ± 0.008**
P_2	98 ± 3	0.144 ± 0.012
P_1P_2I	88 ± 2	0.157 ± 0.007**
P_1P_2II	97 ± 4	0.137 ± 0.011

Water Content and Retention

The hydration behavior of the four types of hydrogels, P_1, P_2, P_1P_2I, and P_1P_2II, were determined in terms of the ability to absorb and retain water. The results summarized in Table 1 revealed that P_2 and P_1P_2II absorbed about the same amount of water. Both of the gels have remarkable water absorbing capacity ranging from 34 to 36 times the weight of dry gels. In addition, both P_2 and P_1P_2II are able to maintain the absorbed water for a period longer than that observed with P_1 and P_1P_2I gels, as the absorbed water evaporated from P_2 and P_1P_2II at the lowest rate. Although there is only a slight difference in water retention found between P_1 and P_1P_2I gels, P_1P_2I composite gel absorbed more water than P_1 gel.

DISCUSSION

In this study we investigated the effect of pectin on the architecture of pectin and polyacrylamide composite hydrogels; especially, on the microstructure of polyacrylamide phases in the composites. Pectin and specifically, pectinic acid, is a polyacid. The intermolecular interaction between a polyacid and polyacrylamide is dependent on (1) the ionization of polyacid and (2) the structural compatibility between the polymers. At low ionization, polyacids function as hydrogen donors, and thus can intermolecularly hydrogen-bond to polyacrylamide, which is a proton acceptor, to form an intermolecular complex. At some point as ionization increases, the two polymers will act independently. Model systems to demonstrate this kind of behavior are the polymerization of acrylic acid or methacrylic acid in the presence of polyacrylamide [23-25]. The polyacrylic acid and polyacrylamide are compatible with each other, both are highly water soluble and their molecular chains are highly flexible. Thus, the intermolecular interaction between the two polymers are efficient as the polyacids are deionized, the two polymers mix at segment level or at molecular level, resulting in an interpenetrating network (IPN) structure. Pectin is a natural polyacid, but it has a completely different chemical structure than polyacrylic acid. The backbone of pectin consists predominately of poly(galacturonic acid) blocks interrupted by inserted rhamnose segments with attached neutral sugar branches. The galacturonic acid is methyl esterified to various degrees, depending on the sources of pectin. The number and the distribution of carboxylic groups along the backbone chains of pectin, as well as the side branches, specifically control the electrostatic properties and viscometric behavior of the polymer [26].

In the current experiments, the pectin has a DE of 30% and its residual carboxylate groups are in the sodium form. In aqueous solution, pectin polymers may exist as a complex mixture of associated network structures, branched structures and linear structures in the form of rods, segmented rods and kinked rods [27-30]. These chemical and physical structures of pectin may inhibit the hydrogen-bonding between pectin and polyacrylamide. Furthermore, the differences in the structure and solubility between the two polymers contribute to their incompatibility and the water partition in the polymers-water heterogeneous system. As expected, the polymerization of acrylamide in the presence of a viscous pectin solution resulted in a heterogonous composite (P_1P_2I gel) instead of a complex with IPN structure. As the polymerization progressed, the newly formed hydrogel entrapped pectin inside the network and forced it to further aggregate. Networks of pectin macromolecules tend to entrap a large volume of water to balance the osmotic pressure and to buffer the electrostatic repulsion rising from their pendent anionic groups [31-33]. Thus, the water distribution between the pectin phase and the acrylamide phase was found to be uneven. This was demonstrated by the SEM examination. As illustrated in Fig. 1B and C, there is a larger pore volume in the pectin phase than in the acrylamide phase. Furthermore, pores in the pectin phases are bigger than those found in the acrylamide phases. Possibly, these pore spaces were created by entrapped water which was removed by lyophilization.

Accompanying the water partition to the pectin phase, the aggregates of pectin macromolecules should tend to disentangle from the network to form a separated pectin layer and a polyacrylamide layer. On the other hand, the polyacrylamide networks tend to shrink and re-pack the polymer chains in a denser and clustered pattern. Ultimately, the tightly packed acrylamide zones prevent the escape of pectin aggregates. As shown in Fig. 1C to E, these two phases are tightly packed together. At the adjacent areas of phases, the two polymers are closely approached and adherent to each other. Apparently, the water partition to the pectin phase increases the density of the polyacrylamide phase. This may contribute to the increase in storage modulus and the decrease in lost tangent of P_1P_2I composites as compared with that measured from dry P_1 gels (Fig. 4). In response to the surrounding heavy polyacrylamide phases, the pectin phase also developed a relatively dense structure after lyophilization, differing from what was observed in native plant cell walls and from what developed from pectin solutions (Fig. 2A).

In the absence of acrylamide, the lyophilization of a pectin solution created a three-dimensional porous scaffold. The structure, under SEM, exhibits a repeating network of solvent cavities at the size of about 100 micrometers and polymeric strands at the size of 1 micrometer (Fig. 2A). Since the thickness estimated for an individual pectin strand is between 0.5 and 0.8 nm by AFM method [34] and around 1 nm by X-ray scattering method [35,36] data from this study suggests that the wall of cavities may represent aggregates of a huge number of polymer molecules. This conclusion arises from AFM images, which revealed an arrangement of short fibrils and/or granules in the construction of the cellular walls (Figure 2B). Furthermore, SEM images (Figure 2A) reveal that numerous triangular junctions were formed in the adjacent areas of cavities, mimicking the structure of middle lamella of plant cell walls. Such an organization would potentially enhance the physical strength of gel structure. Indeed, the pectin scaffold is able to maintain its three-dimensional structure even after it is filled with an acrylamide solution which is followed by polymerization of the acrylamide and lyophilization of the composite which results (Fig. 2C).

The compressive mechanical properties as a function of temperature was determined by dynamic mechanical analysis (DMA) for pectin, polyacrylamide and composites there of (Fig. 4). The initial decrease in the E' value of the pectin aero gel (P_2) with increasing temperature (Figure 4A) may reflect segmental motion of pectin molecules due to an incipient glass transition. This may indicate that $CaCl_2$ insolubilized pectin with minimal cross-linking having taken place. Thermal energy in combination with decreased polymer-polymer interactions due to air spaces could allow destructuring pectins' sponge-like structure. The recovery of E' to its initial value at higher temperatures may result from losses in air spaces to an extent which permits increased polymer-polymer interactions. Previously, we found that the tensile storage modulus E' for neat high methoxyl pectin films was practically constant over the temperature ranging from -100°C to 200°C which was explained by strong cooperative polymer-polymer interactions due to hydrogen bonding [37]. The data in Figure 4 reveals that lyophilized polyacrylamide unlike lyophilized pectin undergoes a glass transition in the 130°C to 140°C range. This behavior would indicate that in the absence of air spaces that cooperative intermolecular hydrogen bonding is stronger for pectin than for polyacrylamide. Nevertheless at lower temperatures where air spaces are present in lyophilized pectin, cooperative intermolecular hydrogen bonding is stronger for polyacrylamide than for pectin.

The cross-linking of acrylamide monomers in the dry pectin scaffolds resulted in another porous network penetrating through the pectin networks. Thus, the P_1P_2II gels have a double-network structure, which contributed to the increasing in E' value and the decrease in E'' value of P_1P_2II composite gels obtained from small deformation testing (DMA) (Fig. 4). This complex structure was observed using SEM even after lyophilization. It is rather surprising that P_1P_2I and P_1P_2II have similar DMA in that P_1P_2II is more porous than P_1P_2I. It would appear that cross-linked networks of polyacrylamide within pectin pores is as efficient at preventing the onset of molecular motion with increasing temperature as is increasing the packing density as occurs with P_1P_2I.

Water partition between the solid pectin phase and the liquid polyacrylamide phase is considered to play a key role in the construction of the composite. The dry pectin scaffolds demonstrated the highest capacity to absorb and retain water (Table 1) among the four hydrogels. Therefore, the water entrapped in polyacrylamide gels, which is located in the pore spaces of pectin scaffolds, is supposedly absorbed by the walls of pores prior to the process of lyophilization. We speculate that the porous pectin structure not only provides spaces for the deposition of polyacrylamide gels, but also functions as a blotting paper to remove the water held by the polyacrylamide gel. To verify this hypothesis, acrylamide was allowed to polymerize and cross-link inside a pectin scaffold, P_1P_2III. In this experiment the walls of the pectin scaffold were saturated with water but there was little or no water allowed to remain in the pore spaces. Therefore, water absorbed in the pectin walls inhibited the transfer of water from the acrylamide phase to the pectin phase. The resulting polyacrylamide shows a tightly packed network-like structure (Fig. 3A and B), which combines the characteristics of polyacrylamide phases observed with P_1P_2I and P_1P_2II composite hydrogels. In another experiment, a solution of acrylamide monomers was laid on the top of a dry porous pectin scaffold (P_1P_2IV) and allowed to polymerize and lyophilize. A polyacrylamide network of filamentous polymer strands was obtained (Fig. 3C), resembling the structure found in P_1P_2II composite hydrogels (Fig. 2C). Results from the above experiments confirm that in order to maintain the physical structure of cross-linked polyacrylamide, it is critical to remove entrapped water in the polyacrylamide hydrogel by transferring it to dry pectin. Furthermore this should be done before subjecting the composite to lyophilization.

CONCLUSIONS

The microstructure of pectin and polyacrylamide composite hydrogels could be determined by the physical status of pectin, which regulated the coordination of water partition and phase separation in the composites. The water partition from a liquid polyacrylamide phase to another liquid pectin phase resulted in a composite with tightly packed structure. The water partition from a liquid polyacrylamide phase into a sponge-like pectin scaffold left residual filamentous networks of polyacrylamide imprinted in the pore spaces of the scaffold. This procedure limits the effect of freeze-drying on possible mechanical damage to the physical structure of resulting composite.

Finally, we believe the methodology developed here could prevent the irreversible deactivation of polymers during lyophilization. Deactivation may occur during formulation in carrier systems of many environmentally sensitive biomacromolecules including proteins, polypeptides, and others.

REFERENCES

[1] Th. F. Vandamme; A. Lenourry, C. Charrueau, and J-C.Chaumeil, *Carbohydr. Polym.* **48**, 219 (2002).

[2] S. H. Christensen, in *Food Hydrocolloids III*, M. Glicksman, Ed., CRC Press, Boca Raton, 1984, Chap. 9.

[3] R. P. Singh, T. Tripathy, G. P. Karmakar, S. K. Rath, N. C. Karmakar, S. R. Pandey, K. Kannan, S. K. Jain, and N. T. Lan, *Current Science*, **78**, 798 (2000).

[4] R. Semdè, A. Amighi, M. J. Devleeschouwer, and A. J. Moës, *Inter. J. Pharm.* **197**, 169 (2000).

[5] V. R. Sinha, and R. Kumira, *Inter. J. Pharm.,* **224**, 19 (2001).

[6] D. Dhara, G. V. N. Rathna, and P. R. Chatterji, *Langmuir*, **16**(6), 2424 (2000).

[7] J. Kost, and R. Langer, *Adv. Drug Deliv. Rev.*, **46**, 125 (2001).

[8] G. Chen, Y. Imanishi, and Y. Ito, *Macromolecules*, **31**(13), 4379 (1998).

[9] N. A. Pappas, and R. Langer, *Science*, **264**, 1715 (1994).

[10] B. Jeong, Y. H. Bae, D. S. Lee, and S. W. Kim, *Nature*, **388**, 860 (1997).

[11] Z. Hu, X. Zhang, and Y. Li, *Science*, **269**, 525 (1995).

[12] M. Zecca, A. Biffs, G. Palma, C. Corvaja, S. Lora, K. Jerabek, and B. Corain, *Macromolecules*, **29**(13), 4655 (1996).

[13] Y. Cohen, O. Ramon, I. J. Kopelman, and S. Mizrahi, *J. Polym. Sci., B: Polym. Phys.*, **30**, 1055 (1992).

[14] G. Johansson, in *Partitioning in Aqueous Two-phase Systems*, H. Walter, D. E. Brooks, and D. Fisher, Eds, Academic Press, New York, 1985, Chap. 7.

[15] M. A. Malik, A. Nadler, and J. Letey, *Soil Technol.*, **4**, 255 (1991).

[16] K. Kajiwara, and S. B. Ross-Murphy, *Nature*, **355**, 208 (1992).

[17] G. Y. N. Chan, P. A. Kambouris, M. G. Looney, G. G. Qiao, and D. H. Solomon, *Polymer*, **41(1)**, 27 (2000).

[18] J. Elisseeff, W. McIntosh, K. Anseth, S. Riley, P. Ragan, and R. Langer, *J. Biomed Mater. Res.*, **51**, 164 (2000).

[19] T. Miyata, T. Uragami, and K. Nakamae, *Adv. Drug Deliv. Rev.*, **54**(1), 79(2002).

[20] K. G. Lapsley, F. E. Escher, and E. Hoehn, *Food Structure*, **11**, 339 (1992).

[21] J. T. V. Marle, A. C. M. Clerkx, and A. Boekestein, *Food Structure*, **11**, 209 (1992).

[22] J. Brandrup, and E. H. Immergut, Eds., *Polymer Handbook*, John Wiley & Sons, New York, 1975, P. III-146.

[23] F. Diez-Pena, I. Quijada-Garrido, P. Frutos, and J. M. Barrales-Rienda, *Macromolecules*, **35**(7), 2667 (2002).

[24] F. O. Garces, K. Sivadasan, P. Somasundaran, and N. J. Turro, *Mocromolecules*, **27**, 272 (1994).

[25] M. T. Garay, M. C. Llamas, and E. Iglesias, *Polymer*, **38**, 5091 (1997).

[26] M. Rinaudo, in *Pectin and Pectinases*, J. Visser, and A. G. J. Voragen, Eds, Elsevier Science, New York, 1996, Chap. 2.

[27] M. L. Fishman, P. Cooke, B. Levaj, D. T. Gillespie, and S. M. Sondey, *Arch. Biochem. Biophys.*, **294**, 253 (1992).

[28] M. L. Fishman, P. Cooke, A. Hotchkiss, and W. Damert, *Carbohydr. Res.*, **248**, 303 (1993).

[29] M. L. Fishman, H. K. Chau, P. Hoagland, and K. Ayyad, *Carbohydr. Res.*, **323**, 126 (2000).

[30] M. L. Fishman, H. K. Chau, F. Kolpak, and J. Brady, *J. Agr. Fd. Chem.*, **49**, 4494 (2001).

[31] M. Yalpani, *Polysaccharides*, Elsevier, New York, 1988, Chap. 4.

[32] A. Mallam, F. Horkay, A-M. Hecht, and E. Geissler, *Macromolecules*, **22**, 3356(1989).

[33] J. M. BeMiller, in *Chemistry and Function of Pectins*, M. L. Fishman, Ed., American Chemical Society, ACS Series, Washington DC, 1986, Chap. 1.

[34] A. N. Round, A. J. MacDougall, S. G. Ring, and V. J. Morris, *Carbohydr Res.*, **303**, 251 (1997).

[35] M. D. Walkinshaw, and S. Arnott, *J. Mol. Biol.*, **153**, 1055 (1981).

[36] M. D. Walkinshaw, and S. Arnott, *J. Mol. Biol.*, **153**, 1075 (1981).

[37] M. L. Fishman, D. R. Coffin, J. J. Unruh, and T. Ly, *J. Macromol. Sci.-Pure Appl. Chem.*, **A33**, 639 (1996).

In: Homolytic and Heterolytic Reactions: Problems and Solutions ISBN 1-59033-980-0
Editors: G.E. Zaikov, et al., pp. 137-155

Chapter 5

KINETICS OF N,N-DIMETHYLAMINOETHYLMETHACRYLATE POLYMERIZATION IN SOLUTIONS AND INVERSE EMULSIONS INITIATED BY AIBN AND POTASSIUM PERSULFATE

N. M. Beylerian, R. V. Yeghoyan, V. V. Grigorian, R. M. Hakopian and R. S. Harutyunian
Yerevan State University, Department of Physical and Colloid Chemistry. A. Manoogian St., Yerevan, 375025, Armenia. E-mail: norbey@ysu.am

ABSTRACT

The kinetics of N,N-dimethylaminoethylmethacrylate (DMAEM) polymerization has been studied in some polar solvents and in their mixtures with waters elementary reactions level, and in inverse emulsions stabilized by lecithin initiated by oil as well as water soluble initiators. It has been established that water acts on polymerization rate (R_p) acting on macroradicals conformation and their reactivity which results in decreasing both chain propagation and termination rates constants. But, in whole, in presence of water the ratio $k_p/\sqrt{k_t}$ is being increased on which depends R_p if R_{in} remains constant. Such behavior of water is used to control comonomers relative reactivities (r_1 and r_2). By such a way the DMAEM molar ratio has been increased in vinylacetate (VA)-DMAEM copolymer. Oil and water soluble initiators [AIBN and potassium persulfate (P)] are used to initiate DMAEM polymerization in inverse emulsions stabilized by lecithin (Le). It has been established that in both cases R_p is greater in inverse emulsions. It is shown that DMAEM forms an effective initiating system with P as tertiary amine. So DMAEM takes part in chain initiating, propagation and transfer reactions. It plays also the role of crosslinking agent. Le shows unusual behavior. At $[\mathrm{Le}]_0 = 1\%$ by weight with respect to the oil phase (toluene) R_p has maximum value. This result does not depend on the initiator nature. It may be explained assuming that chains are being grown in micelles polar zones by enhanced rate and at the same time Le may transfer the chain with degradation which results in R_p decrease. The both effects depend on Le concentration.

Keywords: Dimethylaminoethylmethacrylate, lecithin, inverse emulsion, radical polymerization, kinetics.

1. Introduction

During the last 30 years waters-soluble, in particular cationic, polymers are in the center of researchers' attention. Among them are dialkylaminoesters of acrylic acid as well as their derivatives (DAAEs) [1-5]. In a great extent it is due to the fact that they emphasize polyelectrolyte properties.

Logunova [6] and Kolesnikov [7] have obtained water-soluble polyelectrolytes on the basis of β-aminoesters of methacrylic acid. The properties of polyelectrolytes in a great extent depend on the solvent nature and their conformation peculiarities, which have been studied in [8]. It is well established that polyelectrolytes have large applications in different areas. PolyDAAEs are also effective crosslinking agents [9,10]. They easily form water-soluble quaternary ammonium salts (QS) which are more reactive.

Among DAAEs particular interest presents Dimethylaminoethylmethacrylate (DMAEM). Yet it is tertiary amine, ester and vinyl compound. Thus it may react with water, acids, peroxides and can be polymerized as monomer and copolymerized. It can be grafted onto Polyacrylamide [11, 12].

DMAEM could not be considered as a water-soluble monomer. In the water/oil systems DMAEM is distributed between both phases [13]. For this reason its polymerization is being carried out in polar solvents (SH) and in water-SH mixtures. There are very few publications concerning DMAEM polymerization in microemulsions [14].

1. 1. Some Considerations Concerning the Water Action on Polymerization Rate (R_p) of Monomers

It is well known that solvents are not a simple medium in which solved reagent molecules may become in contact. They take direct part in liquid phase reactions in particular polymerization as a result of intermolecular interactions between SH and reagent molecules (specific solvation). The SH action may be the result of non-specific salvation, too [15].

Apart in the case of polymerization the SH influences on macromolecules as well as the growing macro-radicals behavior should be considered too, e.g. macromolecules conformation dependence on SH quantity as well as on its nature. In this connection water presents particular interest because, on one hand, it is the most available, ecologically pure solvent, and on the other hand, it possesses very attracting physicochemical properties.

Bhattacharyya and Nandy [16,17] have revealed that in presence of water the R_p of some vinyl monomers is being increased. They assume that water acts on macroradicals conformation which results in termination rate constant's k_p decrease. Similar effect is established in the case of other monomers polymerization [18, 19].

In [20,21] the authors have shown water's positive action on DMAAs and their corresponding QS R_p. The comonomers relative activities (r_1 and r_2) also depend on water presence. The explanation was the same [22,23]. In presence of water there is some decrease in the overall energy of activation (E_p) [19,24].

It is worthy to note that polyelectrolyte properties of PolyDMAEM are more relevant when it is obtained in presence of water [25]. In this case the water action is discussed in [24-29]. In [30] it is shown that in the case of polymerization of vinylacetate (VA) the water presence brings to enhancement of both R_p and mean molecular mass ($\overline{MM}$).

The medium influence may be expressed by means of H-bonding between SH and reagent molecules. It is interesting to note that H-bonding may result in either increase or decrease of reagent molecules reactivity [31-35]. This question in more detail is discussed in [36].

The probability of Charge Transfer Complex (CTC) formation between vinylmonomer and SH cannot be neglected. The CTC formation in principle may act on $k_p/\sqrt{k_t}$ ratio [37, 38]. According to [37-39] CTC formation results only in k_p increase; it does not act on k_t. In principle CTC may be formed also between SH molecules and growing macroradicals [40]. This question is discussed in [41].

The solvent may act on the medium viscosity too on which depends k_t in a more extent than k_p. In [42] this question is discussed in the case of some QS radical polymerization.

The kinetics of ionizing monomers in a great extent depends on the medium pH. In this case electrostatic interactions must be considered [43, 44]. However it is important to consider the possibility of DMAEM hydrolysis as ester which is significant at $pH < 1$ and $pH > 8$ [20, 45]. The role of electrostatic interactions is more important in the case of two ionizing comonomers copolymerization [46, 47].

1. 2. The Water Action on VA Polymerization in Homogeneous SH-Water Mediums [48-52]

The water influence quantitatively and in detail has been studied by us in the case of VA polymerization in CH_3OH and CH_3OH+H_2O solutions initiated by benzoyl peroxide, persulfate- triethanolamine, AIBN as well as using photoinitiation. To maintain the system's homogeneity Gibbs triangle method (VA- H_2O- SH) has been used to pick them up by suitable concentrations. In all cases in presence of water the R_p increases, the $\overline{MM}$, too.

TEMPO has been used as effective inhibitor (2,2′,6,6′-tetramethyl-4-oxy-piperidine-1-oxyl) to determine R_{in}-the first elementary reaction rate. The correctness of $RNO^{\bullet}$ use is confirmed because the following three requirements are satisfied: (i) in its presence clear induction periods (τ_{in}) are being obtained, (ii) there is linear correlation between τ_{in} and $[RNO^{\bullet}]_0$:

$$R_{in} = f\frac{[RNO^{\bullet}]_0}{\tau_{in}} = k_{in}[I]_0 \quad (1)$$

where $f = 1$ for $[RNO^{\bullet}]_0$ [53], $[I]_0$ is the initiator's initial concentration, and (iii) after τ_{in} the kinetic curves in the steady-state are parallel.

In all cases it is strictly established that in the steady-state experimental data obey the kinetic law of the "ideal radical polymerization":

$$R_p = \frac{1}{\sqrt{2}} \cdot \frac{k_p}{\sqrt{k_t}} \cdot R_{in}^{1/2}[M] \quad (2)$$

R_p is determined by dilatometric method. The ratio $k_p/\sqrt{k_t}$ has been determined using rotating sector method:

$$k_p/\sqrt{k_t} = \frac{2\tau_s R_{p(photo)}}{[M]} \text{ and } [R^{\bullet}]_s = \frac{R_{p(photo)}}{K_p[M]} \quad (3)$$

where τ_s - is the mean-life of growing macromolecules in seconds and $[R^{\bullet}]_s$ is their steady-state (stationary) concentration.

In Tables 1 and 2 some kinetic data obtained at different temperatures are summarized. From these data it follows: (i) in presence of water the both rate constants (k_p and k_t) decrease, but k_t decreases in more extent. In whole the ratio $k_p/\sqrt{k_t}$ increases, so R_p increases too. It should be noted that water has practically no action on R_{in}; (ii) the water does not affect the activation energy (E_p and E_t), so its action reflects mainly on the entropy of activation (ΔS_0).

For polyVA the water being "thermodynamically bad solvent" results in macroradicals compactness. So they become rolled into a ball which adversely affects the rate of quadratic termination than the rate of propagation reaction. H-bond formation is also probable:

$$R_n^{\bullet} + H_2O \Leftrightarrow [R_n^{\bullet}...H..OH] \quad (4)$$

This assumption makes possible to explain why in the presence of water both R_p and $\overline{MM}$ are being increased (see Table 3). To generalize the conclusion apart CH_3OH, THF and 1,4-dioxane are studied considering that they are good proton acceptors.

Table 1 Absolute values of k_p and k_t at [VA] = 6.7M and CH_3OH:H_2O = 2:1 (by volume)

$T°K$	Reaction Medium	$10^{-3} \cdot k_p$	$10^{-8} \cdot k_p$
		$M^{-1}s^{-1}$	
313	CH_3OH	4.97	5.60
	CH_3OH+H_2O	4.67	2.42
318	CH_3OH	7.50	6.25
	CH_3OH+H_2O	7.28	2.67
323	CH_3OH	11.20	6.98
	CH_3OH+H_2O	8.92	3.00
328	CH_3OH	16.6	7.41
	CH_3OH+H_2O	13.55	3.18

Table 2 k_p and k_t temperature dependence [$k_i = k_i^0 exp(-E_i/RT)\ M^{-1}s^{-1}$]

Reaction medium	$E_p(\pm 2)$ [Le]$_0$	$10^{-13} \cdot k_p^0$ $M^{-1}s^{-1}$	$E_t(\pm 2)$ $kJ \cdot mol^{-1}$	$10^{-11} \cdot k_t^0$ $M^{-1}s^{-1}$
CH_3OH	61.1	8.42	16.3	3.32
CH_3OH+H_2O	60.7	6.30	16.1	1.15

Table 3 [VA] = 6.7 M, [AIBN] = 1 10 $^{-2}$ M, and T = 323 K

Reaction medium	$[H_2O]$, M	$10^4\ R_p,\ M \cdot s^{-1}$	$10^{-3}\overline{M}_\eta$
in bulk	0 ([CH_3OH]=0)	3.93	426
CH_3OH	0	3.36	194
CH_3OH+H_2O	8.17	3.95	272
THF	0	2.28	14
THF+H_2O	6.7	2.63	44
	8.2	2.71	52
1,4-dioxane (D)	-	2.34	76
D+ H_2O	3.26	2.97	11
	6.7	3.22	138

In general:

$$R_p = a + b[H_2O] \tag{5}$$

1.3. The DMAEM Polymerization Kinetics in Some Organic Polar Solvents and in their Mixtures with Water

The practical interest of PolyDAAEs particularly PolyDMAEM has been shown in the Introduction. According to our studies [13] DMAEM is distributed between water and water insoluble SH. DMAEM is soluble in polar organic solvents as well as in organic solvent-water mixtures. From the literature as well as our own experimental data follows the positive role of water which plays in the case of water insoluble or with limited water solubility monomers polymerization.

Taking into consideration these circumstances we have in detail studied the DMAEM polymerization kinetics in alcohols, DMF, FA, 1,4-dioxane, THF, acetone and in their mixtures with water using already described methods [54-59].

In all cases: $[AIBN]_0 = 1.5\ 10^{-2}$ M, [DMAEM] = 4.5 M the temperature range was 313 ÷ 338° K.

It should be noted that R_{in} practically does not depend on the reaction medium used by us which is of the same order as K_{dec} at 323° K. The obtained data concerning the overall R_p at 323° K are summarized in Table 4.

Table 4. The overall polymerization activation energy in different media

Reaction medium	$[H_2O], M$	$E_{pol}(\pm 2)\ kJ \cdot mol^{-1}$	$10^{-8} k^0_{pol}\ M^{-1}s^{-1}$
CH_3OH	-	73	0.72
CH_3OH+H_2O	8		4.71
C_2H_5OH	-	66	0.14
$C_2H_5OH+H_2O$	8		0.33
n-C_4H_9OH	-	73	1.0
n-$C_4H_9OH+H_2O$	8		1.8
DMF	-	67	0.22
DMF+ H_2O	12.0		0.35
FA		69	0.81
FA+ H_2O			1.00
1,4-dioxane (D)	0	62	0.05
$D+H_2O$	12.0	63	0.10
THF	-	69	0.14
$THF+H_2O$	12.0		0.34

From those data it follows that water mainly acts on foreexponential factor (K^0_{pol}).

The absolute propagation and termination rate constants values determined by rotating sector method at 313 K and $[DMAEM] = 4.25 \div 4.50M$ are brought in Table 5.

In this case again water results in k_p and k_t decrease but in whole the $k_p/\sqrt{k_t}$ ratio is being increased because k_t decreases in a more extent. This is the reason why $\overline{M}$ increases in presence of water.

Using Flory-Fox formulae the mean quadratic distance between end groups in the macromolecule $\left[\left(\overline{h^2}\right)^{1/2}\right]$ has been determined (see Table 6) for PolyDMAEM sample with $\overline{M}_\eta = 8.3 \cdot 10^5$.

Table 5. The propagation and termination absolute rate constants at 313 K

Reaction medium	$[H_2O]$, $mol\ L^{-1}$	$10^{-3} \cdot k_p$, $mol\ (L\ s)^{-1}$	$10^{-7} \cdot k_t$, $mol\ (L\ s)^{-1}$	$10^{-5}\overline{M}_w$
CH_3OH	0	0.78	10.0	-
CH_3OH+H_2O	8	0.65	2.3	
C_2H_5OH	0	1.76	15.9	-
$C_2H_5OH+H_2O$	8	1.96	5.1	
303°K $n\text{-}C_4H_9OH$	0	2.86	70.4	-
$n\text{-}C_4H_9OH+H_2O$	8	2.28	20.4	
$(CH_3)_2CO$	0	2.10	15.2	6.44
$(CH_3)_2CO+H_2O$	12.2	1.95	3.2	17.5
DMF	0	1.95	15.1	2.4
DMF+ H_2O	12.0	1.80	4.2	7.9
FA	0	2.17	6.40	-
FA+ H_2O	10.0	1.52	3.0	
1,4-dioxane (D)	0	0.28	1.3	8.2
D+H_2O	12.0	0.174	0.16	20.0

Table 6. The mean quadratic distance between end groups in polyDMAEM sample

Medium	CH_3OH	CH_3OH+H_2O $\varphi = 0.75$	CH_3OH+H_2O $\varphi = 0.5$	CH_3OH+H_2O $\varphi = 0.25$	H_2O (extrapolated value)
$10^6\left(\overline{h^2}\right)^{1/2}$ *cm*	9.51	16.2	16.7	9.60	6.20
Medium	DMF	DMF+H_2O 3:1	DMF+H_2O 1:1	DMF+H_2O 1:3	
$10^6\left(\overline{h^2}\right)^{1/2}$ *cm*	6.84	7.13	9.2	7.1	

It is clear that the $\left(\overline{h^2}\right)^{1/2}$ dependence upon water content may be described by a "bell" shape curve. This could be explained assuming that water acts in two ways: up to $\varphi \le 0.5$ water results in increase of macromolecule size while at $\varphi > 0.5$ it behaves as "thermodynamically bad" solvent. The size increase may be due to the insertion of definite quantity of H-bonded molecules between macromolecule's end groups. In all cases the k_t is affected in a more extent than k_p.

We have determined the intrinsic viscosity $[\eta]$ of aforementioned polyDMAEM sample in pure CH_3OH and DMF. The result is: $[\eta]_{CH_3OH} = 2.21 L\cdot g^{-1}$ and $[\eta]_{DMF} = 1.10 L\cdot g^{-1}$. This fact indicates that DMF is a "thermodynamically bad" solvent with respect to methanol. Therefore the macromolecule size is smaller in DMF.

1.4. VA + DMAEM Copolymerization in CH_3OH and $CH_3OH + H_2O$ solutions [61-63]

From the exposed data follows that in principle it is possible to change polyVA and polyDMAEM macroradicals reactivity. It is well known that monomers' reactivity ratios r_1 and r_2 are very sensitive toward macroradicals as well as monomers reactivities. If our assumption is true one may observe a clear dependence of r_1 and r_2 on the water content in the reaction medium.

For this purpose VA+DMAEM copolymerization has been studied in CH_3OH and CH_3OH+H_2O solutions initiated by AIBN at 333 K in all experiments $[\text{AIBN}] = 1.10^{-2} M$ DMAEM is noted by M_1 and VA by M_2. DMAEM may be considered as ionizing monomer while VA is not.

Classic methods have been used to determine r_1 and r_2. The obtained experimental data are summarized in Table 7.

Table 7. r_1 and r_2 dependence on medium nature for VA + DMAEM couple

Reaction medium					Monomers' reactivities ratios
CH_3OH (9.5M)	CH_3OH+H_2O $\varphi_\theta = 1.5:1$ $[CH_3OH]$=5.7M $[H_2O]$=8.54M	$\varphi_\theta = 1:1$	$\varphi_\theta = 1:1$ [KCl]=0.27M	$\varphi_\theta = 1:1$ [KCl]=0.65M	
1.1	1.8	2.6	0.79	0.66	r_1
0.33	0.16	0.1	0.11	0.10	r_2

The presented data show that with increase in water r_1 increases, but r_2 decreases. On the other hand the increase of the medium ionic strength (adding KCl to the reaction medium) results in r_1 increase while r_2 is less sensible.

DMAEM is a tertiary amine. In the presence of the water the following process occurs:

$$R_3N + HOH \Leftrightarrow R_3\overset{+}{N}H\,OH \Leftrightarrow R_3NH + HO^-,$$

and the increase in the ionic strength may result in to suppress the ionization. According to literature data $R_3\overset{+}{N}H$ is a more reactive monomer than the corresponding R_3N.

Our experiments show also hat the increase of water content in the reaction medium results in increase of DMAEM units in the copolymer. This fact one more time shows that the water enhances DMAEM's reactivity.

The study of the rheological properties of polyDMAEM samples obtained in presence of water [64] as well as of the new VA+DMAEM copolymer [62, 63] has shown that both macromolecular compounds reveal definitely more stressed polyelectrolyte properties.

2. DISCUSSION

The detailed kinetic study of DMAEM polymerization in some polar solvents and in their mixtures with water showed the important role which water molecules play in the chain propagation and termination reactions. It is due to the water action on macroradicals (macromolecules in general) conformation as well as on their reactivity. The macroradical+H2O interaction by means of H-bonding also should be considered. This circumstance is used to control the copolymerization between VA and DMAEM. Changing r_1 and r_2 adding water into the reaction mixture a copolymer is obtained with enriched DMAEM units.

2.1. DMAEM Polymerization Kinetics in Inverse Emulsions

2.1.1. The Initiator is AIBN [65]

Inverse emulsion has been prepared using lecithin (Le) as detergent. The oil phase was toluene (T). In all experiments $W/T = 1:3$ (by volume). The polymerization is driven up to $45 \div 50\%$ conversion.

The rate law has been established studying R_p dependence on DMAEM (M), Le and AIBN concentrations at 323°K at constant $W/T = 1:3$. The obtained kinetic data are summarized in tables 8 and 9.

Table 8 R_p dependence on $[AIBN]_0$ at $[M]_0 = 0.4\ mol\ L^{-1}$, [Le] = 1 % (by weight of toluene)

$10^2 \cdot [AIBN],\ mol \cdot l^{-1}$	0.2	1.0	2.0	4.0	6.0
$10^5 \cdot R_p,\ Ms^{-1}$	0.48	1.0	1.41	1.89	2.50

It is easy to show that $R_p \sim [AIBN]_0^{1/2}$.

Table 9. $\mathbf{R_p}$ **dependence on** $\mathbf{[M]_0}$ **at** $\mathbf{[AIBN]_0 = 2\ 10^{-2}}$ ***mol L***$^{-1}$ **and [Le] = 1 %**

$[\mathrm{M}]_0$, $mol \cdot l^{-1}$	0.1	0.4	1.0	2.0
$10^5 \cdot R_p$, Ms^{-1}	0.32	1.41	1.65	7.00

From those data it follows that $R_p \sim [\mathrm{M}]_0$. The study of R_p dependence on $[\mathrm{Le}]_0$ showed that it is complex.

Table 10. $\mathbf{[AIBN]_0 = 2\ 10^{-1}}$ ***mol. L***$^{-1}$**,** $\mathbf{[M]_0 = 0.4}$ ***mol L***$^{-1}$**, W/T = 1:3, and T = 303 K**

$[\mathrm{Le}]_0$ %	0	0.5	1	2	4
$10^5 \cdot R_p$, Ms^{-1}	0.80	1.12	1.40	1.20	1.15

Those data show: (i) DMAEM R_p is greater in inverse emulsions than in solutions. At $[\mathrm{Le}]_0 = 1\%$ $(R_p)_{inv.em.} : (R_p)_{sol} = 1.75$, (ii) at $[\mathrm{Le}]_0 = 1\%$ R_p has maximum value.

From data brought in tables 8-10 it follows that:

$$R_p = K[\mathrm{AIBN}]^{0.5}[\mathrm{M}][\mathrm{Le}]^x \tag{6}$$

Kinetic data at $[\mathrm{Le}]_0 = 1\%$ in the temperature range 313÷333 K obey the Arrhenius law. The overall polymerization activation energy is equal to 63 *kJ mol* $^{-1}$.

The unusual R_p dependence on $[\mathrm{Le}]_0$ obliged us to study the chain initiation mechanism to reply the question whether R_{in} depends on $[\mathrm{Le}]_0$.

As it was mentioned inhibitory method has been applied to determine R_{in}. Again TEMPO was the initiator.

The kinetic data are brought in Table 11.

Table 11. $\mathbf{[M]_0 = 0.1}$ ***mol L***$^{-1}$**, [Le] = 1 %, W/T = 1:3, T = 323 K**

$10^4 \cdot [R\dot{N}O]_0$, M	0	1	2	4	8	$10^2[\mathrm{AIBN}]_0$ M	$10^6 R_{ind} M \cdot \mathrm{min}^{-1}$
$\tau_{ind}(\pm 1)$, min	1	-	33	67	131	2	6.06 ± 0.03
	1	32	63	127	-	1	3.20 ± 0.02

From those data it follows that at 323°K

$$R_{in} = k_{in}[\mathrm{AIBN}] \tag{7}$$

where $k_{in} = 0.5 \cdot 10^{-5} s^{-1}$.

In absence of monomers and Le at 323°K the AIBN $k_{dec} = 0.25 \cdot 10^{-5} s^{-1}$ [60]. It should be noticed that within the frame of classic considerations $k_{in} = 2Fk_{dec}$, where F is the initiation efficiency and k_{dec} – the initiator's decomposition rate constant.

One may assume that: (i) even in the presence of Le the chains are being terminated by quadratic (bimolecular) mechanism ($R_{in} \sim [\mathrm{AIBN}]_0$ and $R_p \sim [\mathrm{AIBN}]_0^{1/2}$), and (ii) DMAEM and Le practically do not participate in the chain initiation step.

To confirm this conclusion R_{in} dependence on temperature has been studied to be sure that results obtained at 323°K are not accidental and it is true at least for some temperature range. Obtained kinetic data are presented in Table 12.

Table 12. K_{in} dependence on temperature: [AIBN]$_0$ = 2 10^{-2} M, [DMAEM]$_0$ = 0.4 M, [RNO$^\cdot$]$_0$ = 4 10^{-4}, W/T = 1:3, [Le]$_0$ = 1 %

T K	313	323	328	333
$10^6 k_{in} s^{-1}$	1.15	5.0	10.5	21

Those data obey Arrhenius law:

$$k_{in} = (1.90 \pm 0.10) \cdot 10^{15} \exp[-(127100/RT)] \; s^{-1}$$

According to [60] $k_{dec} = 1.58 \cdot 10^{15} \exp[-(129000/RT)] \; s^{-1}$ and [66] $k_{dec} = 1.0 \cdot 10^{15} \exp[-(128300/RT)] \; s^{-1}$.

So the done conclusion is correct. As for the Le action on R_p we assume that it acts on $k_p / \sqrt{k_t}$ ratio. Le is a zwitterion type surfactant. DMAEM is a polar monomer. The chains may grow in the polar layers of the inverse micelles with an enhanced rate. The increase of Le initial concentration may result in intermolecular interactions between opposite by charged centers. This results in decrease of the polarity of the reaction zone. Taking into consideration the fact that the increase in [Le]$_0$ results in $\overline{MM}$ decrease one may assume that a chain transfer by degradation is possible too.

These are hypothesis which request further confirmation.

2.1.2. The Initiator is Potassium Persulfate (P) [67]

According to literature data, DMAEM polymerization may be initiated by radical initiators. Among them there are not peroxides. The main reason is that DMAEM as was already mentioned is a tertiary amine which with a high rate may react with peroxides. Our preliminary studies showed that, in fact, when P being used, there is a very fast initiation, then in a result of complete consumption of P the polymerization comes to a stop. Is is possible to find out conditions at which P may be used. The problem is solved considering the following two circumstances: (i) confirming that in fact the system P+DMAEM is a peroxamine type initiator, and, if it is so, (ii) regulating the free DMAEM concentration changing as well the medium pH.

2.1.3. P+DMAEM System as an Effective Initiator for Radical Polymerization

The kinetics of acrylamide (AA) polymerization initiated by the cited system has been studied. According to our earlier studies the system $P + R_1R_2R_3N$ systems are very effective initiators for radical polymerization [68], particularly for AA polymerization [69, 70].

Varying $[AA]_0$ in the range $0.25 \div 1M$, $[P]_0 = (1 \div 5)10^{-3}M$, $[DMAEM]_0 = (0.5 \div 6)10^{-3}M$ and at 303°K it has been established that:

$$R_p^0 = k_{pol}[P_0]_0^{1/2}[DMAEM]_0^{1/2}[AA]_0 \tag{8}$$

where R_p^0 is the initial polymerization rate.

From (8) it follows that the initiation rate law should be:

$$R_{in} = k_{in}[P_0]_0[DMAEM]_0 \tag{9}$$

which is very well established using the inhibitory method. (9) shows that R_{in} does not depend on AA concentration which follows from data brought in Table 13.

Table 13. $[P]_0 = 2\ 10^{-3}$ M, $[DMAEM]_0 = 2.5\ 10^{-3}$ M, $[RNO]_0 = 5\ 10^{-5}$, and T = 303 K

$[AA]_0$ M	0.15	0.25	0.50	0.75	1.00	1.20
$\tau_{ind}(\pm 1)$ min	29	28	27	29	29	27

The study of k_{in} dependence on temperature in the range $293 \div 313°K$ allowed to derive

$$k_{in} = (1.60 \pm 0.07) \cdot 10^9 \exp[-(5680 \pm 1700)/RT]M^{-1}\min^{-1} \tag{10}$$

$k_{in} = 0.34\ \ M^{-1}\min^{-1}$ at 303° K.

According to [33] DMAEM may be hydrolyzed. The main products are $(CH_3)_2NC_2H_4OH$ and $CH_2{=}C(CH_3)\text{-}COOH$. At 303 K and $[DMAEM]_0 = 6 \cdot 10^{-2}M$ the hydrolysis extent is 10% during 10 hours. Taking into consideration our experimental conditions ($[DMAEM]_0 = 2 \cdot 10^{-3}$ and reaction duration 2 hours) we can assume that DMAEM hydrolysis may be neglected. This conclusion is confirmed on the ground of kinetic data obtained earlier concerning the elementary reaction of P with $(CH_3)_2NC_2H_4OH$ – one of the DMAEM hydrolysis product

$$S_2O_8^{2-} + (CH_3)_2NC_2H_4OH \rightarrow HSO_4^- + \dot{S}O_4^- + (CH_3)_2N\underset{H}{\dot{C}}CH_2OH \quad (11)$$

studied by iodometric analysis

$$\left(k_{in} = 5.6 \cdot 10^6 \exp(-43260/RT)\right)\min^{-1},$$

and ESR method

$$\left(k_{in} = 1.4 \cdot 10^7 \exp(-45560/RT)\right)\min^{-1}$$

in both cases in presence of $RNO^\bullet$ [71,72]. At 303 K $k_{in} = 0.14 \cdot M^{-1}\min^{-1}$ while $k_{in} = 0.34 \cdot M^{-1}\min^{-1}$ when the initiating system was P+DMAEM. Therefore $(CH_3)_2NC_2H_4OH$ practically is absent in the reaction medium. So the system P+DMAEM in fact is an effective initiating system.

2.2. The Kinetics of DMAEM Polymerization Initiated by P in Aqueous Solutions in Presence of H_2SO_4

It is well established that conjugated with amines acids $\left[(R_1R_2R_3NH)^+\right]$ do not react with peroxides particularly with P [73, 74]. The first step was to study the dependence of R_p upon pH. In the following table the values of initial R_p obtained at different concentrations of added sulfuric acid $(0 \div 0.4M)$ are presented.

Table 14. $[P]_0 = 2\ 10^{-3}$ M, $[DMAEM]_0 = 0.4$ M, T = 303 K

$[H_2SO_4]$, M	0	0.20	0.25	0.30	0.35	0.40
pH	9.4	8.25	7.45	2.0	1.7	1.45
$10^3 R_p^0 M, \min^{-1}$	7.0	7.0	5.2	3.0	1.8	0.41

The decrease in R_p^0 with pH decrease is obvious.

Therefore in case of absence of H_2SO_4 occurs a fast bimolecular reaction P+DMAEM. So $R_{in} \neq \text{const}$ and $R_p \rightarrow 0$. This means that steady-state cannot be established. This is the case stated by Tobolsky [75]. It is called “dead-end polymerization”.

Studying R_p dependence on temperature in the range $T = 303 \div 333^\circ K$ at pH=1.45 it has been obtained $E_{pol} = 69.3\ kJ \cdot mol^{-1}$. In strong acid medium R_{in} is very low because the concentration of free DMAEM is low. To disclose the mechanism of chain initiation the kinetics of DMAEM polymerization has been studied in presence of $RNO^{\bullet}$.

As could be expected after the induction period the polymerization does not occur in steady-state regime. The induction periods are estimated by extrapolation of parallel kinetic curves. Used data are presented in Table 15.

Table 15. [DMAEM]$_0$ = 0.4 M, [P]$_0$ = 2 10^{-3} M, [H_2SO_4] = 0.41M, T = 323 K and [RNO]$_0$

$10^5 \cdot [\dot{RNO}]_0\ M$	0	0.625	2.5	5.0
τ_{ind} min	0	11	41	80

(when $[P]_0 = 1 \cdot 10^{-3}$, $\tau_{ind} = 41 \min$)

It is easy to show that

$$R_{in} = k_{in} \frac{[RNO]_0}{\tau_{ind}} = k_{in}[P]_0 \quad (12)$$

$k_{in} = 3.1 \cdot 10^{-4}\ \min^{-1}$ at 323 K and pH=1.45. It is interesting to note that the obtained value is approximately equal to the value determined for persulfate decomposition at the same temperature and at pH=1 [76]. This result unambiguously shows that in strong acid medium there is not P+DMAEM bimolecular reaction and the chains are being initiated as a result of $HS_2O_8^-$ monomolecular decomposition. The mechanism of this reaction in detail is discussed by us [77].

This conclusion is confirmed determining R_{in} dependence on temperature. E_{in} was equal to $105.4\ kJ \cdot mol^{-1}$. According to [76] $E_{dec} = 109.6\ kJ \cdot mol^{-1}$.

2.3. The Kinetics of DMAEM Polymerization Initiated by P in Inverse emulsions [67]

Stable inverse emulsions have been obtained in presence of lecithin and using $[H_2O]/[toluene] = w/oil = 1:3$ system [65]. In the following tables 16 and 17 are brought kinetic data concerning R_p dependence on $[P]_0$, $[DMAEM]_0$, and $[Le]_0$. In all cases $T = 303°K$ and w/oil=1:3 are presented.

Table 16. [DMAEM]$_0$ = 0.4 M, [Le]$_0$ = 1 % [by mass with respect to the toluene (the oil phase)]

$10^3[P]_0\ M$	0.5	1.0	2.0	4.0
$10^6 \cdot R_p\ Ms^{-1}$	5.05	6.95	10.2	16.0

From these data it follows that $R_p \sim [\mathrm{P}]_0^{1/2}$ which shows that growing chains are being terminated by quadratic mechanism.

Table 17. $[\mathrm{P}]_0 = 2\ 10^{-3}$ M, $[\mathrm{Le}]_0 = 1$ %

$[\mathrm{DMAEM}]_0$ M	0.2	0.4	1.0	1.5	1.75	2.0
$10^6 \cdot R_p$ Ms^{-1}	6	14.2	33.3	48.8	70.0	115

The obtained kinetic data show that the order (n) with respect to DMAEM is not simple. At $[\mathrm{DMAEM}]_0 < 0.4$ $n \approx 1$, but at $[\mathrm{DMAEM}]_0 \geq 0.4M$ n becomes >1. It could be conditioned by the fact that primary free radicals are being formed by two parallel reactions:

$$\mathrm{P} - \quad \xrightarrow{k_1} \quad S\dot{O}_4^- \quad +$$

$$\xrightarrow[k_2]{}$$

$$R_{in} = (k_1 + k_2[\mathrm{A}])[\mathrm{P}]_0 \text{ and}$$

$$R_t = k_t\left[R_n^\bullet\right]^2.$$

So

$$R_p \sim \left[\mathrm{R}_\mathrm{n}^\bullet\right][\mathrm{A}] \sim [\mathrm{P}]_0^{1/2}\left(k_1 + k_2[\mathrm{A}]\right)^{1/2}[\mathrm{A}] \qquad (13)$$

and in fact n must be >1. n=1 when $k_1 >> k_2[\mathrm{A}]$.

Table 18. $[\mathrm{P}]_0 = 2\ 10^{-3}$ M, $[\mathrm{DMAEM}]_0 = 0.4$ M

[Le] %	0	0.25	0.50	0.75	1.00	1.50	2.00	4.20	5.20
$10^6 \cdot R_p$ Ms^{-1}	8.0	10.0	10.4	12.0	14.0	12.1	11.5	8.0	4.0

These data show that R_p dependence on $[\mathrm{Le}]_0$ may be presented by bell-shape curve with a maximum at $[\mathrm{Le}]_0 = 1\%$. Similar phenomenon was established in the case when AIBN was used as initiator (see table 10).

From R_p dependence on T the E_{pol} is determined: it is equal to $67 \pm 2\ kJ \cdot mol^{-1}$ which practically does not differ from E_{pol} value obtained when AIBN was used as initiator.

It should be noted that the homolysis activation energy of AIBN and P at pH>9 is approximately the same: $\sim 130\ kJ \cdot mol^{-1}$.

So the Le behavior does not depend on initiator nature (water-soluble or oilsoluble). Probably the change in $[\mathrm{Le}]_0$ results in changes in micelles structure on which may depend $k_p / \sqrt{k_t}$ ratio. But as was stated Le may take part also in chain transfer but with degradation. The major part of obtained polyDMAEM is crosslinked which did not allow to determine the mean polymerization degree and to study $\overline{MM}$ dependence on different parameters including $[\mathrm{Le}]_0$.

On the basis of obtained kinetic data the following empiric rate law is derived:

$$R_p^0 = k[\mathrm{P}]_0^{1/2}[\mathrm{DMAEM}]_0^n[\mathrm{Le}]_0^x \tag{14}$$

where $n > 1$ and x is a complex function of $[\mathrm{Le}]_0$. This law is discussed considering some hypothesis.

Conclusion

The overall rate of DMAEM polymerization is approximately 1.5 greater in inverse emulsions than in homogenous mediums. This phenomenon does not depend on the initiator nature. DMAEM is distributed between aqueous and oil phases. In both cases it does not participate in the chain initiation step if it does not form redox system with the initiator. One may assume that DMAEM as tertiary amine forms an effective redox system with P which initiates its own polymerization. It is also a crosslinking agent. R_p dependence on [Le] has unusual form which may be due to the fact that the chains are being grown in inverse micelles polar zones. It results in R_p increase and micelles structure depends on surfactants (e.g. Le) concentration. On the other hand it may transfer the chains with degradation which results in R_p decrease.

References

[1] Alfrey T., Fuoss R.M., Moravetz H., Pinner S.H. // *J. Am. Chem. Soc.*, 1952, v. 74, p. 438 - 441

[2] Alfrey T., Overberger C.G., Pinner S.H. // *ibid.* 1953, v. 75, p. 4221 - 4223

[3] Imoto M., Otsu T., Oba T. // *Makromol. Chemie,* 1955, v. 16, p. 10

[4] Alfrey T., Pinner S.H. // *J. Poly. Sci.,* 1957, v. 23, p. 533 - 537

[5] Longi p., Pelinno E., Greco F., Mazzochi R. // *Chim. e Ind.,* 1964, v. 46, p. 156 - 159

[6] Logunova I.I., Gavrina R.K., Koulikova S.I. // *Vysokomol. Soedinenya* (USSR), 1969, v. B 11, No. 5, p. 355 - 358

[7] Kolesnikov G.S., Teblina N.V., Skripchenko N.I. // *ibid.*, 1971, v. A 13, No. 9 p. 2139 - 2143
[8] Scheinker A.P., Kozlova N.V., Bounet E.V., Abkin A.D. // *Doklady Academyi Naouk USSR*, 1981, v. 258, No. 4, p. 953 - 957
[9] Ponarin E.F., Gavrilova I.I. // *Vysokomol. Soedinenya*, 1977, v. B 19, No. 4, p. 251 - 254
[10] Harutyunian R.S., Grigoryan V.V., Beylerian N.M., Yeghoyan R.V., et al // *USSR patent, № 1,548185*, 1989
[11] Gonzalez-Jaiz J.M., Fernandez-Torroba M.A., Pizarro C. // *Europ. Poly. J.*, 1997, v. 33, p. 475 - 480
[12] Siyam T., Abd-Ellatif Z. // *Sci. Tech. Poly. Adv. Matter*, 1997, p. 165 - 169
[13] Harutyunian R.S., Grigoryan.J.D., Simonyan G.S., Aroyan S.H., Grigoryan V.V., Grigoryan M.V., Beylerian N.M. // *J. Phys. Chem.* (Russia), 2002, v. 76, № 5, p. 846 - 856
[14] Baade W., Hunkeler D., Hamielec A.E. // J. *Appl. Poly. Sci.*, 1989, v. 38, No.1, p. 185 - 201
[15] Loupy A., Haudrecky A. // *Effects de milieu en synthèse organique*, Ed. Masson, Paris, 1996
[16] Bhattacharyya B.R., Nandy U. // *J. Poly. Sci.*, A1, 1966, v. 4, №10, pp. 2675-2682
[17] Bhattacharyya B.R., Nandy U. // *J. Indian Chem. Soc.*, 1971, v. 48, №11, pp. 1033-1038
[18] Sheikloutdinov E.M., Kourmanaliev O.M., Toul'baev Sh. S., Ermaganbetov M.E. // *Vysokomol. Soed., Short Commun. (ser. B)*, 1979, v. 21, №1, pp. 61-63 (USSR)
[19] Sheikhoutdinov E.M., Ermaganbetov M.E., Toul'baev Sh. S., Kourmanaliev O.M. // *ibid* 1986, v. 28, №10, pp. 735-737
[20] Martinenko A.I., Rouziev R.D., Nechaeva A.B., Djalilov A.T., Topchiev D.A., Kabanov V.A. // *Ouzbek. Chem. J.*, 1979, № 2, pp 59-63
[21] Rouziev R.D., Djalilov A.T., Topchiev D.A., Kabanov V.A. // *Izv. Vouzov. Chem. i Chem. Tech. (USSR)*, 1984, v. 27, № 5, pp. 590-592
[22] Yamamoto T., Siki Sh., Kamachi M., Yamamoto T., Hiroba M. // *J. Chem. Soc. Japan, Chem. and Ind. Chem.*, 1987, v. 27, № 8, pp. 1548-1568
[23] Hyglein M.B., Rehab M.M. // *Eur. Poly. J.*, 1987, v. 23, № 10, pp. 825-828
[24] Moustafa A.B., Badran A.J. // *Acta Polym.*, 1980, v. 31, № 2, pp. 82-84
[25] Khmelenko V.N., Rouziev R. // *Ouzbek. Chem. J.*, 1985, № 1, pp. 56-58
[26] Konsoulov V.B. // *Vysokomol. Soed. (ser. B), Short Commun.*, 1980, v. 22, № 7, pp. 488-491
[27] Lisovtzev V.V., Rostokin G.A., Koulikova A.E., Podgornova V.A., Khamitova I.D. // *Phys. Chem. Principles of Synthesis and Elaboration of Polymers* (in Russian), Gorki, 1984, pp. 8-11
[28] Mel'nik O.A., Sakharova A.A., Ourinize G.M., Kalinin V.N. // *Vysokomol. Soed. (ser. B), (Short Commun.)*, 1986, v. 28, № 9, pp. 710-711
[29] Simonyan G.S., Soghomonian B.M., Beylerian N.M. // *Kin. i Kataliz (USSR)*, 1987, v. 28, № 1, pp. 198-201
[30] Henbin B., Henbin G. // *Acta Polym.*, 1988, v. 39, № 6, pp. 326-328
[31] Spirin Yu.M., Yatzimirskaya T.S. // *Vysokomol. Soed. (ser. A)*, 1976, v. 18,No. 8, pp. 1850-1854

[32] Van der Meer R., Aarts M.W., German A.L. // *J. Poly. Sci., Poly. Chem. Ed.*, 1980, v. 18, № 4, pp. 1347-1357
[33] Konsoulov V.B. // *Vysokomol. Soed. (ser. B), (Short Commun.),* 1980, v.22, № 7, pp. 488-491
[34] Sheinker A.P., Kozlova N.V., Bounet E.V., Abkin A.D. // *Doklady Academyi Naouk USSR*, 1981, v. 258, № 4, pp. 958-960
[35] Zhouravleva I.L., Bounet E.V., Bogachev Yu.S., Shepetko N.N., Sheinker A.P., Abkin A.D. // *Vysokomol. Soed. (ser. A),* 1985, v. 27, № 2, pp. 380-386
[36] Bogachev Yu.S., Zhouravleva I.L., Gromov V.F., Bounet E.V., Teleshov E.N. // *J. Phys. Chem. (USSR)*, 1990, v. 64, № 1, pp. 154-160
[37] Henrici-Olive G., Olive S. // *Z. Phys. Chem.*, 1965, v. 47, № 1, pp. 286-298
[38] Bamford C.H., Bremby S. // *Macromolek. Chem.,* 1967, v.105, № 24, pp. 122-131
[39] Kamachi M. Lian D.Y., Nofakura S. // *Polym. J.,* 1979, v. 11, № 12, pp. 921-928
[40] Elsabec M.Z., Sabaa M.W., Mokhbar S. // *ibid.* 1985, v. 17, № 6, pp. 737-746
[41] Zaitzeva V.V., Zaitzev Yu.S., Koucher R.V. // *Structure of Organic Compounds and Reaction Mechanisms, Kiev, (in Russian),* 1986, pp. 100-126
[42] Topchiev D.A., Tajmetdinov T., Kardashevski A.I., Nechaeva A.V., Kabanov V.A. // *Izv. Academyi Naouk SSSR, (ser. Chemistry),* 1983, № 10, pp. 2232-2236
[43] Topchiev D.A., Kurilova V.A., Karuputadze T.M., Mkrtchian L.A., Kabanov V.A., *International Symposium on Macromolecular Chem.*, Madrid, 1974, Preprints, 48, p. 23
[44] Martinenko A.I., Rajiev R., Nechaeva A.V., Disalilov A.T., Topchiev D.A., Kabanov V.A. // *Ouzbek. Chem. J,* 1979, № 2, pp. 59-63
[45] Ishiga T., Hamielec A.E. // *J. Appl. Poly. Sci.*, 1973, v. 17, p. 1479 - 1484
[46] Kyatourka V.G.P., Radjiounas L.V., *Achievements in the Field of Technology and Sciences in Lithuania (Abstract of the Conference),* Vilnius, 1989, p. 43
[47] Krouglova V.A., Anenkov V.V., Axalintov I.V., Zaitzeva V.V. // *Izv. Vouzov. Chem i Chem. Tech. (USSR)*, 1990, v. 33, № 10, pp. 103-108
[48] Beylerian N.M., Yeghoyan R.V., Markarian G.A. // *Arm. Chem. J.*, 1973, v. 26, p. 442
[49] Beylerian N.M., Yeghoyan R.V., Kniazian L.B. // *ibid.* 1973, v. 26, p. 985
[50] Beylerian N.M., Mkhitaryan S.L., Avakyan A.K. // *XVIII Conference. on Macromolecules (USSR)*, Kazan, 1973, p. 28 (Abstracts)
[51] Yeghoyan R.V., Beylerian N.M., Marmaryan G.A. // *Arm. Chem. J.,* 1974, v. 27, p. 369 - 372
[52] Yeghoyan R.V., Grigorian V.V., Simonian L.G. // *Vysokomol. Soed. (ser. B) (Short Commun.),* 1988, v. 30, pp. 8-10
[53] Kabanov V.A., Topchiev D.A. in *Polymerization of Ionizing Monomers*, Ed. Naouka, Moscow, 1975 (in Russian)
[54] Yeghoyan R.V., Grigorian V.V., Beylerian N.M. // *Arm. Chem. J.,* 1979, v.32, pp. 93-96
[55] Yeghoyan R.V., Galstian L.S., Beylerian N.M. // *ibid.*, 1979, v. 32, pp. 520-525
[56] Yeghoyan R.V., Hakopian F.T., Beylerian N.M. // *ibid.*, 1979, v.32, № 9, pp. 704-707
[57] Yeghoyan R.V., Grigorian V.V., Beylerian N.M. // *ibid.*, 1992, v. 12, № 9, pp. 570-574
[58] Grigorian V.V., Yeghoyan R.V. // *Vysokomol. Soed. (ser. B) (Short Commun.),* 1986, v. 86, p. 566 - 567
[59] Yeghoyan R.V., Grigorian V.V., Danielian V.H. // *Arm. Chem. J.,* 1985, v. 39, p. 708 - 713

[60] Van Hook V., Tobolsky A. // *J. Am. Chem. Soc.,* 1958, v. 80, p. 779 - 784
[61] Yeghoyan R.V., Grigorian V.V., Soghomonian B.M., Beylerian N.M. // *Arm. Chem. J.,* 1984, v. 37, p. 543 - 547
[62] Grigorian V.V. // *Kinetics of DMAEM Homo- and Copolymerization in Water-Organic Mediums,* PhD Thesis, Yerevan State University, 1991
[63] Yeghoyan R.V. // *Water Influence on Kinetics of Some Vinyl Monomers Radical Homo- and Copolymerization in Organic Solutions and on Physicochemical Properties of Obtained Polymers.* Doctoral Thesis, Yerevan State University, 1998
[64] Harutyunian R.S., Yeghoyan R.V. // *Trans. Of the Yerevan State University*, 1989, № 3, pp. 86-88
[65] Beylerian N.M., Grigorian V.V., Aroyan S.H., Harutyunian R.S. // *J. Surface Sci. and Technology,* 2001, v. 17, Pt. 3 / 4, pp. 149 - 156
[66] Bevington J. // *Trans Far. Soc.* 1955, v. 51, p. 1392
[67] Beylerian N.M., Hakopian R.M., Grigorian V.V., Harutyunian R.S. // *J. Surface Sci. and Techn.* (published)
[68] Beylerian N.M. *Peroxamine Systems as Sources of Free Radicals and Peculiar Initiators for Radical Polymerization*, Doctoral Thesis, 1973, Yerevan State University
[69] Hakopian R.M., Beylerian N.M., Ohanian I.M. // *Arm. Chem. J.,* 1975, v. 28, p. No 4 263 - 268
[70] Hakopian R.M., Beylerian N.M. // *ibid.*, 1979, v. 32, №5, p. 344 - 347
[71] Ghoukassian T.T., Mkhitarian R.P., Beylerian N.M. // *ibid.*, 1979, v. 32, No. 4 pp. 249 - 253
[72] Mkhitarian R.P., Ghoukassian T.T., Beylerian N.M. // *ibid.*, 1980, v. 33, No. 3, p. 187 - 191
[73] Chaltikyan H.H., Beylerian N.M. // *Izv. Akadem. Naouk Arm. SSR,* 1958, v. 9, № 11, p. 153 - 158
[74] Beylerian N.M., Chaltikyan H.H., Soghomonian B.M., // *Dokladi. Akadem. Naouk Arm. SSR,* 1962, v. 34, № 5, p. 201 - 206
[75] Tobolsky A. // *J. Am. Chem. Soc.,* 1958, v. 80, p. 5927 - 5932
[76] Kolthoff I.M., Miller I. // *ibid.*, 1951, v. 73, p. 3055 - 3061
[77] Beylerian N.M., Vardanian L.R., Harutyunian R.S., Vardanian R.L. // *Macromolecular Chem. Phys.*, 2002, v. 203, № 1, p. 212 - 218

In: Homolytic and Heterolytic Reactions: Problems and Solutions ISBN 1-59033-980-0
Editors: G.E. Zaikov, et al., pp. 157-174

Chapter 6

OXIDATION AND DESTRUCTION OF ARABINOGALACTAN OF SIBERIAN LARCH (LARIX SIBIRICA L.) IN AQUEOUS PHASE

I. M. Borisov[a,b]***, Yu. S. Zimin***[a]***, E. N. Shirokova***[b]***,***
Yu. B. Monakov[a,b] ***and G. E. Zaikov***[c]
[a]Bashkir State University, 32 Frunze Street, 450074 Ufa, Russia
[b]Institute of Organic Chemistry, Ufa Scientific Centre of Russian Academy of Sciences, 71 Prospekt Oktyabrya, 450054 Ufa, Russia
[c]N. M. Emanuel Institute of Biochemical Physics, 4 Kosygin Street, 119991 Moscow, Russia

ABSTRACT

It is shown that the oxidation of natural polysaccharide arabinogalactan proceeds according to the radical mechanism at simultaneous influence of hydrogen peroxide and molecular oxygen on aqueous solutions of the biopolymer. This process is accompanied with oxidative destruction and functionalization of polysaccharide macromolecules and oligomers.

Keywords: Polysaccharides, arabinogalactan, hydrogen peroxide, oxygen, oxidation, destruction, functionalization, radical mechanism, kinetics

INTRODUCTION

Natural polysaccharides having biological activity [1-3] are considered now as perspective ecologically pure raw material for manufacturing of pharmaceutical products and additives in the food and cosmetic industries. In the present work the method of oxidizing modification is used for making new properties to arabinogalactan (AG). The ecologically pure system "hydrogen peroxide + molecular oxygen" is chosen as an oxidizer of arabinogalactan in aqueous phase. In the present work the data about kinetic laws of oxidation, oxidative destruction and oxidative functionalization of arabinogalactan in water-peroxide solutions are given.

EXPERIMENTAL PART

The arabinogalactan with molecular mass 40000 is used in experiment. It was prepared by the water extraction from the larch needles. It is known [4, 5] that highly ramified chain (AG) consists of a sequence of structural fragments the most frequently repeating from which look like:

→3) - β - D – Galp – (1 →	→3) - β - D – Galp – (1	→3) - β - D – Galp – (1 →
6	→	6
↑	6	↑
1	↑	1
β - D – Galp	1	Araf – (1→ 3) - β - L - Araf
6	β - D – Galp	
↑		
β - D – Gal – 1		c
a	b	

The average structure of the basic chain can be displayed as a combination

→[a → a → a → b → c → a → a →b] →

The extraction and purification of AG from water-soluble phenolic compounds including dihydroquercetine were carried out on polyamide sorbent. Thus, an aqueous solution of polysaccharide containing the trace quantities of flavonoids was obtained. Molecular mass of arabinogalactan was determined by viscosimetry. Water-peroxide solutions of AG were oxidized by molecular oxygen in a glass thermostated reactor of a bubbling type. The samples were periodically taken from the reactor. Volume of a reactionary mixture was 0.01 l, the speed of air supply was 3 l/h (except for the stipulated cases). At the same time series of experiments without air barbotage were conducted in which the AG oxidation was carried out by oxygen formed at H_2O_2 thermal decomposition. After the reaction finish, the polymeric fraction of the oxidized AG was separated from the oligomeric one by acetone precipitation (volume ratio of a reaction mixture to acetone was 1:4). The oligomeric fraction was separated from the liquid above the precipitate by removing acetone and water.

The analysis of the functional groups of the polymeric and oligomeric fractions was conducted by ^{13}C NMR and IR spectroscopy methods. ^{13}C NMR spectra were recorded on a spectrometer BRUKER AM-300 (working frequency 75.47 MHz) with broadband suppression on protons and in a JMODXH regime. 3-5% AG solutions in D_2O and internal DSS standard were used. ^{13}C NMR spectra were recorded at temperature +35°C with a delay between 15 s impulses. IR spectra were recorded in vaseline oil on a spectrometer UR-20. The concentration of the carboxyl groups was determined by alkalimetry (KOH). The total concentration of the peroxide reaction products (H_2O_2 + products of AG oxidation) was determined by iodometry with KJ and subsequent titration of generated J_2 by a $Na_2S_2O_3$ solution. Galactose was determined by reaction on hexoses with anthrone reagent. The impurities of proteins and of nucleic acids were analyzed on UV spectra at 220-245 nm. The value of specific rotation was measured on a Perkin-Elmer polarimeter (model 141). The characteristic viscosity of the 10% aqueous solutions of the polymeric and oligomer fractions of the oxidized arabinogalactan was measured at 30 ± 1°C in Ubellhode viscosimeters with the hung level. The kinematic viscosity of the 10% aqueous solutions of arabinogalactan was determined in Ubellhode viscosimeters with the hung level at 90.0 ± 0.5°C.

RESULTS AND DISCUSSION

In a reactionary system "AG + H_2O + H_2O_2 + O_2" arabinogalactan is oxidized according to the radical mechanism [6], including stages of initiation, continuation and termination of a chain.

When heating this reactionary mixture at 85-95°C the change of peroxy compounds concentration in time is described by the reaction equation of the first order.

$$\ln [\text{-O-O-}]_t = \ln [\text{-O-O-}]_0 - k_{eff} \cdot t \quad (I)$$

where k_{eff} is the effective rate constant of peroxy compounds consumption; $[\text{-O-O-}]_0$ and $[\text{-O-O-}]_t$ are the initial and current concentrations of peroxy compounds.

The effective rate constant of peroxy compounds consumption was found by transformation of kinetic curves in coordinates of equation (I). The carboxyl groups are accumulated during oxidation of polysaccharide. The rate of carboxyl groups accumulation (V_{COOH}) changes depending on time: the maximal meaning V_{COOH} is observed after a period of induction and then the rate of -COOH accumulation falls (Fig. 1). To find a maximal rate V_{COOH}, kinetic curves of -COOH accumulation were subjected to polynomial analysis.

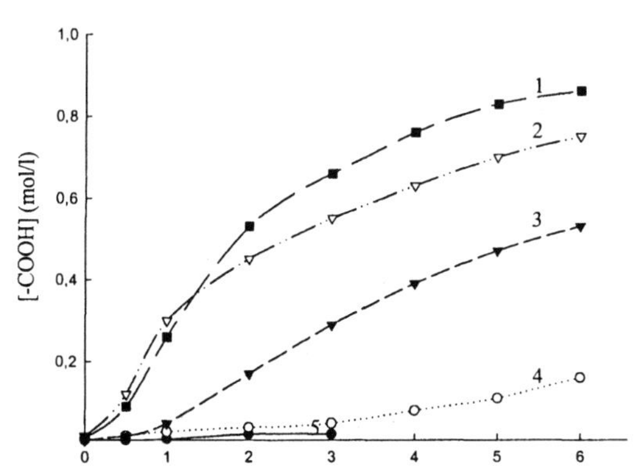

Figure 1. Kinetic curves of the carboxyl group accumulation at various temperatures; temperature (°C) – 95 (1), 90 (2), 80 (3), 70 (4), 60 (5); $[AG]_0$ = 10 wt %, $[H_2O_2]_0$ = 1 mol/l

Initiation

In the investigated system the origin of radicals occurs at catalyzed decomposition of hydrogen peroxide by of variable-valence metal ions [7]

$$H_2O_2 + M^{n+} \rightarrow HO^- + HO^\bullet + M^{(n+1)+} \quad (1)$$

The rate of carboxyl groups accumulation and the effective rate constant of peroxy compounds decomposition increase at introduction of $FeSO_4$ in to the "AG + H_2O + H_2O_2 + O_2" system (Fig. 2). Natural arabinogalactan contains the trace quantities of variable-valence metals compounds [8] as impurities. Therefore the weak initiation of oxidation reaction in the investigated system occurs according to reaction (1) even in the absence of $FeSO_4$ additives. The trace quantities of variable-valence metal ions can come in a reactionary mixture also with distilled water, which was not exposed to special purification from M^{n+} impurities.

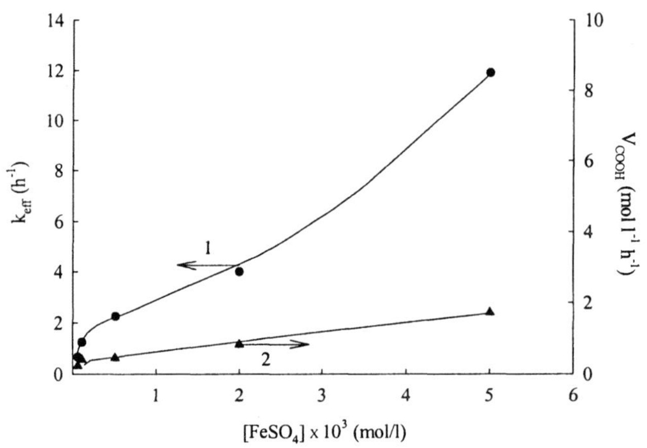

Figure 2. Dependence of the effective rate constant of the peroxy compound consumption (1) and of the maximal rate of carboxyl group accumulation (2) on $FeSO_4$ concentration; 90°C, $[AG]_0$ = 10 wt %, $[H_2O_2]_0$ = 1 mol/l

Hydroxyl radicals are very active in detachment reactions of hydrogen atoms from C–H bonds. For example, the hydrogen atom detachment rate constants are equal to $2.8 \cdot 10^9$ and $1.9 \cdot 10^9$ l/mol·s in $HO^\bullet$ + cyclo-[$O(CH_2)_2O(CH_2)_2$] and $HO^\bullet$ + $CH_2(OH)CH(OH)CH_2OH$ reactions, respectively, in aqueous phase at 298 K [9]. It is necessary to expect that the hydroxyl radicals will be highly active in reactions with all C–H bonds of arabinogalactan. Most likely, the primary place of the hydrogen detachment in AG macromolecules (representing balls or globules in a solution) will be determined by availability of these bonds for attack by $HO^\bullet$ radicals, instead of their durability. Therefore free valence in carbon-centered macroradicals formed after homolysis of C–H bonds in reactions with $HO^\bullet$ radicals, can be located both in a basic chain (core) and in lateral branches of arabinogalactan (PH):

$$HO^\bullet + PH \rightarrow H_2O + P^\bullet \quad (2)$$

where $P^{\bullet}$ is the set of various AG carbon-centered macroradicals.

It is known that carbon-centered radicals quickly attach oxygen turning into peroxyl ones [10]

$$P^{\bullet} + O_2 \rightarrow PO_2^{\bullet} \quad (3)$$

It takes place also for macroradicals, in particular for alkyl radicals of polyolefins [10]. Thereof, when concentration of the dissolved oxygen is higher of a certain value, the rate of process ceases to depend on it, and the radical process of oxidation is limited by reactions of peroxyl macroradicals.

The similar dependence on the concentration of oxygen, which was varied by argon or air purge of a reactionary mixture, is also observed at arabinogalactan oxidation (Table 1). The data of Table 1 give the basis to assume that an arabinogalactan oxidation, as well as a polyolefins oxidation, is limited not by formation of peroxyl macroradicals but by their subsequent reactions.

Table 1. Effective rate constant of peroxy compound decomposition and the maximal rate of carboxyl group accumulation as a function of the air barbotage rate; 90°C, $[H_2O_2]_0$ = 1.1 mol/l, $[AG]_0$ = 10 wt %

Gas barbotage rate, l/h	Argon	Air			
	3	In absence of barbotage	1	3	5
k_{eff}, h^{-1}	0.16±0.03	0.63±0.04	0.63±0.04	0.66±0.04	0.58±0.06
V_{COOH}, mol/(l·h)	0.10	0.25	0.21	0.21	0.23

As shown in [10], the continuation of a chain reaction at polyolefins oxidation is mainly carried out intramolecularly (peroxy radical of polymer attacks its own C-H bonds). Apparently, similar processes also take place at the arabinogalactan oxidation in water medium.

It is possible to distinguish the following possible reactions of $PO_2^{\bullet}$ peroxy radicals of various structures.

a) The detachment of a hydrogen atom from C(3)–H bond of a fragment → 3,6) - β- D Galp (1→

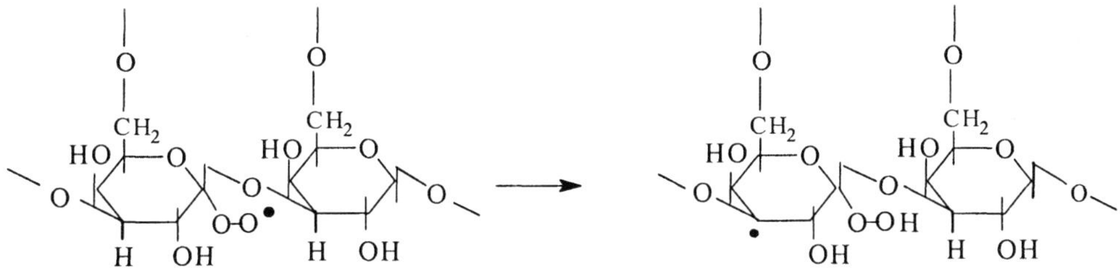

(4)

Furthermore, the new formed $P^{\bullet}$ radical attaches oxygen and arisen peroxy radical, in its turn, tears off a hydrogen atom from C(1)–H bond of the following macroradical fragment →

3,6) - β- D Galp (1→. Owing to such go-ahead transfer of free valency an accumulation of hydroperoxyl groups at glycoside bond occurs.

b) The detachment of a hydrogen atom from C(3)–H bond of the next fragment →3,6) - β- D Galp (1→ with subsequent destruction of the carbon-centered radical

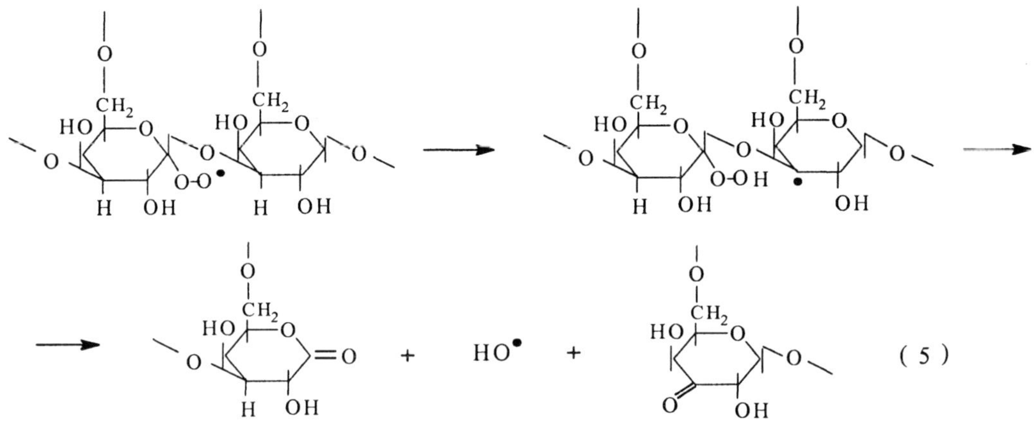

(5)

Probably, the formation of AG oligomers with lactone and ketone end groups occurs according to this reaction. It proves to be true by presence of weak-field singlet signals (168.2 and 202.5 ppm) in a ^{13}C NMR spectrum.

c) The detachment of a hydrogen atom from C(4)–H bond of the fragment → 3,6) - β - D Galp (1→

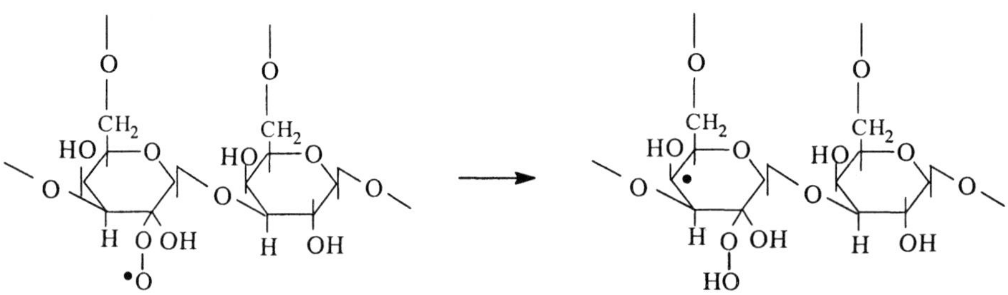

(6)

The $PO_2^{\bullet}$ radicals in lateral chains of arabinogalactan macromolecules, for example in β D Galp (1→, participate also in total process

c)

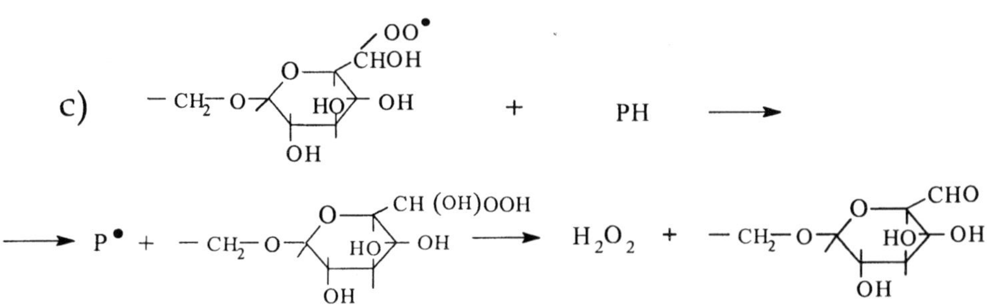

(7)

Then the aldehyde groups are oxidized by molecular oxygen according to radical-chain mechanism turning into carboxyl ones [11]. The accumulation of -COOH groups is fixed on a ^{13}C NMR spectrum at 178.9 ppm. The rate of carboxyl group accumulation is calculated as V_{COOH}.

In the fragment → 6) - β - D Galp peroxy radical is isomerized, tearing off hydrogen from C(6) in → 3,6) - β - D Galp (1→

e)

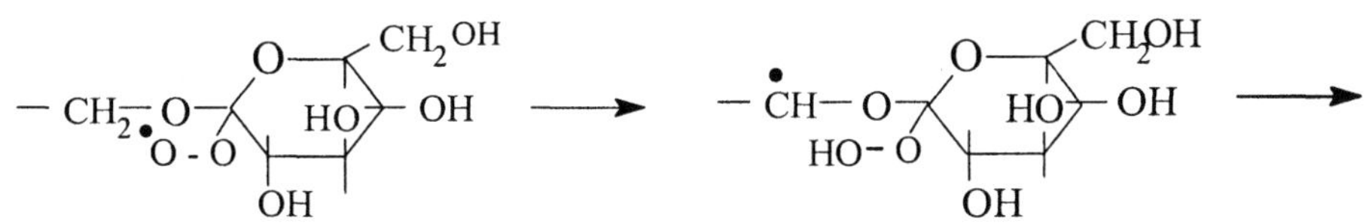

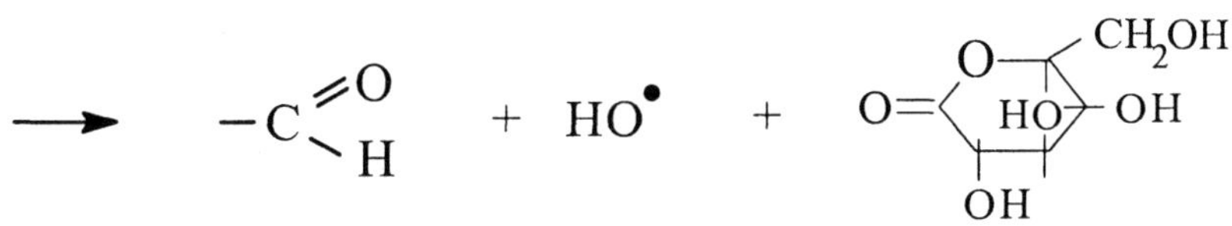

(8)

The formed aldehyde group is also further oxidized into carboxyl one.

The accumulation of carboxyl groups can occur also at hydrolysis of lactones formed on (5) and (8) reactions at AG oxidation in water medium

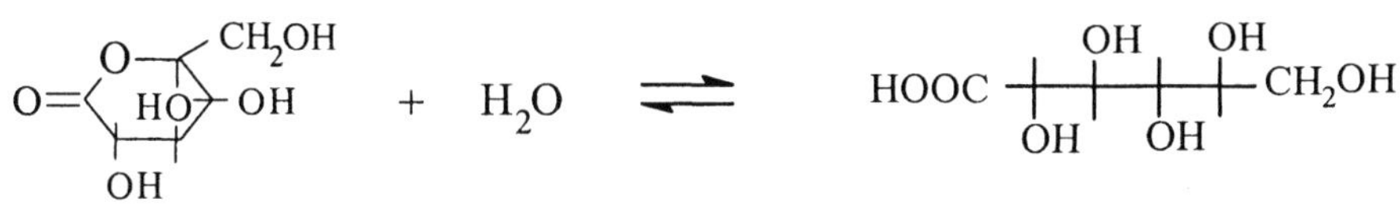

(9)

and consequently the total contents of carboxyl groups and lactones is determined by alkalimetry analysis. It is necessary to note, that (7) - (9) reactions are also possible with participation of arabinose fragments: -L - β - Arap - (1→; 3) - AraA.

The effective constant of the consumption rate of peroxy compounds and maximal -COOH accumulation rate grow with an increase of the initial arabinogalactan concentration at the fixed $[O_2]$ and $[H_2O_2]_0$ concentrations in the "AG + H_2O + H_2O_2 + O_2" system (Fig. 3). These dependences were linearised in logarithmic coordinates $\ln k_{eff} = f(\ln[A\Gamma]_0)$ and $\ln V_{COOH} = f(\ln [A\Gamma]_0)$, from which the reaction orders of the consumption of peroxy compounds ($n_{o\text{-}o} = 1.50 \pm 0.19$ without barbotage and $n_{o\text{-}o} = 1.50 \pm 0.25$ at barbotage by air) and accumulation of carboxyl groups ($n_{COOH} = 1.19 \pm 0.08$ without barbotage and $n_{COOH} = 1.16 \pm 0.05$ at barbotage by air) were calculated.

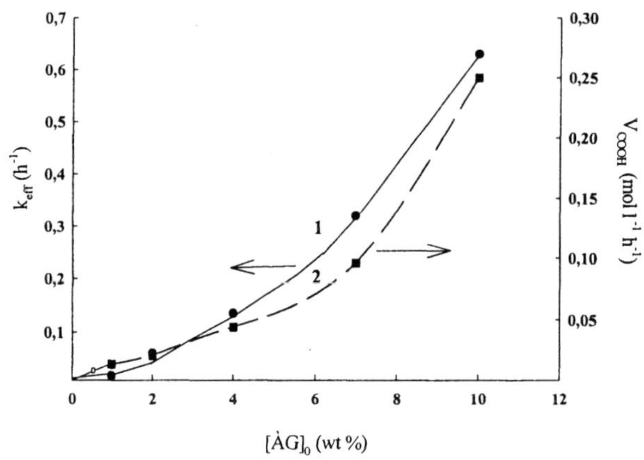

Figure 3. Dependence of the effective rate constant of the peroxy compound consumption (1) and of the maximal rate of carboxyl group accumulation (2) on the initial arabinogalactan concentration; 90°C, $[H_2O_2]_0$ = 1 mol/l

Table 2. The degree of peroxy compound concentration decrease (hydrogen peroxide and peroxides of oxidized arabinogalactan) as a function of the initial polysaccharide concentration; 90°C, $[H_2O_2]_0$ = 1.1 mol/l

$[AG]_0$, wt %	1	2	4	7	10
Degree of peroxy compound concentration decrease, %	11	37	72	85	97

It is necessary to note, that the degree of the consumption of H_2O_2 (together with peroxides of oxidized AG) depends on the initial arabinogalactan concentration (at $[H_2O_2]_0$ = const) grows with the increase of $[AG]_0$ (Table 2). For example, at $[AG]_0$ = 10 wt % in a reaction mixture the hydrogen peroxide is consumed practically completely, whereas at $[AG]_0$ = 1 wt % only 11 % of hydrogen peroxide are consumed, and then the H_2O_2 concentration remains practically unaltered with time. The data of Fig. 3 and Table 2 can be explained on a basis of the following hypothesis. In work [10] it was shown that the carbon-centered macroradicals of polyolefins cause induced decomposition of hydroperoxy groups. Probably, the carbon-centered $P^•$ macroradicals forming at arabinogalactan oxidation in "AG + H_2O + H_2O_2 + O_2" system also induce H_2O_2 decomposition, for example according to the reaction

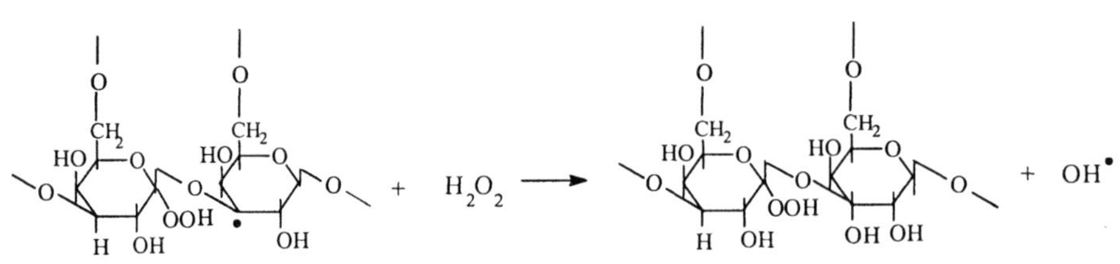 (10)

The second possible route of the hydrogen peroxide consumption is a balanced joining of H_2O_2 to forming carbonyl groups according to Bayer-Villigiere [10-13], with subsequent decomposition of labile peroxide:

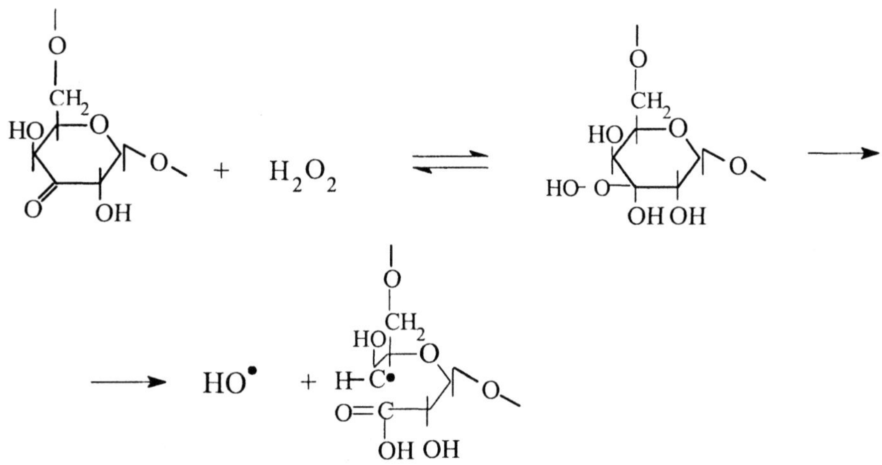

(11)

Increase of V_{COOH} with growth of $[AG]_0$ in the investigated system is connected with the increase of reaction (11) rate, owing to increasing of formation rate of -COOH precursors, namely, of lactone and aldehyde groups (reactions (7) - (9)).

The maximal rate of -COOH group accumulation also grows with the increase of initial hydrogen peroxide concentration at the fixed meanings $[AG]_0$ in experiments both with air barbotage and without barbotage (Fig. 4). The data of Fig. 4 were processed in coordinates ln $V_{COOH} = f(\ln [H_2O_2]_0)$ for calculation of the reaction order with respect to hydrogen peroxide. The reaction order of carboxyl group accumulation with respect to H_2O_2 is 0.48 ± 0.08.

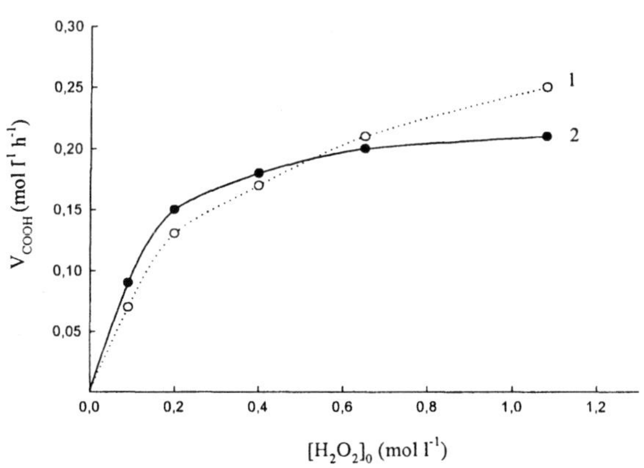

Figure 4. Dependence of the maximal rate of carboxyl group accumulation on the initial hydrogen peroxide concentration without air barbotage (1) and with air barbotage (2); 90°C, $[AG]_0 = 10$ wt %

It is necessary to note that in the investigated system "AG + H_2O + H_2O_2 + O_2" the carboxyl groups are accumulated only in that case if H_2O_2 is spent. The stoichiometry of this process calculated as the ratio of the accumulated carboxyl group concentration to the concentration of the consumed peroxy compounds ([-COOH]/Δ[-O-O-]) at the same instant remains unaltered, within the experimental error, in the course of the reaction and constitutes, for example, 0.6 ± 0.1 at 90°C.

On the contrary, the effective constant of peroxy compounds consumption rate, as distinct from V_{COOH}, decreases with an increase of $[H_2O_2]_0$ at constant meanings of $[AG]_0$ = 10 wt % (Fig. 5). The formal processing of Fig. 5 data in coordinates ln k_{eff} = f (ln $[H_2O_2]_0$) gives a negative value of reaction order: n = −0.66 ± 0.15. The negative reaction order with respect to H_2O_2 indicates that not only H_2O_2 consumption takes place in the "AG + H_2O + H_2O_2 + O_2" system but also accumulation of peroxide products of arabinogalactan oxidation and subsequent consumption of AG hydroperoxides. Probably, the consumption of peroxides at high $[H_2O_2]_0$ is compensated to the greater extent than at low $[H_2O_2]_0$. It occurs at the expense of AG hydroperoxides accumulation. Since the total contents of peroxy compounds is analyzed by iodometry, the decrease of a specific rate of peroxy compounds consumption (k_{eff}) is experimentally observed with growth of $[H_2O_2]_0$.

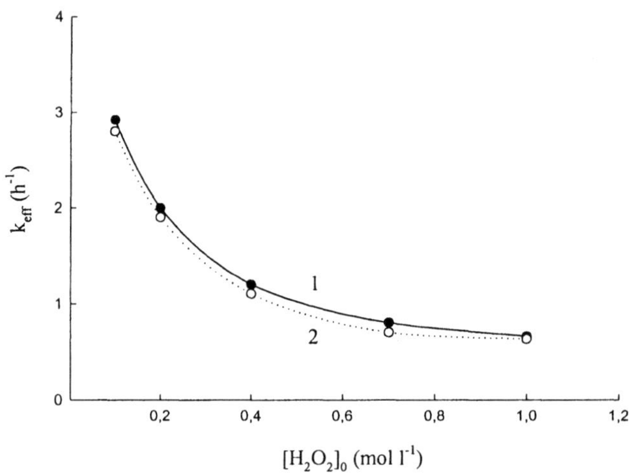

Figure 5. Dependence of the effective rate constant of the peroxy compound consumption on the initial hydrogen peroxide concentration without air barbotage (1) and with air barbotage (2); 90°C, $[AG]_0$ = 10 wt %

Basing on the present hypothesis, it is also possible to explain unusual form of kinetic curves of the peroxy compounds consumption depending on temperature. The present kinetic curves also reflect simultaneous proceeding at least of three processes: a) the consumption of hydrogen peroxide; b) the accumulation of peroxide products of the arabinogalactan oxidation; c) the consumption of AG peroxy compounds. The peroxide decomposition reactions predominate at the increased temperatures (85-95°C) and consequently the kinetic curves of the peroxy compounds consumption are linearized at these temperatures in coordinates of the equation (I). When decreasing the experimental temperature the rate of peroxy compounds destruction is lowered and the role of reactions of AG oxidation peroxide products formation increases, owing to the predominant accumulation of peroxide products on initial stages of the reaction and then their consumption prevails. The indicated laws are exhibited both in a case of blowing of a reactionary mixture by air with rate 3 l/h, and in an absence of air barbotage.

The effective rate constants of peroxy compounds consumption, calculated with help of the equation (I), linearly depend on temperature in the Arrhenius coordinates:

$$\ln k_{eff} = (39 \pm 5) - (118 \pm 15)\cdot 10^3/RT \quad \text{(II)}$$

(without air barbotage; correlation coefficient 0.998; R = 8.31 J/mol·degree),

$$\ln k_{eff} = (44 \pm 18) - (134 \pm 53)\cdot 10^3/RT \quad \text{(III)}$$

(with air barbotage; a correlation coefficient 0.978).

The values of maximal V_{COOH} linearly depend on temperature in the Arrhenius coordinates:

$$\ln V_{COOH} = (32 \pm 6) - (90 \pm 17)\cdot 10^3/RT \quad \text{(IV)}$$

(correlation coefficient 0.990).

Stage of Termination

The data of Table 1 allow us to assume, that peroxyl macroradicals participate not only in a limiting stage of the arabinogalactan oxidation, but also in termination of radical process

$$PO_2^{\bullet} + PO_2^{\bullet} \rightarrow \text{Molecular products} \quad (12)$$

It is known [14] that phenols react with peroxyl radicals and in consequence inhibit oxidative process. Really, the effective rate constant of peroxy compounds consumption and maximal -COOH accumulation rate are reduced on introduction of the phenol additives (Fig. 6) in a reactionary mixture "AG + H_2O + H_2O_2 + O_2" (the choice of PhOH as inhibitor is conditioned by its good solubility in water). These data testify that the consumption of peroxy compounds and accumulation of carboxyl groups on AG oxidation proceed according to the radical mechanism and the phenol additives (radical inhibitor) inhibit this process. Obviously, the Fig. 6 data can be explained as a result of interaction of phenol with $PO_2^{\bullet}$.

The presence of an induction period on carboxyl group accumulation kinetic curves (Fig. 1) is probably conditioned by the presence of trace impurities of a phenolic type in arabinogalactan composition, which inhibit an oxidation of biopolymer macromolecules [1, 15].

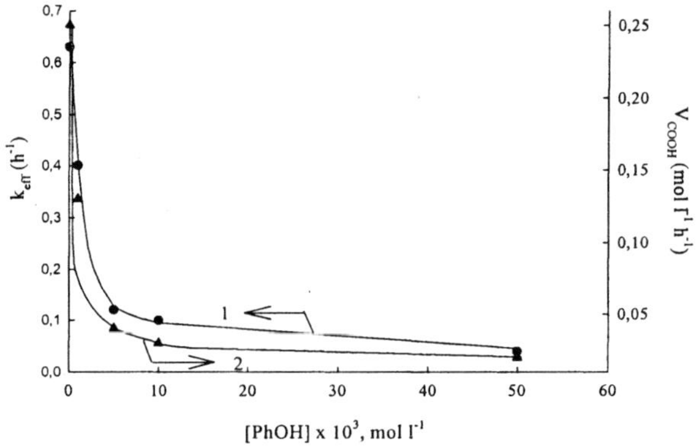

Figure 6. Dependence of the effective rate constant of the peroxy compound consumption (1) and of the maximal rate of carboxyl group accumulation (2) on phenol concentration; 90°C, $[AG]_0$ = 10 wt %, $[H_2O_2]_0$ = 1 mol/l

Oxidative Destruction

The kinematic viscosity is reduced at heating the water-peroxide solutions of arabinogalactan at the 90°C (Fig. 7); the viscosity does not change at heating AG aqueous solutions in the absence of H_2O_2. The degree of the kinematic viscosity reduction depends on the content of hydrogen peroxide in a reactionary system and grows at $[H_2O_2]_0$ increase (Table 3).

The characteristic viscosity is also reduced at heating aqueous solutions of arabinogalactan in a presence of hydrogen peroxide and dissolved oxygen (AG + H_2O + H_2O_2 + O_2) (Table 4). The degree of the characteristic viscosity reduction grows with increase of the initial hydrogen peroxide concentration in a solution (Table 4).

Table 3. Relative decrease of the kinematic viscosity (ν_k) of AG solutions as a function of the initial hydrogen peroxide concentration; 90°C, $[AG]_0$ = 10 wt %, t=6h (ν_k^0 and ν_k^∞ are the kinematic viscosities of an AG solution in the beginning and at the end of the experiment)

$[H_2O_2]_0$, mol/l	0.5	0.8	1.0	2.0	2.5
$(V_k^0 - V_k^\infty)/V_k^0 \bullet 100$ %	11	15	16	20	24

Table 4. Relative decrease of the characteristic viscosity of arabinogalactan aqueous solutions as a function of the initial hydrogen peroxide concentration; 90°C, $[AG]_0$ = 10 wt %, $[\eta]_0$ = 0.033 dl/g, t=6h ($[\eta]_\infty$ is the characteristic viscosity of an AG solution at the end of the experiment)

H_2O_2, mol/l	0.10	0.20	0.65	1.10
$([\eta]_0 - [\eta]_\infty)/[\eta]_0 \bullet 100\%$	0	3	9	15

The initial concentration of hydrogen peroxide in the system "AG + H_2O + H_2O_2 + O_2" also influences on the yield of the oligomeric and polymeric fractions of the polysaccharide (Table 5): the yield of oligomers grows with increase of $[H_2O_2]_0$.

Table 5. Yields of the oligomeric and polymeric fractions of destructed AG as a function of the initial hydrogen peroxide concentration; 90°C, $[AG]_0$ = 10 wt %

$[H_2O_2]_0$ (mol/l)	Yields of fractions (wt %)	
	Oligomeric	Polymeric
0.8	54	42
1.0	73	24
2.0	85	11
2.5	89	4

The data of Fig. 7 and Tables 3-5 specify that the destruction of polysaccharide macromolecules occurs in the water-peroxide solutions of arabinogalactan, in consequence the viscosity of the solutions is reduced. The destruction of AG is caused by proceeding of radical oxidative processes and, the most likely, takes place on a stage of a chain development.

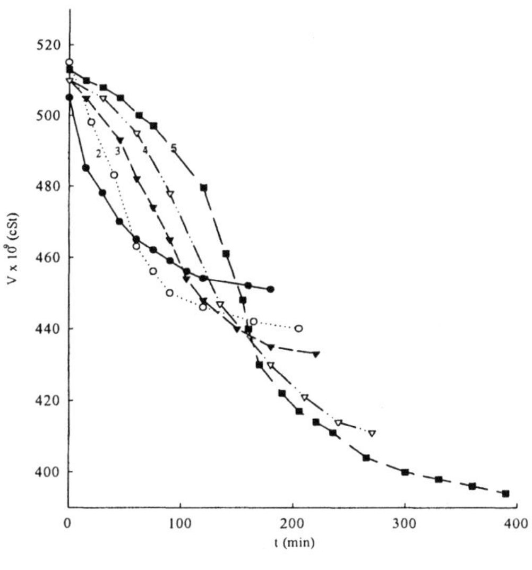

Figure 7. Dependence of kinematic viscosity on initial hydrogen peroxide concentration; 90°C, $[AG]_0$ = 10 wt %, H_2O_2 concentrations (mol/l) – 0.5 (1), 0.8 (2), 1.0 (3), 2.0 (4), 2.5 (5)

It has been shown in [10] that the oxidative destruction of carbon-chain polymers is caused by decomposition of peroxyl and alkoxyl macroradicals. Obviously, the oxidative destruction of arabinogalactan also occurs as a result of decomposition of oxygen-centered and carbon-centered radicals. The formation of radical intermediate compounds in course of oxidative process is possible both in the basic chain and in lateral fragments of AG macromolecules. Therefore the following reactions of destruction are the most probable ones:

(a) Destruction of radicals formed at oxidation of lateral fragments of the AG macromolecules according to the reaction (8);
(b) Destruction of radicals formed at oxidation of the basic chain of the AG macromolecules

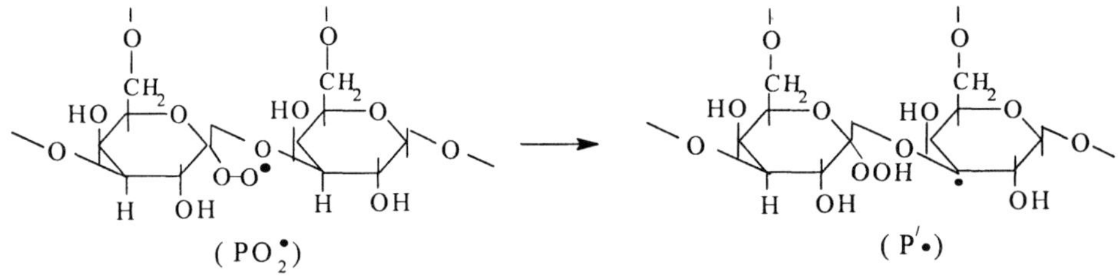

(5)

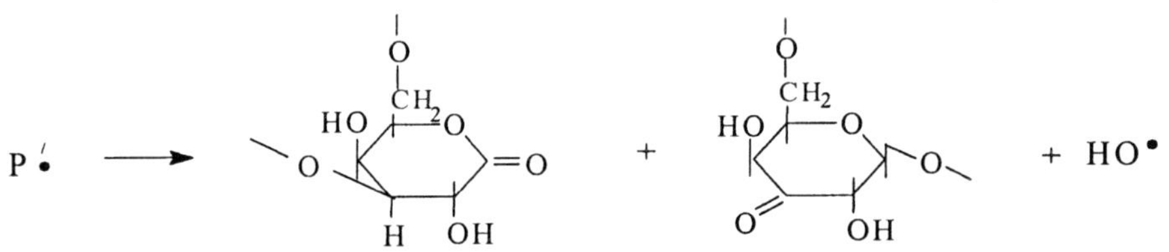

(6)

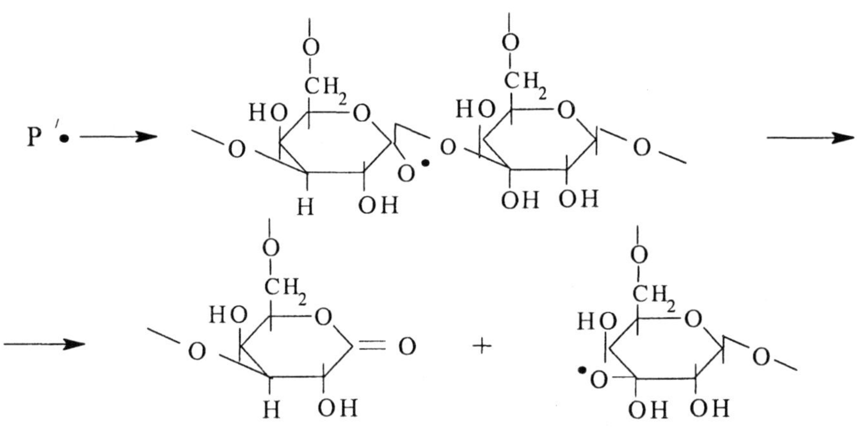

(7)

The consideration of the kinematic viscosity change dynamics in a course of the reaction (Fig. 9) specifies that the destructive processes show themselves the most clearly at low concentrations of hydrogen peroxide ($[H_2O_2]_0 \leq 1$ mol/l) in the AG solution. At high $[H_2O_2]_0$ values the kinematic viscosity is insignificantly reduced on the initial stage of reaction and then the destruction is accelerated (Fig. 9). It is probably connected with a case that at high $[H_2O_2]_0$ various carbon-centered and peroxyl macroradicals are formed with a high rate and in significant concentration on an initial stage of AG oxidation. These macroradicals can intermolecularly react with each other, resulting in an increase of kinematic viscosity of a solution (Fig. 8). In similar macromolecules the same functional groups as in initial AG are maintained and consequently they also can be involved in reactions of destruction on deep stages.

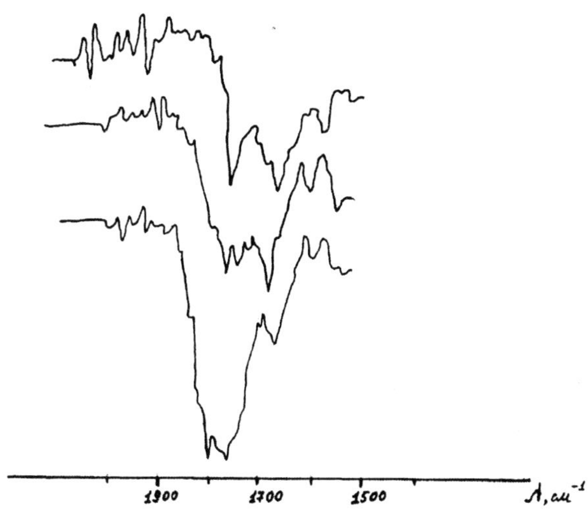

Figure 8. IR spectra of original AG (1), the high-molecular weight AG fraction after oxidative destruction at 90°C (2) and the oligomeric AG fraction after oxidative destruction at 90°C (3)

Oxidative Functionalization

The oxidative destruction of the biopolymer and the functionalization of macromolecules and oligomers take place at addition of hydrogen peroxide to the AG aqueous solutions. It results in a change of element composition of reaction products (Table 6).

As it is evident from Table 6, the part of oxygen increases in an oxidized sample. The content of galactoses is essentially reduced at affecting of H_2O_2 on aqueous AG solution. The significant change of specific rotation magnitude also testifies to change of product composition in polysaccharide oxidation reaction. The vibrations at 3200-3600 cm^{-1} (OH-groups) as the strong and wide band appear at the IR spectrum of AG. There are also the vibrations at 1050-1100 cm^{-1} (pyranose and furanose rings) and at 890-910 cm^{-1} (deformation vibrations of C_1–H). The presence of the uronic acid residues in the oxidized arabinogalactan leads to appearing of the absorbency band of a moderate intensity at 1690 cm^{-1} and of the small intensity band at 1730 cm^{-1}. After AG oxidation by molecular oxygen in the presence of hydrogen peroxide the absorbency bands of moderate and strong intensities appear in the range 1765-1750 cm^{-1} of the IR spectra of the polymeric and oligomeric fractions (Fig. 8). These bands are characteristic for the vibrations of the carbonyl group. It follows from the IR-spectra that the content of the >C=O is higher in the oligomeric products compared with the oxidized macromolecules.

Table 6. Composition of original arabinogalactan, polymeric and oligomeric fractions of oxidized polysaccharide; 90°C, $[H_2O_2]_0 = 1$ mol/l, $[AG]_0 = 10$ wt %, t = 6 h

Compound	Non-oxidized AG	Fraction of oxidized AG	
		Polymeric	Oligomeric
C_{exp}, %	40.18	38.75	37.64
H_{exp}, %	7.49	7.24	6.21
O_{exp}, %	52.33	54.01	56.15
Ash	Is absent	Is absent	Is absent
Hexoses, %	71.8	46.3	20.0
Protein, %	1.2	Is absent	Is absent
$[\eta]_{char}$	0.033	0.028	0.017
$[\alpha]_D^{20}$	+11.9	+8.4	+5.3

The ^{13}C NMR spectrum and structural composition of an original polysaccharide are identical to the spectrum and AG composition of Larix sibirica L. timber [4, 5]. The analysis of the high-molecular fraction spectrum, extracted from AG after oxidation, shows that the fraction consists of structural fragments not subjected to an oxidation of monosaccharide links and of significant quantity (30 % mol) of uronic acids. The presence in the carbon spectrum (Table 7) of characteristic four doublet signals at 177-180 ppm corresponding to carboxyl atom of carbon indicates formation of uronic acids in various structural fragments of a partial arabinogalactan oxidation product. The signals of end galactopyranuronic groups are the most intensive in ^{13}C NMR spectra. The chemical shift values of these signals coincide with data obtained earlier [16]. There are two essential alterations in ^{13}C NMR spectra at arabinogalactan oxidation. The first one is the significant reduction of characteristic signal intensities of three-replaced link →3,6) -β - Galp - (1→, namely: two wide doublet signals of C(1) atom at 106.0 ppm and of C(3) atom at 83.0 ppm and triplet of C(6) atom at 68.5 ppm. The second one is the occurrence of narrow doublet signals at 95.3, 83.0, 75.1 ppm and singlet signal at 178.6 ppm. The described alterations point out that the destruction of the basic polysaccharide chain with a detachment of lateral chains and with a formation of →3) - β - GalpA - (1→ uronic acid links occurs at arabinogalactan oxidation.

The ^{13}C NMR spectrum of oligomeric fraction of arabinogalactan oxidation products contains a wider set of structural units. The decrease of monosaccharide group atom signal intensities and growth of uronic acid signal intensities is observed in this spectrum in comparison with a high-molecular weight fraction spectrum. The total content of uronic acids in a low molecular weight fraction reaches 70 % mol. Besides signals of these structures, weak-field singlet signals of carbonyl atom of carbon at 168.2 and 202.5 ppm appear in spectra of an oligomeric fraction, which essentially differ from a band of resonance signals of uronic acid carboxyl group (177-180 ppm). The chemical shift values of these weak-field signals in a spectrum of oligomeric fraction give the basis to assume that the oxidative destruction of the basic polysaccharide chain (core) with formation of end galactopyranoselactone and galactopyran-3-ulose functional groups in reaction products also occurs at AG oxidation by hydrogen peroxide.

Table 7. The ^{13}C NMR spectra of arabinogalactan oxidation products; 30°C, D_2O, DSS

Fraction of oxidized arabinoga-lactan	Fragment	Chemical shifts (ppm)					
		C(1)	C(2)	C(3)	C(4)	C(5)	C(6)
High-molecular weight	β - GalpA – (1→	95.9	71.9	73.7	72.2	75.2	178.9
	β - Galp – (1→	105.3	72.6	74.1	71.3	71.3	63.7
	→3,6) -β - Galp – (1→	106.4	71.6	84.5	69.1	74.9	68.5
	→6) -β - Galp – (1→	105.8	72.3	73.4	71.0	74.6	70.5
	→3) -β - GalpA – (1→	106.0	72.5	83.7	73.0	75.1	178.6
	-L -β - Arap – (1 →	99.1	71.3	71.0	71.8	64.7	
Low-molecular weight	β - GalpA– (1→	95.9	71.8	73.8	72.1	75.2	179.5
	β - Galp – (1→	105.3	72.7	74.6	71.8	71.1	63.7
	→3,6) -β - Galp – (1→	106.5	71.8	84.4	69.0	74.8	68.6
	→6) -β - Galp – (1→	105.7	72.6	73.4	71.1	74.6	70.4
	-β - Arap – (1 →	99.4	71.6	70.8	73.4	64.7	
	→ 3)- Ara	95.2	70.1	74.6	70.8	65.9	

CONCLUSION

In the water-peroxide solution the arabinogalactan is oxidized by molecular oxygen according to the radical mechanism. Oxidation of arabinogalactan is intensified by introduction of initiating systems (sources of radicals) and is braked by addition of inhibitor (phenol). The functionalization takes place at a polysaccharide oxidation. Therefore it is necessary to expect, that the occurrence of additional functional groups in arabinogalactan oxidation products will give them new chemical properties. The oxidative destruction of polysaccharide macromolecules occurs also in the water-peroxide solution of arabinogalactan. The variation of hydrogen peroxide initial concentration allows to regulate a degree of arabinogalactan destruction and an yield of the oligomeric fraction.

REFERENCES

[1] Ernest V. Groman, Daming Gou: *Carbohydrate Research*, **301**, 69 (1997).
[2] O. Arifkhoddzaev: *Khimiya prirodnykh soedineniy*, **3**, 185 (2000) (in Russian).
[3] Yu. S. Ovodov: *Bioorganicheskaya khimiya*, **24**, 483 (1998) (in Russian).
[4] G. F. Antonova, A. I. Ysov: *Bioorganicheskaya khimiya*, **10**, 1664 (1984) (in Russian).
[5] S. Karacsonyi, V. Kovacik, J. Alfoldi, M. Kubackova: *Carb. Res.*, **134**, 265 (1984).
[6] M. Borisov, E. N. Shirokova, V. A. Babkin, G. A. Tolstikov, Yu. B. Monakov: *Dokl. RAN*, **134**, 265 (2002) (in Russian).
[7] A. Ya. Sychev, V. G. Isak: *Uspekhi khimii*, **64** (12), 1183 (1995) (in Russian).
[8] G. F. Antonova, N. A. Tyukavkina: *Khimiya drevesiny*, **2**, 89 (1983) (in Russian).
[9] E. T. Denisov, T. G. Denisova: *Izv. AN. Ser. Khim.*, **1**, 38 (1994) (in Russian).

[10] E. T. Denisov: *Oxidation and Destruction of Carbochain Polymers*. Leningrad, Khimiya, 1990 (in Russian).
[11] E. T. Denisov, N. M. Mizkevich, V. E. Agabekov: *The Mechanism of the Liquid-phase Oxidation of Oxygen-Containing Compounds*. Minsk, Nauka i technika, 1975 (in Russian).
[12] G. Strukul: *Angew. Chem. Int. Ed.*, **37**, 1198 (1998).
[13] V. L. Antonovskii: *Khim. fizika*, **15**, 49 (1996) (in Russian).
[14] V. A. Roginskii: *Phenolic Antioxidants: Reactionary Ability and Efficiency*. Moskva, Nauka, 1988 (in Russian).
[15] G. F. Antonova, N. A. Tyukavkina: *Khimiya drevesiny*, **4**, 60 (1976) (in Russian).
[16] S. Shashkov, V. I. Grishkovets, V. Ya. Chirva: *Bioorganicheskaya khimiya*, **8** (10), 1393 (1982) (in Russian).

In: Homolytic and Heterolytic Reactions: Problems and Solutions ISBN 1-59033-980-0
Editors: G.E. Zaikov, et al., pp. 175-195

Chapter 7

RELATION BETWEEN MORPHOLOGY AND THERMAL, MECHANICAL AND FRACTURE PROPERTIES IN RUBBER MODIFIED DIVINYLESTER RESINS

María L. Auad[1], Julio Borrajo[2] and Mirta I. Aranguren[2*]

1. Department of Materials Science. University of Southern California (USC). 3651 Watt Way, VHE # 602, Los Angeles, CA, 90089-0241 – USA

2. Institute of Materials Science and Technology (INTEMA). University of Mar del Plata – National Research Council (CONICET). Av. Juan B. Justo 4302, (7600) Mar del Plata – ARGENTINA. E-mail: marangur@fi.mdp.edu.ar

ABSTRACT

The system initial miscibility, the final morphology, as well as the related fracture and mechanical behavior of vinyl ester resins (DVER) of different molecular weights cured with styrene (St) and modified with two different liquid rubbers are presented and discussed. The selected elastomers are: carboxyl terminated poly(butadiene-*co*-acrylonitrile), (CTBN) and a reactive rubber (vinyl terminated poly(butadiene-*co*-acrylonitrile), (VTBN). The initial miscibility of the modified systems is affected by the resin molecular weight, the concentration and nature of the elastomer and the temperature of the system. The thermodynamic study of the systems allows to model the location of the initial mixture in the one phase or two phases regions in a quasi-ternary thermodynamic diagram. The use of the Flory-Huggins theory and an expression for the binary interaction parameter, which is a single function of the temperature, was utilized to analyze the miscibility of the different systems. The resulting final morphologies of the modified thermosets correspond to a continuous main phase (rich in the St-DVER copolymer) with simple rubber rich inclusions or with inclusions with a complex internal structure, where phase separation due to a polymer induced phase separation process (PIPS). In particular, the low molecular weight resin cured with St and modified with 10% of CTBN leads to a continuous structure with microvoids that generates a material of low density and poor mechanical and fracture properties. On the other hand, the use of

---

* To whom the correspondence should be addressed.

the more reactive vinyl-ended elastomer, VTBN, leads to a much finer distribution of the elastomeric phase and to a more compact morphology, with gradual reduction of the mechanical performance of the modified resins and improved fracture behavior.

Keywords: Divinylester resins, liquid rubbers, cloud-point curves, Flory-Huggins analysis, interaction parameters, phase morphology.

INTRODUCTION

Divinylester resins (DVER) are one of the most important poly-unsaturated monomers used in composite formulations with industrial and biomedical applications. The materials formulated with these resins show valuable properties, such as excellent resistance to corrosion and solvents, good adhesion, high glass transition temperature and modulus, as well as good electrical insulation [1].

Like most thermosetting matrices, DVER have been blended with several modifiers to improve their properties. For example, St-DVER thermosetting systems have been modified with liquid elastomers, such as carboxyl terminated poly (butadiene-co-acrylonitrile) (CTBN) and vinyl terminated poly (butadiene-co-acrylonitrile) (VTBN), in order to improve their fracture toughness. All these systems show two-phase morphologies constituted by domains rich in the St-DVER copolymer and others domains rich in the additive [2, 3, 4].

The understanding of the thermodynamic phase behavior of this reactive system is important for the development, production, and processing of polymeric materials with low profile or toughening modifiers. During copolymerization, the reactive system is constituted by four components: St, DVER, the rubber additive and the formed copolymer. At a given conversion, the phase transformation diagram is represented by a tetrahedron with one component in each vertex. The St-DVER-rubber triangular face of the tetrahedron represents the phase behavior for the reactive system at zero conversion, meaning the ternary phase diagram for the physical mixture of the three initial components. The characteristics of this ternary phase diagram and the initial composition of the ternary homogeneous (or heterogeneous) mixture, greatly determine the beginning of the phase separation by the polymer induced phase separation mechanism (PIPS), and the morphology generated during the copolymerization.

Studies on similar ternary reactive systems formulated with styrene, unsaturated polyester (UP) prepolymer and low-profile additives (LPA) have demonstrated that the morphology developed can be correlated with the initial system miscibility. Thus, the location of the composition coordinates representing the initial system in the ternary phase diagram [5-9] determines the course of the phase separation during copolymerization, which is mostly dependent on the miscibility of UP-St binary, since it presents less miscibility than the other two pairs.

In DVER based systems modified with CTBN (or VTBN), poor DVER-rubber miscibility has been cited as the required property needed to achieve the suitable morphology for obtaining toughening or low-profile effects [9-12].

In general, phase diagrams of binary and ternary physical mixtures are severely affected by the molecular properties of each component, such as molecular weight, polydispersity, chemical copolymer composition, the presence of specific chain end groups and molecular association. [13-19].

In this work, the miscibility of elastomer modified St-DVER systems was experimentally and theoretically analyzed, as well as the correlated morphologies developed during curing and the resulting final properties.

EXPERIMENTAL

Materials and Sample Preparation

Two divinylester resins of low and high molecular weight, DVERL and DVERH, were synthesized by reacting epoxy resins, diglicidyl ether of bisphenol A (DGEBA MY 790, Ciba Geigy, equivalent weight 176.2 g/eq. and DGEBA Araldite GT 6071, Ciba Geigy, equivalent weight 450-465 g/eq.), with methacrylic acid (Norent Plast S.A., laboratory grade reagent) using triphenylphosfine as catalyst (Fluka A.G., analytical reagent). The final conversion reached was higher than 93% in both cases. The molecular weights were measured by gel permeation chromatography (GPC) using a polystyrene calibration. Synthesized DVERs were stabilized with 300 ppm of hydroquinone. A commercial DVER resin, DVERC, (PALATAL A 430, BASF AG) was also used in the study. The molecular weights of the three resins are shown in Table 1.

Table 1. Molecular weights of the reactants and modifiers.

	Styrene (St)	**DVERL** Synthesized	**DVERC** Commercial	**DVERH** Synthesized	**CTBN**	**VTBN**
Mn (gr/mol)	104	583	1015	1236	3600	3600
Mw (gr/mol)	104	606	1766	2662	6501	6498
Mw / Mn	1.0	1.04	1.74	2.15	1.81	1.81

The two liquid rubbers used as modifiers were copolymers of butadiene and acrylonitrile (BF Goodrich Co.), which had either carboxyl end groups (CTBN, 1300x8) or vinyl end groups (VTBN, 1300x8). Table 1 also summarizes the characteristics of these components.

The crosslinking reaction of the DVERs was realized with the addition of styrene in a weight proportion of DVER: St = 55:45, an usual commercial formulation. The samples were cured at 50°C for two hours and then postcured at 150°C during two more hours. The reaction was initiated by an amine-accelerated system, using 2% wt. of benzoyl peroxide (Luzidol 75%, Akzo Chemicals S.A.) as initiator and 0.4% wt. of N, N-dimethyl aniline (Akzo Chemicals S.A.) as promoter. All the materials were used as received.

In order to make samples for compression testing, the reactive mixture of monomers (with or without additives) was injected into glass cylinders of 6 mm diameter previously sprayed with a silicone release agent. Compression specimens were carefully machined from the cylinders up to achieve the final dimensions (length/diameter = 1.5-2).

Plates for bending tests (3 mm thickness) and fracture measurements (6 mm thickness) were obtained by casting the mixtures into a mould consisting of two glass plates coated with a silicone release agent, spaced by a rubber cord and held together with clamps.

Electron Microscopy

Fractured specimens were gold coated and then observed by scanning electron microscopy (SEM), using a Jeol JSM 35 CF scanning electron microscope.

Physical and Mechanical Tests

The density of the cured copolymers modified with different amounts of elastomeric additives was determined using picnometry, by immersion of the samples in distilled degassed water at 20°C.

Temperature scans in dynamic mechanical tests were performed on rectangular bars, 1-2 mm thick (with a precision of ± 0.1 mm), using a Perkin Elmer 7e, and three point bending geometry with a span of 15 mm. The frequency of the test was 1 Hz and the heating rate 10°C/min. The applied static stress was 0.5 MPa and the dynamic stress 0.1 MPa.

Compression test specimens were deformed between metallic plates lubricated with molybdenum disulfide in a hydraulic INSTRON Universal Testing Machine Model 8501 according to ASTM D 695-85.

Flexural modulus and strength were measured using three points bending geometry, according to ASTM D 790-86 specifications. Fracture mechanics measurements were made at room temperature, also in three-point bending mode at a crosshead displacement rate of 10 mm/min. The stress intensity factor at the onset of crack growth, K_{IC}, was calculated following the ESIS Protocol recommendations using single edge notched specimens (SEN) [20]. Flexural and fracture tests were carried out using an electromechanical INSTRON Universal Testing Machine model 4467.

RESULTS AND DISCUSSION

Thermodynamics and Phase Separation

A thermodynamic analysis of experimental binary and ternary liquid-liquid systems formulated with divinyl ester resins (DVER), styrene (St) and the liquid rubbers CTBN or VTBN have been reported by Auad et. al. [9]. The onset of immiscibility was determined at the point where the initially homogeneous transparent system became cloudy, from which data cloud point curves (CPCs) were generated. The Flory-Huggins model was applied to the analysis of the quasi-binary and quasi-ternary CPCs measurements [17,18,20,21].

Flory-Huggins general description of the mixing Gibbs free energy in a multicomponent system with polydisperse polymers can be described by the following equation:

$$\Delta \overline{G^{mix}} = \frac{\Delta G^{mix}}{MRT} = \sum_{i} \sum_{j=1}^{N_i} \frac{\phi_{ij}}{r_{ij}} \ln \phi_{ij} + \sum_{i<k} \chi_{ik} \phi_i \phi_k \quad (1)$$

which gives the dimensionless mixing free energy change per mole of lattice sites. The symbols i,k =1, 2, 3 represent components; j = 1, 2 ,..., N_i the polymerization degree of different molecular species inside of the i component molar mass-fraction distribution; ϕ_{ij} is the volumetric fraction of the j molecular species of the i component and $\phi_i = \sum_j \phi_{ij}$ is the volumetric fraction of the i component; $\chi_{ik} = \chi_{ki}$ is the composition independent binary interaction parameter. M is the total number of lattice sites, $r_{ij}=V_{ij}/V_r$ is the relative size of the ij molecular species and V_r is the reference volume, usually taken as the molar volume of the smaller component or the smaller polymer monomeric unit.

Expressions for the chemical potentials of each molecular species can be obtained from equation (eqn 1) given,

$$\frac{\Delta \mu_{ij}}{r_{ij} RT} = \frac{1}{r_{ij}} + \frac{\ln \phi_{ij}}{r_{ij}} - \sum_i \sum_{j=1}^{N_i} \frac{\phi_{ij}}{r_{ij}} + \sum_{k \neq i} \chi_{ik}\phi_k (1 - \phi_i) - \chi_{kl}\phi_k \phi_l \qquad (2)$$

Thermodynamic requirements for liquid-liquid phase equilibrium, at the cloud-point conditions, in a mixture with polydisperse components are given by the following equations:

$$\Delta\mu_{ij}^{\alpha} = \Delta\mu_{ij}^{\beta} \qquad (3)$$

where α and β represent the mother and emergent phases in equilibrium at the cloud point conditions, respectively.

Numerical solution of the equilibrium equations (3) by the Kamide method [9, 15, 17, 18] with the previous knowledge of the quasi-binary and quasi-ternary experimental CPCs, allow to obtain the binary interaction parameters at different temperatures. These values can be fitted linearly with equation (4):

$$\chi_{ij} = a_{ij} + \frac{b_{ij}}{T} \qquad (4)$$

Constants a and b for all quasi-binaries are reported in Table 2.

Table 2. Constants *a* and *b* of the interaction parameters (equation 4)

Binary Pair	a	b (K)
St-DVER	-0.161	158.516
St-CTBN	-0.194	44.316
St-VTBN	-0.306	94.171
DVER-VTBN	-0.0058	37.479
DVER-CTBN	-0.051	15.561

Using the Flory-Huggins model and the obtained expression for the interaction parameter it is possible to perform an inverse calculation of the theoretical CPC for each quasi-binary system (eqn. 1) and to analyse the validity of the use of the interaction parameter, χ, linear equation (eqn. 4).

St(1)–DVER(2) Quasi-Binary System

Cloud-points corresponding to the St-DVERL solutions could not be measured, due to the low molecular weight of the resin and the associated high solubility in St. On the other hand, St-DVERC solutions showed measurable cloud-points below room temperature. Figure 1 shows the experimental and calculated CPCs for the quasi-binary system St-DVERC, as well as the calculated shadow curve (ShC) and spinodal curve (SC). At each temperature, ShC represents the composition of the emergent phase in equilibrium with the mother phase located in the CPC. Moreover, SC represents the locus were the homogeneous quasi-binary solutions become thermodynamically unstable, outside the SC quasi-binary homogeneous solutions can exist, but inside SC cannot and must be phase separated. The three curves (CPC, ShC and SC) have a common point, which is the critical point (CP) of the quasi-binary system.

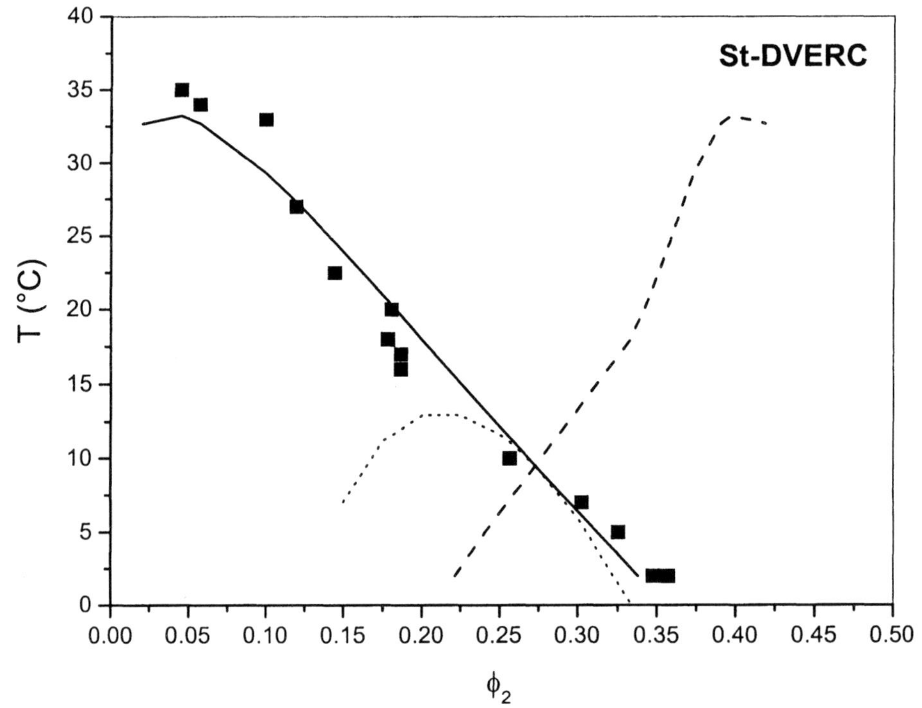

Figure 1: St-DVERC quasi-binary system; ■ experimental cloud-point data; __ calculated cloud-point curve; ---- calculated shadow curve; ...... spinodal curve.

As can be observed, the fitting of the experimental and calculated CPCs is very good, even at the left side of the critical point where the effect of the DVER polydispersity on the miscibility is very important. In the framework of the Flory-Huggins theory, binary interaction parameters are only temperature dependent and not concentration or molecular weight dependent, as it was assumed in eqn. 4. Under this assumption, it is possible to assign to the unmeasured binary St-DVERL the same χ-parameter calculated from the experimental CPC of the St-DVERC solutions.

St(1) – CTBN(3) Quasi-Binary System

As in the St-DVERL system, the cloud-points corresponding to the liquid-liquid phase separation in St-CTBN and St-VTBN solutions could not be measured during cooling because St solidification takes place before liquid-liquid phase separation occurs. However, at a constant temperature and pressure, the CPC and SC of the ternary system are tangent at the critical point. This property was used to calculate the unknown χ-parameter for the St-CTBN and St-VTBN pairs from the experimental data of the respective quasi-ternary systems [9]. This procedure was repeated at different temperatures and, from the adjusted χ values, the a and b parameters of equation (eqn. 4) were obtained for the St-rubber pairs. Figure 2a shows the experimental and calculated CPCs for the St-DVERL-CTBN quasi-ternary system at 50ºC, as well as the corresponding ShC and SC. Figure 2b shows similar results for the same system at 70ºC. The CPCs, calculated using the linear correlation for the interaction parameter (eqn. 4), are in very good agreement with the experimental data in the whole range of compositions.

DVER(2)-CTBN(3) Quasi-Binary System

Figure 3 shows the experimental and calculated CPCs for the DVERL-CTBN quasi-binary. It shows a very good fitting between the experimental and calculated CPC in a wide range of concentrations and temperatures, suggesting, that equation (eqn. 4) is appropriate to describe this quasi-binary system. Figure 3 also shows the calculated shadow curve (ShC) and spinodal curve (SC).

Similar calculations were done for the quasi-ternary systems formulated with the VTBN rubber and the obtained values for a and b parameters are shown in Table 2.

MORPHOLOGY DESCRIPTION

Neat (copolymers) St-DVER Networks

The St-DVER mixtures constitute homogeneous systems that produce cured networks that are transparent yellow solids. The neat systems fracture in a brittle way without showing any special features in the fracture surfaces and thus, showing no signs of plastic deformation. This behavior is consistent with that of a single-phase thermoset material, as expected from thermodynamic studies [2].

Although this is the observed behavior at the micron-scale, combined techniques of Laser Ablation and Atomic Force Microscopy have shown that the morphology of neat networks of cured divinyl ester resins are constituted by the agglomeration of microgels into clusters at the nanoscale [22, 23]

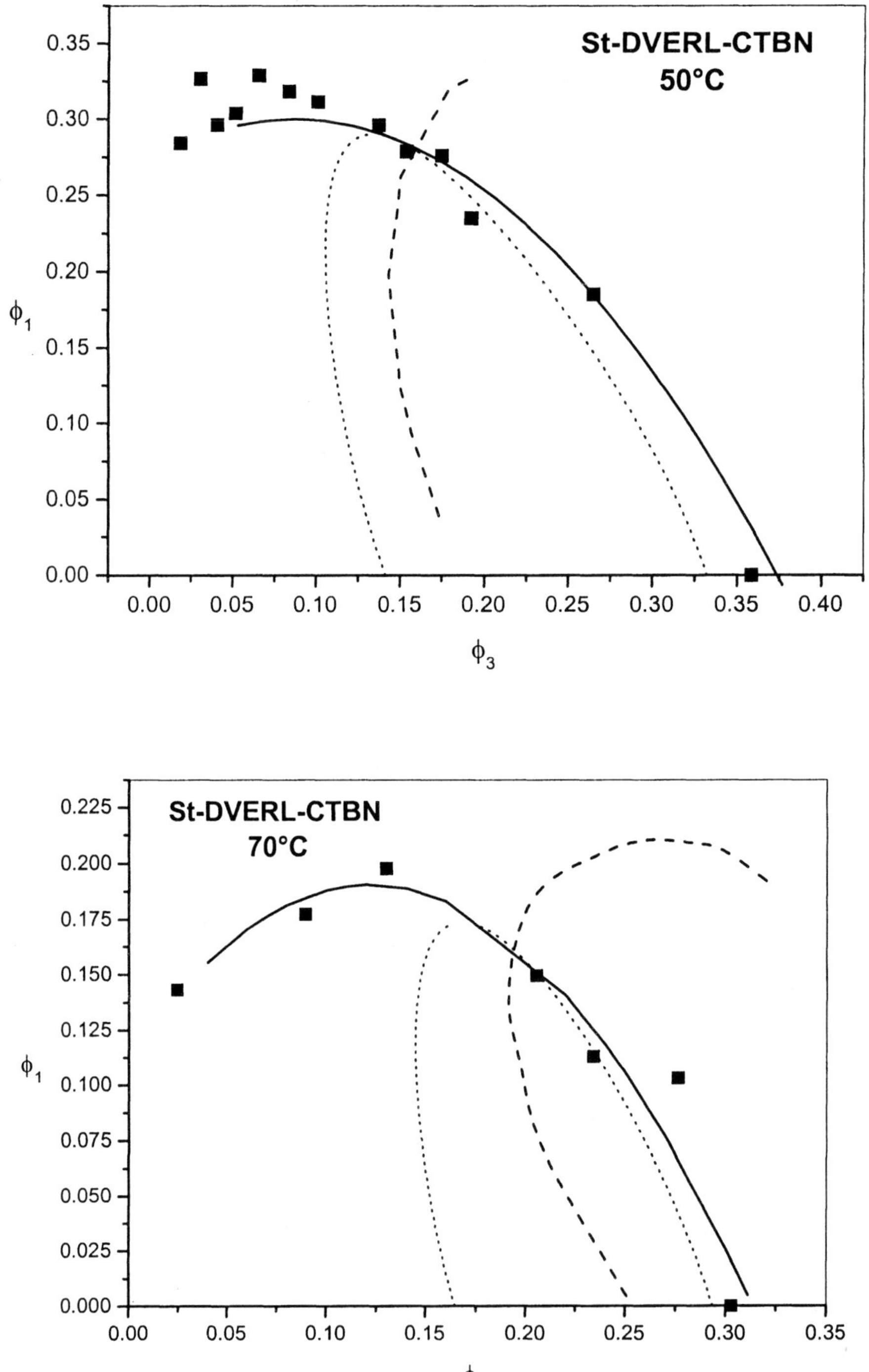

Figure 2. St-DVERL-CTBN quasi-ternary system at 50°C (a) and 70°C (b); ■ experimental cloud-point data; __ calculated cloud-point curve; ---- calculated shadow curve; ...... spinodal curve.

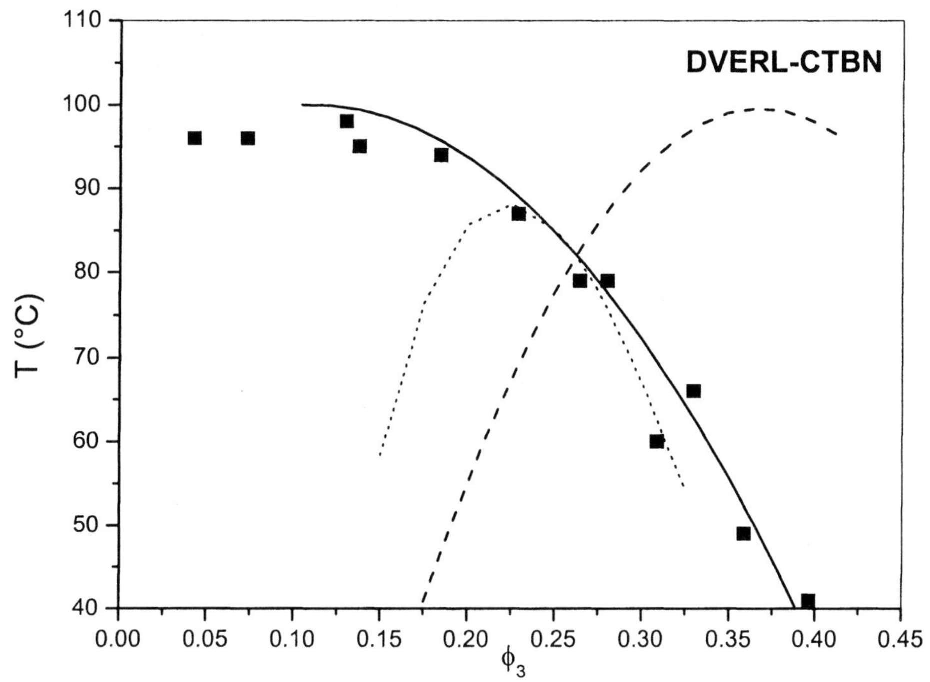

Figure 3. DVERL-CTBN quasi-binary system; ■ experimental cloud-point data; __ calculated cloud-point curve; ---- calculated shadow curve; ...... spinodal curve.

Modified Networks

Phase Diagrams and Morphology of the Modified Materials

The final morphologies of thc clastomer-modified thermosets are qualitatively different depending on the molecular weight of the resin, the type and concentration of the elastomer and the curing temperature [3, 4]. If a low molecular weight vinylester resin is used, all the components are initially miscible, but they can form a heterogeneous system if a high molecular weight resin is used. The last case is usually found in commercial modified DVER systems.

The effect of the resin molecular weight can be easily understood analyzing the phase diagrams of the initial systems. Open circles in Figure 4 represent typical industrial formulations for modified systems (5%, 10% and 15% by weight content of rubber). The quasi-ternary phase diagram shows the CPC and SC for the St-DVERC-CTBN and St-DVERL-CTBN systems at 30°C. The spinodal curve for the modified St-DVERC system at 80°C is also included for comparison.

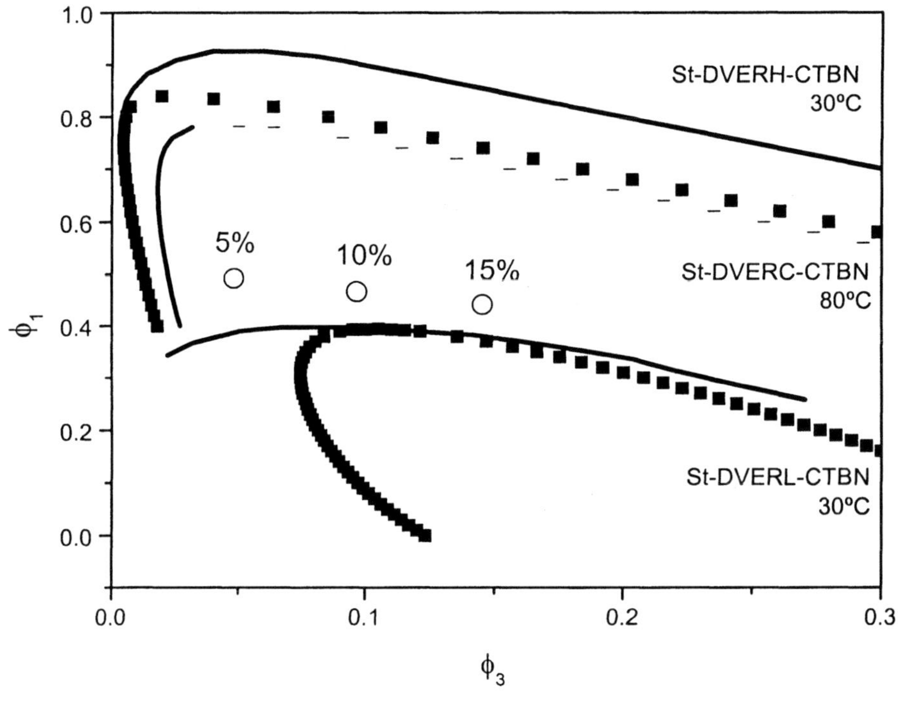

Figure 4. Calculated quasi-ternary CPC and SC at 30°C for St-DVERH-CTBN and St-DVERL-CTBN system. SC for St-DVERC-CTBN system at 80°C. O typical industrial formulations: 5, 10, 15 % by weight content of rubber.

The position of the circled points indicates that the DVERL mixture is homogeneous at these compositions, which lie just over the CPC. On the other hand, at the same compositions, the DVERC mixture is phase separated in a wide range of temperatures, even before the curing process starts, prediction that has been experimentally confirmed. In consequence, materials obtained from the modified DVERC mixtures will be heterogeneous from the beginning of the cure reaction and the final morphology will be greatly influenced by the initial mixing step. Actually, this morphology will be very different from that developed in the DVERL modified system, which is the result of the phase separation originated by the PIPS mechanism from an initially homogeneous solution.

Thus, depending on the molecular weight of the original resin, the type and concentration of the modifier and the temperature of the reaction, materials of very different morphologies are obtained, and this has a strong correlation to the varied final properties measured for this type of materials [2, 8, 24]

Low Molecular Weight Resin (DVERL) Networks

The mixture of St-DVERL and CTBN is initially transparent, but as the reaction proceeds, the formed copolymer St-DVERL shows partial miscibility in the mixture and separates forming nodules. The reaction continues inside these nodules, although with a different stoichiometry as the bulk mixture so that, crosslinking density increases more rapidly in the interior of the nodules (microgelation). The St is retained preferentially in the monomeric phase, which is also enriched in the elastomer additive. As the reaction proceeds, the presence of the copolymer nodules becomes more evident as their geometry is better defined and the nodules end up surrounded by elastomer. Finally, in the last stage of the reaction, and as a result of the different contraction of the copolymer rich and the elastomer rich phases, microvoiding takes place. The generation of this internal microvoiding is a well-known result of the addition of low profile additives (LPA) to unsaturated polyester and vinylester resins. This mechanism allows reducing the overall macroscopic contraction of the thermoset during curing. However, massive microvoiding may lead to a catastrophic deterioration of the mechanical properties of the modified thermoset, as it will be further discussed.

Figure 5 a, b shows the fracture surface of the St-DVERL-5%CTBN. Although, the surface is very rough, no clear nodular structure is visible. The formation of nodule-aggregates is incipient and the fracture path is tortuous, which indicates large energy dissipation during the fracture process. At higher concentrations, a nodular co-continuous microstructure appears (Figure 5 c, d), which is associated to extensive microvoiding. This microstructure spans the whole sample, so that the sample consists in St-DVERL nodules, barely overlapped and surrounded by an elastomer rich phase, where extensive microvoiding has taken place. Obviously, this change in microstructure has a profound effect on the mechanical and fracture properties of the materials, as it will be discussed in further sections.

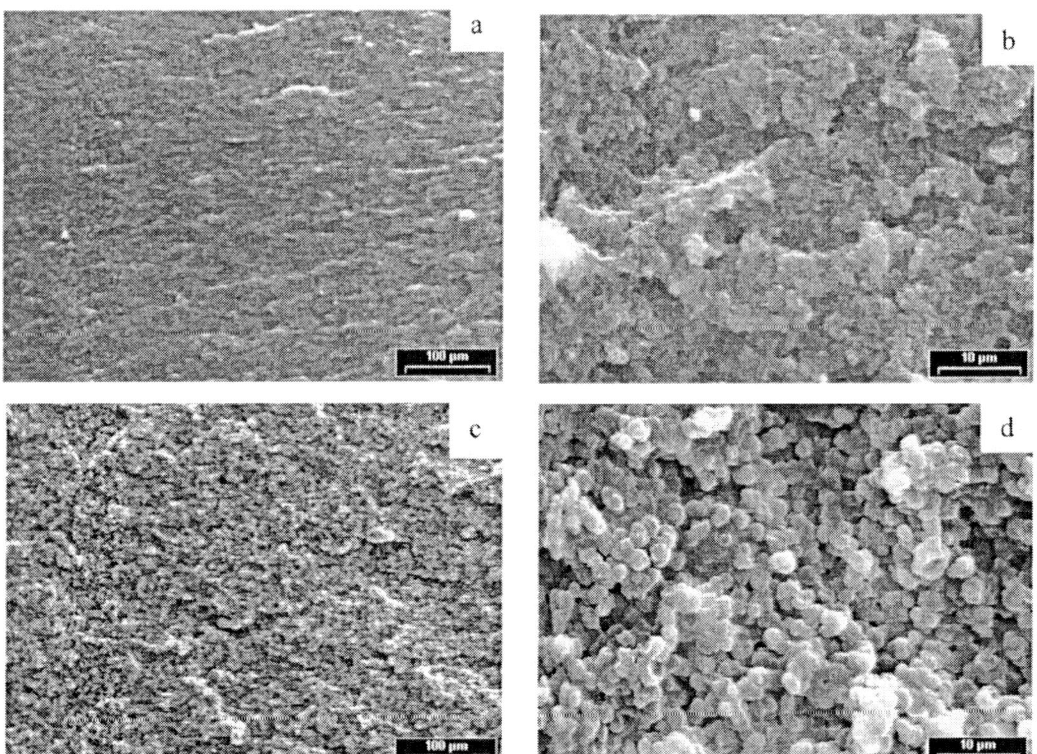

Figure 5. Fracture surfaces of CTBN modified St -DVERL networks. (a) and (b) 5% CTBN. (c) and (d) 10% CTBN.

Comparison of Figures 5 a, b with respect to 5 c, d illustrates the increasing segregating effect of higher CTBN concentrations, which leads to the formation of clear nodular structures.

High Molecular Weight Resins (DVERC, DVERH):

The use of high molecular weight resins results in a thermoset with a morphology with two main regions: one that corresponds to a rich St-DVER region with or without rubber inclusions and a second one that shows an incipient nodular St-DVER formation surrounded by elastomer.

Figures 6 a-d show different magnifications of the St-DVERC prepared at 5 and 10% (by weight) of CTBN. Large, more or less spherical regions appear showing a complex internal structure. These complex domains are formed by St-DVERC nodules not completely developed and highly packed or coagulated, which are surrounded, as in the particulated structure discussed above, by the CTBN elastomer. The complex domains, with sizes in the range of 20-60 μm, are originated at the start of the reaction. Initially two separated macrophases are present: the low-density CTBN-rich phase, which will constitute the minority phase in the final material and the high-density CTBN-poor phase, which will constitute the majority of the continuous phase. Both separated macrophases could be considered as independent reactors during the curing step. Phase separation process by the PIPS mechanism takes place at different rates in each of the two initially homogeneous macrophases. Inside the spherical domains, rich in the CTBN modifier, a nodular structure is generated in the same way than in the DVERL system, with a continuous phase rich in the rubber component. Outside the domains, the continuous phase undergoes phase separation forming little, well dispersed CTBN rich spherical particles. The continuous phase shows a flaky structure that looks like the fracture surface of the cured St-DVER neat network, which is a brittle material [2]. These two regions–complex morphologies are typical of St-UP-LPA systems and mainly contribute to control the volume shrinkage during curing, although it has been reported that some toughening was also obtained [25, 26]. From the results reported for other multiphase systems, small particulate domains with complex structure are expected to lead to materials with improved properties, while large inclusions may act as points of failure in the material.

There is a clear interface between the two main regions described above and microvoiding is observed in the interior of the complex elastomer-rich domains (Figure 6).

An increment on the amount of the droplets (nodular regions) with increasing elastomer concentration is observed at low magnification. The nodules do not grow as much as in the DVERL system, because of the higher viscosity of the St-DVERC system.

Similar characteristics were observed in the fracture surfaces of the St-DVERH-CTBN system. However, in this case the mixture seems to have segregated most of the elastomer to the large droplets, so that fewer small inclusions are seen in the main phase. Accordingly, the nodules in the CTBN rich phase are more scarce and smeared in the more concentrated CTBN domain (Figure 7 a, b).

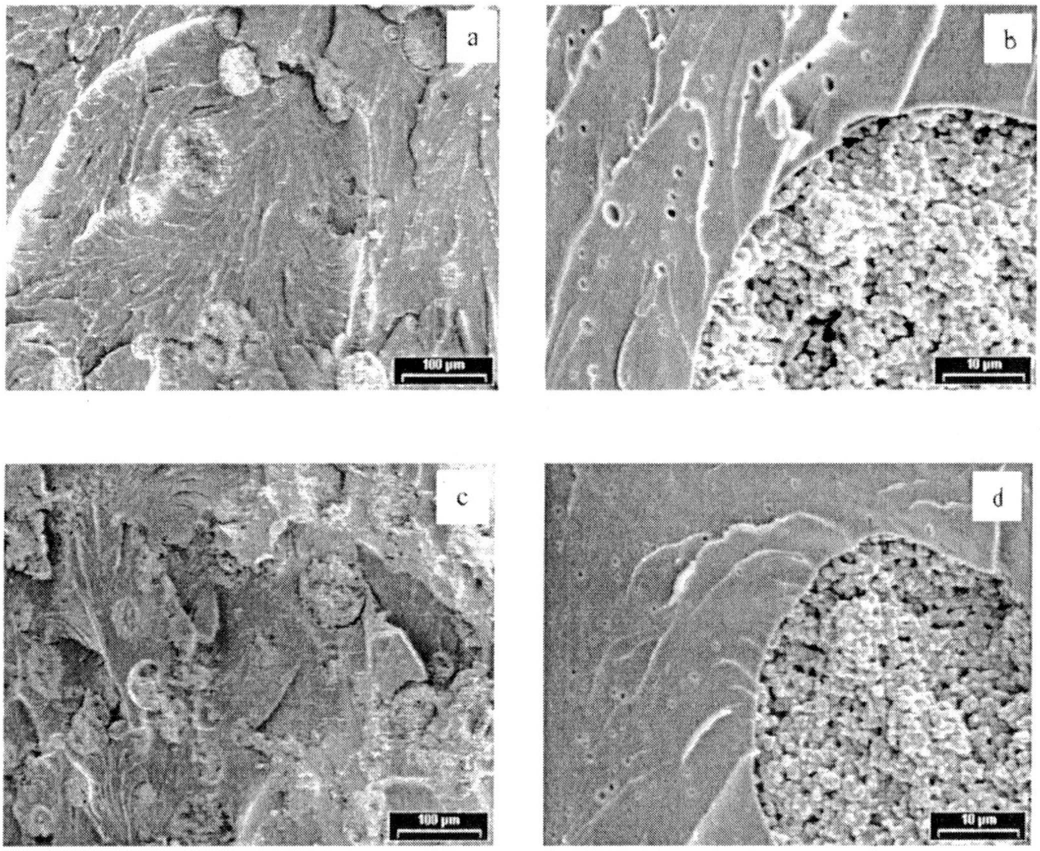

Figure 6. Fracture surfaces of CTBN modified St -DVERC networks. (a), (b) 5% CTBN. (c) and (d) 10% CTBN.

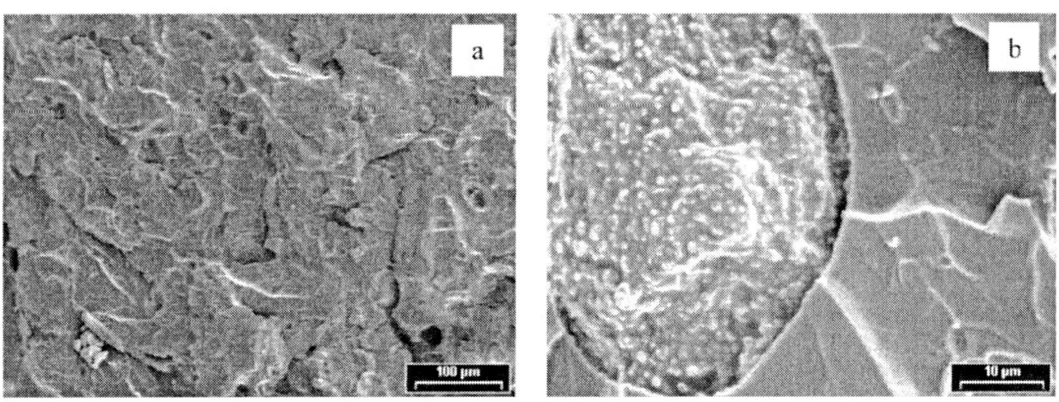

Figure 7. Fracture surfaces of CTBN modified St -DVERH networks. (a), (b) 10% CTBN.

Physical and Mechanical Properties of the Thermosets Dynamic Mechanical Tests: Glass Transition

Neat Systems

Figure 8 shows tan δ and storage modulus, E', measured in dynamic mechanical tests (DMA) for the neat St-DVERL copolymers. The trend observed in the glass transition temperatures, Tg, measured at the maximum in tan δ correlates very well with the crosslinking density expected for these networks. Since the resins are vinyl terminated, they are crosslinked through the final groups to another molecule containing double bonds (i.e. another resin molecule or, with a higher probability, to a styrene molecule). Therefore, the resin with the lowest molecular weight of the series leads to the copolymer with the highest crosslinking density, and thus, with the highest Tg. The same reasoning explains the value of the storage modulus in the rubbery region, E_r', which increases as the molecular weight of the resin decreases, since it is a function of the crosslinking density of the network.

The room temperature behavior is related to the cohesion energy of the material, and thus, to the measured density at room temperature. Good correlation between mechanical properties and material cohesion has been previously reported [3].

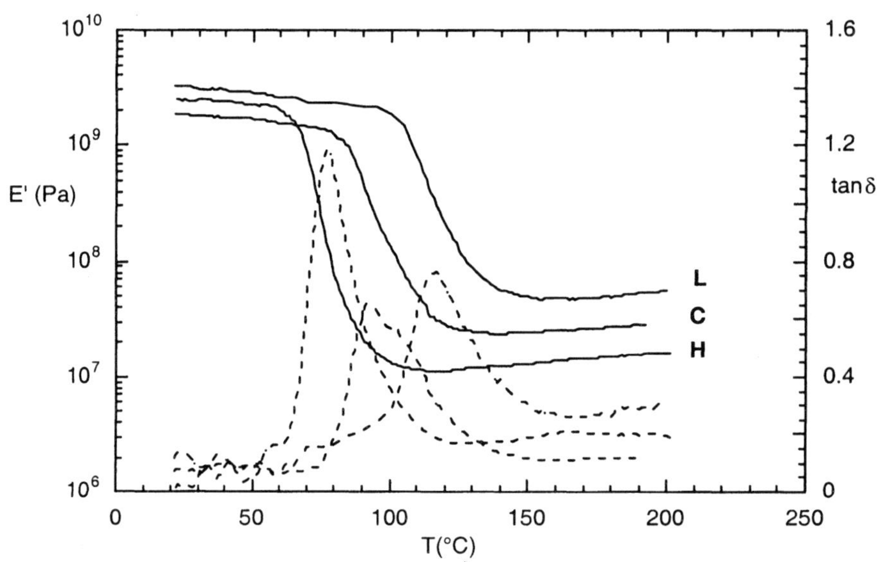

Figure 8. Dynamic mechanical temperature scans of the neat St-DVER.

Modified Networks

The networks modified with different amounts of additives present two transitions, one below room temperature, which corresponds to the glass transition of the elastomer rich phase, and the other at high temperatures, which corresponds to the glass transition temperature of the St-DVER rich phase. The changes in this last transition were followed through the changes in the temperature of the maximum in tan δ.

Figure 9 shows the effect of rubber inclusions in the storage modulus of the glassy state. As it has been observed in other thermoset systems, the elastomer inclusions reduce the room temperature modulus. The microstructure discussed for the St-DVERL-10% CTBN, which showed nodular structure spanning the whole sample and extensive microvoiding, leads to a further reduction of the glassy modulus.

Regarding the Tg of the samples, the temperature value is the result of the phase separation that takes place during curing. As mentioned before, the St is segregated to the monomeric phase, and thus the polymeric phase becomes more compactly crosslinked and Tg increases. It is interesting to observe the width of the transition of the 5% CTBN modified sample. The microstructure showed non-defined nodules, but a rough surface structure, closer to the expected behavior for a continuous material, quite in agreement with the wide transition observed in DMA.

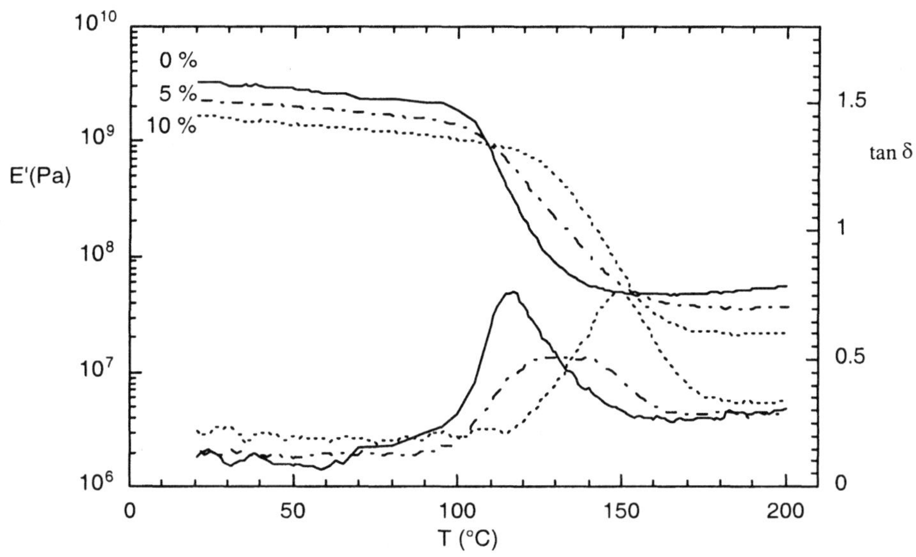

Figure 9. Dynamic mechanical temperature scans of the CTBN modified St-DVERL.

At higher concentration, the effect is more pronounced, but since the separation of the phases is better resolved, the width of the transition of the main phase is reduced again.

On the other hand, the rubbery modulus (at T=Tg+60°C) is a function of the crosslinking density of the network as well as the effect of the elastomer contribution. Note that although Tg increases, E'_r, decreases with the addition of elastomer. This is explained because Tg measures the transition of the copolymer in the nodules, which are highly crosslinked and internally packed, under a reduced St concentration with respect to the nominal stoichiometric ratio. E'_r, on the other hand is a function of the elastically active chains. Many of the crosslinked points inside the nodules are close enough one to the other to be counted as a single macro-crosslinking point. Besides, the connection between different nodules is low at high CTBN concentrations, and this also leads to an overall reduced module.

Figure 10 shows the effect of the additive on the commercial resin system. In this case and since the phase separation takes place at the beginning of the reaction, the St segregation is not important and the difference between the neat and modified samples is less marked, that is, the stoichiometry in both phases is close to the nominal St-DVER ratio of the formulation.

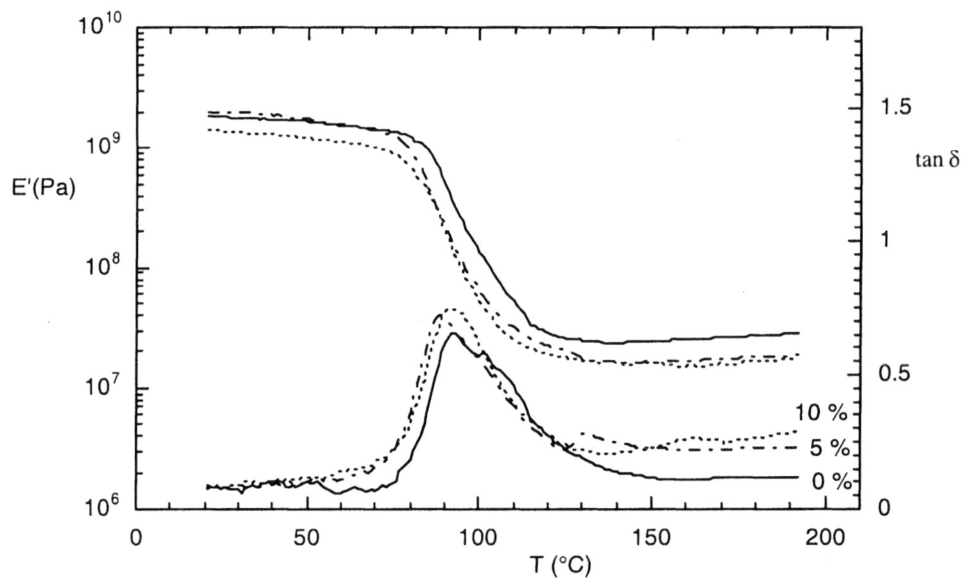

Figure 10. Dynamic mechanical temperature scans of the CTBN modified St-DVERC.

As a result there is little difference in the Tg of the neat and modified systems. Similar behavior was observed in the case of the CTBN-modified St-DVERH systems.

Mechanical and Fracture Behavior

Neat Systems

The mechanical performance for the neat St-DVER tested in flexion, compression and fracture is included in Table 3. The overall flexural response of these thermosets is in the linear range with essentially no plastic deformation under the test conditions. The results for the flexural modulus show a good correlation with the density of the materials [2].

During the compression tests the crosslinked materials show an initial linear region followed by plastic deformation until they finally break, a behavior typical of thermosets that show yield phenomena only in compression. Yield stress values are also reported in Table 3.

Table 3. Physical and mechanical properties of the neat St-DVER copolymers

	Density (g/cm^3)	E f (GPa)	σ_y (MPa)	K_{Ic} ($MPa/m^{1/2}$)
St-DVERL	1.145 ± 0.005	4.04±0.16	113.78±3.45	0.718±0.053
St-DVERC	1.127 ± 0.002	2.74±0.22	87.82±2.92	0.825±0.134
St-DVERH	1.132 ± 0.005	3.46±0.05	101.88±2.90	0.955±0.093

The stress intensity factors, K_{IC}, measured in this work are comparable to those found in the literature (0.75-1.12 MPa/m1/2) for commercial St-DVER systems [10, 11] and obtained from resins of similar molecular weights (Mn~1100 gr/mol) and styrene concentrations (45% wt.). The values of the stress concentration factor, K_{IC}, reported in Table 3 show that the matrix with the larger molecular weight of the initial DVER is tougher than the rest of the networks. This observation is not new in the literature of thermosets. Other authors have previously investigated the effect of the molecular weight between crosslinks, Mc, on the fracture behavior of crosslinked resins. They found that an increment in Mc produces an increment on the fracture toughness of the material [27], although in some cases this change is followed by a slow decrease after passing through a maximum [28]. Since only the terminal groups of the DVER are reactive, the value of Mc correlates with the molecular weight of the initial DVER and explains the observed trend.

Modified Networks

The density average values of the modified copolymers are reported in Table 4. In general, the addition of CTBN generates materials with low density; a consequence of the microvoiding observed in CTBN modified systems. The drop in density is dramatic in the case of the 10% CTBN low molecular weight system, where microvoiding occurs throughout the whole material. Voids notoriously affect the mechanical performance of the modified networks.

Table 4. Physical and mechanical properties of the networks modified with different concentrations of CTBN.

	% CTBN	Density (g/cm^3)	E_f (GPa)	σ_y (MPa)	K_{IC} ($MPa/m^{1/2}$)
St-DVERL	5	1.075±0.012	2.81±0.18	69.13±1.28	0.802±0.054
	10	0.975±0.010	1.13±0.02	42.70±4.05	0.301±0.029
St-DVERC	5	1.098±0.003	2.14±0.03	69.74±0.99	1.526±0.092
	10	1.085±0.005	1.75±0.07	53.47±0.57	1.817±0.045
St-DVERH	5	1.113±0.003	2.85±0.03	69.63±5.12	1.491±0.132
	10	1.105±0.005	2.38±0.03	51.88±3.01	1.408±0.333

Using the rule of mixtures the theoretical density of the material with additives can be calculated and the conclusion is that there is a small but not negligible amount of voids in the materials. In general the fraction of voids increases when the DVER molecular weight decreases and the rubber concentration increases. The calculated void fractions were between 1.3 and 5.7% for the CTBN modified networks, with exception of the St-DVERL-10% CTBN [2, 3]. In this case, the calculated void fraction is 14.2%, hence the mechanical properties are largely reduced, in particular the fracture strength.

As observed in Table 4 the modified materials show enhanced fracture properties with respect to those of the pure matrix. The improvement in toughness occurred together with a reduction in stiffness arising from the addition of the rubber. However, again the St-DVERL-10% CTBN shows a large deterioration in fracture properties. They are negatively affected because the large percentage of voids in the sample acts as points of failure in the material. The material becomes very brittle and cracks find an easy path for growing through the sample [2, 25, 29].

Huang et al. [30] have reported a behavior similar to that described here for unsaturated polyester-styrene and additives such as polyvinylacetate (PVAc) and polyurethane (PU). They found a maximum in the fracture toughness with the addition of 5% of PVAc or with 10% of PU. Those systems also showed microvoid formation and a cocontinuous structure around the maximum in toughness, indicating that the presence of disperse microvoids was more efficient to improve toughness than microvoids confined to a single dispersed phase [31]. The toughness increment was related to the crack tip blunting produced in the matrix due to the presence of the microvoids, which delay the crack propagation. A larger concentration of additives increases the microvoid concentration and at some point the concentration was so high that an adverse effect was observed and the crack propagated through the plane of voids. These two contrary effects produced a maximum in the properties, which was also clearly visible in the St-DVERL presented in this work, where the phase separation and microvoid formation occurred throughout the whole sample.

The two high molecular weight resins systems show a similar behavior, although higher toughness is obtained with the use of the commercial resin. Probably, the synthesized high molecular weight resin, which also shows larger molecular weight dispersion, has a lower performance with respect to the commercial resin, because of the presence of low molecular weight chains.

Summarizing, the K_{IC} value increases with the percentage of additive in the case of the two higher molecular weight resins, where microvoid formation represents a relatively low volume fraction of the material, contributing to the crack blunting and reducing the rate of crack propagation. In the case of the CTBN modification of the St-DVERL network the generation of microvoids is too high and K_{IC} drops because of the propagation of the crack through the voids.

Copolymers Modified with VTBN

The behavior of the systems modified by VTBN is more complex because the elastomer is vinyl end functionalized and can co-react with the unsaturations of the other reactants during the crosslinking. The reacting mixture is composed by the three monomers, St, DVER, and VTBN, and a terpolymer generated by the copolymerization of the three.

The blocks of the copolymer that are rich in the elastomer can segregate during the reaction, generating elastomer-rich regions and St-DVER rich regions. However, this segregation cannot be as neat and well defined as in the CTBN case because of the existence of covalent bonds between the blocks. Figures 11a and 11b show the fracture surfaces of the VTBN modified St-DVERL system at 10% of elastomer.

In this range of concentrations the St-DVERL-CTBN system showed a particulate morphology throughout the entire sample (Figures 5 c-d). As explained above, VTBN is a reactive elastomer and although it has a lower initial miscibility in the St-DVERL mixture than CTBN [5], it co-reacts with the vinylester and styrene molecules, so that the final degree of separation is reduced.

Consequently, the Figures 11 a and b show a co-continuous structure of micron-size domains rich in the St-DVERL copolymer and domains of nodular microstructure, which are rich in VTBN. Both types of regions are co-continuous throughout the sample.

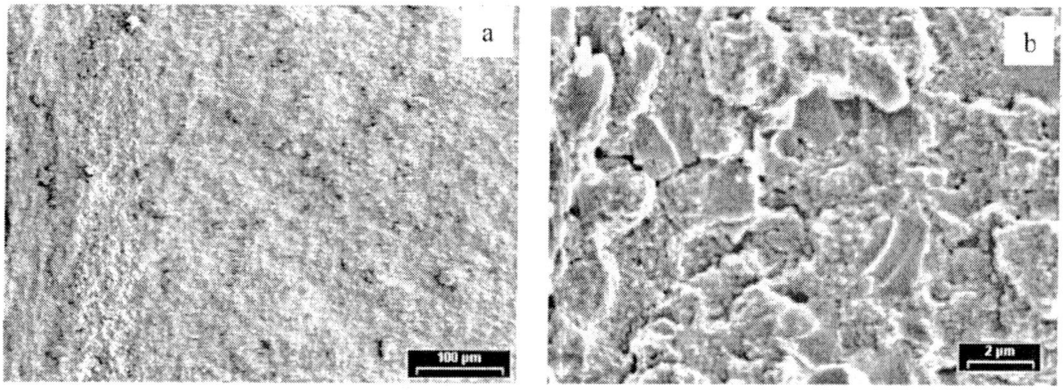

Figure 11. Fracture surfaces of VTBN modified St -DVERL networks. (a), (b) 10% VTBN.

The systems modified with VTBN show a slight decrease in density with the addition of the elastomer (Table 5). The changes are gradual and follow an identical trend for the three different resins. The calculated void fractions were between 0.4 and 1.9 % for the VTBN modified resins, lower that the values calculated for the CTBN modified systems. The reason is the improved cohesion of the material and the almost absent microvoiding.

Table 5. Physical and mechanical properties of the networks modified with different concentrations of VTBN.

	%VTBN	Density (g/cm^3)	Ef (GPa)	σy (MPa)	K_{IC} (MPa/m$^{1/2}$)
St-DVERL	5	1.130±0.002	3.30±0.19	76.6±2.39	1.310±0.053
	10	1.122±0.002	2.68±0.06	64.8±2.18	1.460±0.097
St-DVERC	5	1.119±0.001	2.44±0.03	67.5±1.34	1.615±0.085
	10	1.100±0.018	2.20±0.06	60.03±3.13	1.851±0.170
St-DVERH	5	1.124±0.004	2.79±0.02	69.7±2.79	1.661±0.331
	10	1.103±0.002	2.50±0.02	60.4±3.09	1.804±0.241

The mechanical study of this system indicated a reduction in the modulus of the VTBN modified material (with respect to the neat system), as well as improved fracture behavior. Since phase separation is not as complete as in the CTBN modified systems, there is a better cohesion between phases of the VTBN modified systems and a reduction in stiffness arising from the addition and copolymerization of the reactive rubber. [2]. Similarly, Huang et al. [8] have reported on the effect of improved compatibility of additive in UP-St systems. They observed a stronger interface with less segregation of species, which leads to the improved impact strength of the system, but lower modulus because of the flexibilizing effect of the elastomer in the main phase.

CONCLUSIONS

The Flory-Huggins theory applied to polydisperse systems was successfully utilized to model the quasi-binary and quasi-ternary behavior of divinylester, styrene and CTBN (or VTBN) mixture. The binary interaction parameters were modeled using an expression, which is only an inverse function of the absolute temperature.

The morphologies developed during crosslinking of the DVER with St are a strong function of the initial miscibility of the system. The thermodynamic study indicated that the initial mixture is homogeneous for the low molecular weight resin (DVERL), but is in the two phase region for the high molecular weight systems (DVERC). The latter is the usual case in commercial formulations and so the final microstructures are highly affected by the initial mixing step.

The use of a low molecular weight resin produces materials with nodular microstructures spanning the whole sample, as a result of the PIPS mechanism. Generalized microvoiding also appears.

High molecular weight resins produce final materials with different domains: a St-DVER rich phase with small elastomer inclusions and an elastomer rich phase with internal complex nodular microstructure.

Final properties are a direct function of the final material morphology. Tg is higher for the low molecular weight systems, as a result of a more packed crosslinked microstructure. In general, the addition of CTBN elastomer produces a reduction of the flexural modulus and the compression yield stress of the samples, but with the desired increment in fracture resistance. St-DVERL-10% CTBN modified system was an exception due to the negative effect of generalized microvoiding.

The use of a reactive elastomer, such as VTBN, produces materials with less microvoiding and improved fracture resistance. The flexural modulus is reduced by the presence of the second phase and by the flexibilization of the main phase, St-DVER rich phase that co-react with VTBN.

ACKNOWLEDGEMENTS

The financial supports of the National Research Council (CONICET, Argentina), the National Agency for the Promotion of Science and Technology (ANPCyT, Argentina), and the University of Mar del Plata, are gratefully acknowledged.

REFERENCES

[1] Selly J. L.,*"Encyclopedia of Polymer Science & Engineering"*, 2nd. Edition, Mark-Bikales-Overberger-Menges, Jhon Wiley & Sons, Inc., 12 (1998).

[2] Auad M.L., Frontini P.M., Borrajo J, Aranguren M.I. *Polymer*; 42:7 2723-2730 (2001).

[3] Auad, M.L., Proia, M., Borrajo, J. and Aranguren, M.I., *Journal of Materials Science, 37, 4117-4126 (2002).*

[4] Auad, M.L., Borrajo, J. and Aranguren, M.I., *Journal of Applied Polymer Science*, 89:1, 274-283 (2003).

[5] Suspene L., Fourquier, Q., and Yang, Y.S., *Polymer*, 32:9 1593-1604 (1991).

[6] Bucknall, C.B., Partridge, I.K., Phillips, M.J., *Polymer*, 32:5, 786-790 (1991).

[7] Hang, Y.J., Su, C.C., *J. Appl. Polym. Sci.*, a and b-55:4, 305-318 (1995).

[8] Huang, Y.J., Jiang, W.C., *Polymer*, 39:25 6631-6641 (1998).

[9] Auad, M.L., Aranguren, M.I. and Borrajo, J., *Polymer,* 42:15 6503-6513 (2001).

[10] Pham, S., and Burchill, P. J., *Polymer*, 36:17, 3279-3285 (1995).

[11] Ullett, J.S., and Chartoff R. P., *Polym. Eng. Sci*, 35:12 1086-1095 (1995).

[12] Cook, W. D., Zipper, M. D., and Chung A. C.H., *Polymer*, 39:22 5431-5439 (1998).

[13] Flory, P.J. *"Principles of Polymer Chemistry",* Cornell University Press: Ithaca, NY, (1953).

[14] Tompa, H, *"Polymer Solutions*", Butterwords: London, 182 (1956).

[15] Kenji Kamide, *"Thermodynamics of Polymer Solutions: Phase Equilibria and Critical Phenomena",* A.D. Jenkis Edit., Polymer Science Library 9, Elsevier, (1990).

[16] Painter, P.C. and Coleman, M.M., *Fundamentals of Polymer Science*, Technomic, Lancaster, PA, (1994).

[17] Shirataki H., Matsuda S., and Kamide K., *British Polym. Journal*, 23:2 299-309 (1990).

[18] Shirataki H., Matsuda S., and Kamide K, *Polym International*, 32:3 265-273 (1993).

[19] Lecointe, J.P., Pascault, J.P., Suspène, L. and Yang, Y.S., *Polymer*, 33:15, 3226-3233 (1992).

[20] ESIS Testing Protocol, "*A Linear Elastic Fracture Mechanics (LEFM) Standard for Determining Kc and Gc for Plastics*" (1990).

[21] Borrajo, J., Riccardi, C.C., and Williams, R.R.J., *Polymer,* 35:24, 5541-5549 (1994).

[22] Riccardi, C. and Borrajo, J., *Polym International*, 32:2, 241-248 (1993).

[23] Rey, L., Duchet, J., Galy, J., Sautereau, H., Vouagner, D., Carrion, L.; *Polymer,* 43:16 4375-4338 (2002).

[24] Rey, L., Galy, J., Sautereau, H., *Macromolecules*, 33:18 6780-6786 (2000).

[25] Kinkelaar M., Muzundar S., Lee L.J., *Polym. Eng. Sci.*, 35:10 823-836 (1995).

[26] Suspene, L., Yang, Y.S., Pascault, J.P. In: Riew C.K., Kinloch A.J, editors. Toughened Plastics I – Science and Engineering, *Advance in Chemistry Series* N° 233, ACS, Washington, DC, 163-188 (1993).

[27] Grosbi, G.A., Philips, M.G., *J. Mater. Sci.,* 20:1 182-192 (1985).

[28] Pham, S. and Burchill, P.J., *Polymer,* 36:17 3279-3285 (1995).

[29] Matsumoto, A., Aoki, K., Kukimoto, Y., Oiwa, M., Ochi, M., Shimbo, M.D., *J. Polym. Sci., Polym. Lett,* 21 837-844 (1983)

[30] Cho, K., Lee, D., Park, C.E., and Huh, W., *Polymer,* 37:5 813-817 (1996).

[31] Siebert, A.R., Guiley, C.D., Kinloch, A.J., Fernando, M., Heinsbrock, E.P.L. In: Riew C.K., Kinloch A.J., editors. Toughened Plastics II – Novel Approach in Science and Engineering, *Advance in Chemistry Series* N° 252, ACS, Washington, DC, 151-160 (1996).

[32] Huang, Y. J. and Horng, C. J., *Polymer,* 39:16 3683-3695 (1998).

[33] Huang, Y. J. and Liang, C. M., *Polymer*, 37:3 401-412 (1996).

In: Homolytic and Heterolytic Reactions: Problems and Solutions ISBN 1-59033-980-0
Editors: G.E. Zaikov, et al., pp. 197-232

Chapter 8

A Fractal Treatment of Structural Stabilization of a Polymeric Melts

G. V. Kozlov and G. E. Zaikov
Institute of Biochemical Physics of Russian Academy of Sciences. Kosygin st., 4, Moscow 119991, Russia

Abstract

For characterization of a polymer melt structure the fractal dimension of a macromolecular coil is used. It is shown that the oxygen consumption kinetics in a thermooxidative degradation process is defined by the chemical constitution of polymer and its structure. The quantitative analysis of a kinetic curve in the framework of the fractal analysis is made. It is demonstrated that the transition of kinetic curves of melts oxidation from autodecelerated (sigmoidal) up to autoaccelerated regime is defined by the structural factor, namely, by reaching the fractal dimension of a macromolecular coil. A critical value, at which a number of reactive sites in bulk and surface becomes equal, is calculated. The transition from induction period up to sharp acceleration of a thermooxidative degradation in case of kinetic curves of an autoaccelerated type is due to the change of space type, in which reaction is occured, from fractal up to Euclidean. The effect of melt structure not only on quantitative characteristics of a thermooxidative degradation process, but on qualitative changes in this process, in particular on chemical mechanisms of reaction, is shown.

Keywords: Polymeric melt, thermooxidative degradation, structure, fractal analysis, scaling approach, fractional derivative, chemical mechanism, stabilization.

1. Introduction

The term "structural stabilization" with reference to polymers in general and their melts in particular is known for a long time [1]. However, it is assumed that the structural stabilization is applied to solid state of polymers, where there is a pronounced structure (specially for semicrystalline polymers), whereas polymeric melt is considered as a structureless state. Besides the absence of polymers structural models for any of the mentioned states it is necessary to use indirect methods of the structure estimation. So, authors [1] consider that the idea of structural stabilization consist of such structural-physical modification of material, specially low-scale high-frequent motions responsible for chemical reactions. A reduction of molecular motion decreases a chemical reactivity and increases the material stability [1]. The attempt to allow the influence of topological disorder (a level of polymer chain entanglements) on a process of thermooxidative degradation was made in papers [2, 3]. It is not difficult to see that in both cases indirect characteristics of structure are used.

The widespread development in last 20 years of the fractal analysis methods has allowed to change the present situation. As Vilgis pointed out [4, 5], a macromolecular coil in melt is fractal with the dimension $\Delta_f \cong 2.5$. This results in two very important consequences. In the first place, the direct, not indirect melt structure characteristic is obtained, as the fractal (Hausdorff) dimension Δ_f characterises coil elements distribution in space, i.e., is a purely structural parameter [6]. In the second place, the correct description of fractal objects is possible only within the framework of fractal analysis and any application of Euclidean geometry is only a more or less exact approximation [7]. On this basis in the present review the quantitative structural treatment of polymeric melts thermooxidative degradation in the terms of the fractal analysis is presented.

2. The Main Aspects of the Structural Stabilization Fractal Model

As it is well known [8, 9], the analysis of the experimental data on oxygen consumption at the thermooxidative degradation of different polymers both in open and in closed system has shown that there are three main types (under the other data – four types [10]) of kinetic curves "amount of consumed oxygen-time". $N_{O_2}(t)$ will be considered: curves exponentially decrease with time (autodecelerated), which are described by the following equation [8]:

$$N_{O_2} = N_{O_2}^{\infty}\left(1 - \exp(-k_d t)\right) \tag{1}$$

where $N_{O_2}^{\infty}$ is the limiting amount of oxygen which is capable to be consumed at the oxidation, k_d is the effective constant of oxidation rate.

The dependence (1) is usually explained by the heterogeneity of polymer which defines the noticeable differences in oxidation rates of its various sites. As more reactive sites are oxidized first of all, after their practically complete transformation the rate of the summary process strongly reduces. Besides it was exhibitedthat the value $N_{O_2}^{\infty}$, determined with the help of the equation (1), can be many times lower than the concentration of monomer units in the individual polymer: during the experiment some part of these units behaves as an inert substance [9].

The value k_d depends on the temperature and polymer structure. Therefore, both $N_{O_2}^{\infty}$ and k_d are simply fitting parameters, as their quantitative relation with polymer structure is not clarified. Authors [11] studied the structural sense of parameters $N_{O_2}^{\infty}$ and k_d for a polymeric melt on an example of two block-copolymers polyarylatearylenesulfonoxide (PAASO), obtained at low temperature (PAASO-1) and high-temperature (PAASO-2) polycondensation at three testing temperatures. Studied further PAASO and polyarylates (PAr), obtained by different methods of polycondensation (see table 1), are convenient objects for examination (as polycarbonate, obtained from solutions in different solvents) from that point of view that in each of these series the polymers of an identical chemical structure are explored. Therefore, it is possible to assume that the obtained differences of the characteristics within the limits of each series are caused by the structural state of polymeric melts [11].

If we consider the parameters characterizing a polymeric melt structure the studies of the thermooxidative degradation process of PAASO are made within the temperature range $T = 623 \div 723$ K and the glass transition temperatures T_g range of these copolymers is equal to $472 \div 474$ K. As it is known [12], the temperature of the so-called transition "a liquid 1 – liquid 2" T_{ll} can be estimated as follows:

$$T_{ll} \approx (1{,}20 \pm 0{,}05)T_g \quad (2)$$

From equation (2) and quoted in table 1 the condition $T > T_{ll}$ follows. At T_{ll} there occurs a transition of polymeric melt from "liquid with fixed structure" (where the residual structural ordering is observed [12]) to a true liquid state or "structureless" liquid [13]. Nevertheless, the term "structureless" at $T \geq T_{ll}$ concerns to the structure of the macromolecular coil in melt remains the most important structural factor (in essence, only at $T \geq T_{ll}$) [11].

Table 1. Methods of polycondensation, conditional names and main characteristics of studied polymers [12]

Polymer	The method of polycondensation	The conditional Name	T_g, K	$\bar{M}_W \times 10^{-3}$	$k_d \times 10^4$, s^{-1}*
Polyarylate	Low-temperature	PAr-1	471	76	0,34
	High-temperature	PAr-2	476	72	0,26
	Interfacial	PAr-3	462	69	0,17
Polyarylate-arylenesulfonoxide	Low-temperature	PAASO-1	472	76	0,19
	High-temperature	PAASO-2	474	64	0,24
	Interfacial	PAASO-3	491	66	0,07
	Emulsive	PAASO-4	489	58	0,11

*Footnote: at $T = 623$ K.

As mentioned above, the structure of a macromolecular coil can be exactly described with the help of its fractal dimension Δ_f [14]. The estimation of Δ_f can be made as follows [15]. The formal kinetics of chemical reactions can be described by the following equation:

$$\frac{dQ}{dt} = k(1-Q) \tag{3}$$

where Q is the reaction conversion degree, k is the reaction rate constant.

The general fractal relationship is also used for the description of the chemical reactions kinetics, looks like [16]:

$$Q \sim t^{(3-\Delta_f)/2}. \tag{4}$$

Differentiating the relationship (4) by time t and equating the derivative dQ/dt to a similar derivative in the equation (3), we shall obtain [15]:

$$t^{(\Delta_f-1)/2} = \frac{C_1}{k(1-Q)}, \tag{5}$$

where C_1 is a constant, which can be estimated from the boundary conditions [15].

From this description it follows that the thermooxidative degradation process for the considered copolymers proceeds not in an Euclidean, but in a fractal space with dimension Δ_f. In the latter space the process of degradation can be presented by the way of "devil's staircase" [17]. Its horizontal segments correspond to the time intervals, where the reaction does not occur. In this case the degradation process is described with the usage of fractal time t, which belongs to the points of Cantor's set [18]. If the reaction is consider in an Euclidean space, the time belongs to the set of real numbers.

For the description of the evolutional processes with fractal time the mathematics of fractional derivation and integration will be used [18-19]. In this case the fractional exponent ν coincides with the fractal dimension of Cantor's set and indicates a fraction of the system nonchanged during the time of evolution t. We remind that the Cantor's set is considered in one – dimensional Euclidean space ($d = 1$) and therefore its fractal dimension $d_f < 1$ by virtue of the fractal definition [17]. For the fractal objects in Euclidean spaces with higher dimensions ($d > 1$) as ν it is necessary to accept the fractional part d_f (in our case Δ_f) or:

$$\nu = \Delta_f - (d-1) \tag{6}$$

Then, the value of ν characterizes the fraction of a fractal (macromolecular coil), unchanged during the degradation process. Apparently, the fraction of a macromolecular coil β which is breaking up during the degradation is determined as follows:

$$\beta = 1 - \nu = 1 - [\Delta_f - (d-1)] = d - \Delta_f \tag{7}$$

or, as in the considered case $d = 3$:

$$\beta = 3 - \Delta_f. \tag{8}$$

Further it is natural to assume that oxygen is consumed in a part of a macromolecular coil which is breaking up during the degradation. Then, having calculated the value of $N_{O_2}^{T}$, which is necessary for the oxidation of all aliphatic and aromatic groups of PAASO (which is equal to 24.1 mol O_2 per mol of polymer [11]) it is possible to determine the parameter $N_{O_2}^{\infty}$ as follows [11]:

$$N_{O_2}^{\infty} = \beta N_{O_2}^{T}. \tag{9}$$

The change Δ_f means the variation of the compactness of a macromolecular coil [16]. We should expect that lowering Δ_f, defining the decrease of the coil compactness, will result in increase of N_{O_2} and, therefore, k_d that allows to replace k_d by the structural parameter. It is possible to characterize the compactness degree of a macromolecular coil with the help of its density, ρ. As it is known [17], the value ρ of a fractal is determined as follows:

$$\rho \sim R_g^{\Delta_f - d} \tag{10}$$

where R_g is the gyration radius of a macromolecular coil. For simplicity, it was accepted R_g equal to 100 relative units (the values of molecular weight $\bar{M}_W$ for PAASO-1 and PAASO-2 are close) and density ρ was determined from the following equation for both polymers and all testing temperatures [11]:

$$\rho = 8,2 R_g^{\Delta_f - d} \tag{11}$$

where coefficient 8.2 is defined empirically.

Now, the equation (1) with the allowance of the considered geometrical factors can be written as follows [11]:

$$N_{O_2} = \left(3 - \Delta_f\right) N_{O_2}^{T} \left(1 - \exp^{-t/\rho}\right). \tag{12}$$

The exponent $-(t/\rho)$ of the exponential curve is selected in such a form because of the action ρ is opposite to the action t: the increase of ρ reduces the oxygen consumption and on the contrary. In Fig. 1 the experimental dependences $N_{O_2}(t)$ for both studied polymers at three temperatures of tests are shown. As it is possible to see all kinetic curves $N_{O_2}(t)$ belong to the considered type: the value N_{O_2} decreases exponentially during the degradation. Such behavior dN_{O_2}/dt uniquely indicates the proceeding of the thermooxidative degradation process in a fractal space [20].

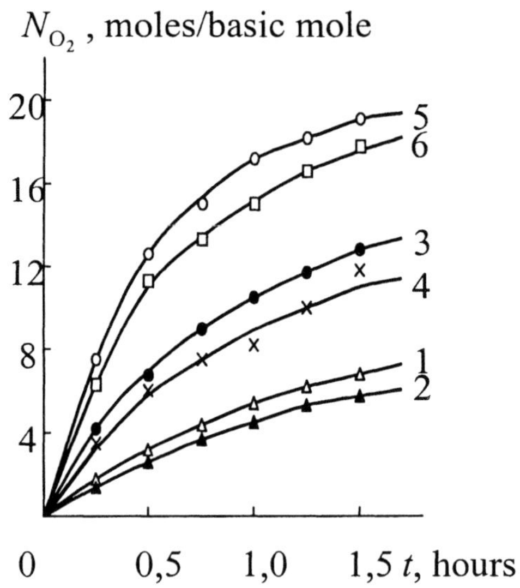

Figure 1. The dependences of consumed oxygen amount N_{O_2} on time t for PAASO-1 (1, 3, 5) and PAASO-2 (2, 4, 6) at the temperatures 623 (1, 2) 673 (3, 4) and 723 K (6, 6) [11].

In Fig. 2 the generalized kinetic curve of the oxygen consumption for PAASO-1 and PAASO-2 at three testing temperatures is shown. As it is possible to see the experimental data are well described by equation (12), not containing the empirical coefficients. Then, the kinetics of the oxygen consumption is defined by the chemical constitution of polymer $\left(N_{O_2}^{T}\right)$ and its structure (Δ_f and ρ) [11].

As follows from equations (10) and (11), the increase of Δ_f results in the increase of the density ρ of a macromolecular coil. Authors [15] assumed that the increase ρ should determined by the decreasing of a rate constant of thermooxidative degradation k_d, as the mentioned change ρ results the difficulty of an oxidant (oxygen) access to the reactivity centres of a polymer macromolecule. In reality, for PAASO and polyarylates on the basis of dichlorodiane 2,2-di(carboxiphenyl) ethylene and diane (PAr) the linear reduction of the function $k_d(\Delta_f)$ was found. This plot allows to determine the limiting values k_d on the basis of the following criterions. The value Δ_f can be determined according to equation [5]:

$$\Delta_f = \frac{d_s(d+2)}{2} \tag{13}$$

where d_s is the spectral (fracton) dimension of a coil.

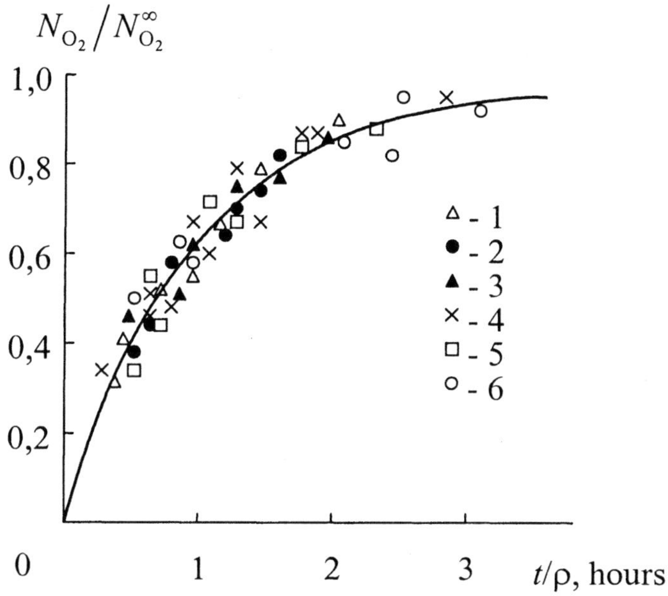

Figure 2. Generalized kinetic curve of the oxygen consumption corresponding to the equation (12), for PAASO-2(1-3) and PAASO-2(4-6) at the temperatures 623 (1, 4), 673 (2, 5) and 723 K (3, 6) [11].

For linear polymers, PAASO and PAr, $d_s = 1$ [21] and then the minimal value is $\Delta_f = 2{,}5$ and maximal (theoretical) value is $\Delta_f = d = 3$. This allows to determine the maximal (at $\Delta_f = 2.5$) and minimal (at $\Delta_f = 3$) values of k_d from the plot $k_d(\Delta_f)$ as 0.32×10^{-4} s^{-1} and 0, respectively. In other words, thermooxidative degradation is possible only for fractal objects. However, as Balankin showed [22], for real physical objects a value of the fractal dimension can be not more then 2.95. This means that the minimal value k_d for studied polymers is different from zero and is 0.35×10^{-5} s^{-1} [15].

In [23] was made the assumption that when determined according to the equations (7) and (8) parameter β can be used for normalization of N_{O_2} in analogue with the parameter $(1 - K)$ (where K is the crystallinity degree) in case of solid-state semicrystalline polymers. The dependences $N_{O_2}/(d - \Delta_f)$ on an aging duration t for PAr and PAASO are shown in Fig. 3. These dependences can be linearized only at the usage of the value $t^{1/2}$ as abscissa. This means that the reaction order of chain termination for PAr and PAASO melts is equal to 0.5. The different slopes of straight plots in Fig. 3a are due to different rate constants of reaction [9]. The most important consequence from results in Fig. 3, linear plots is that their linearization is reached by the usage of fractal parameter $(d - \Delta_f)$. This means that the structure of a polymer melt is described with the help of a macromolecular coil fractal dimension as well as the structure of solid-state semicrystalline polymer with the help of its crystallinity degree [9].

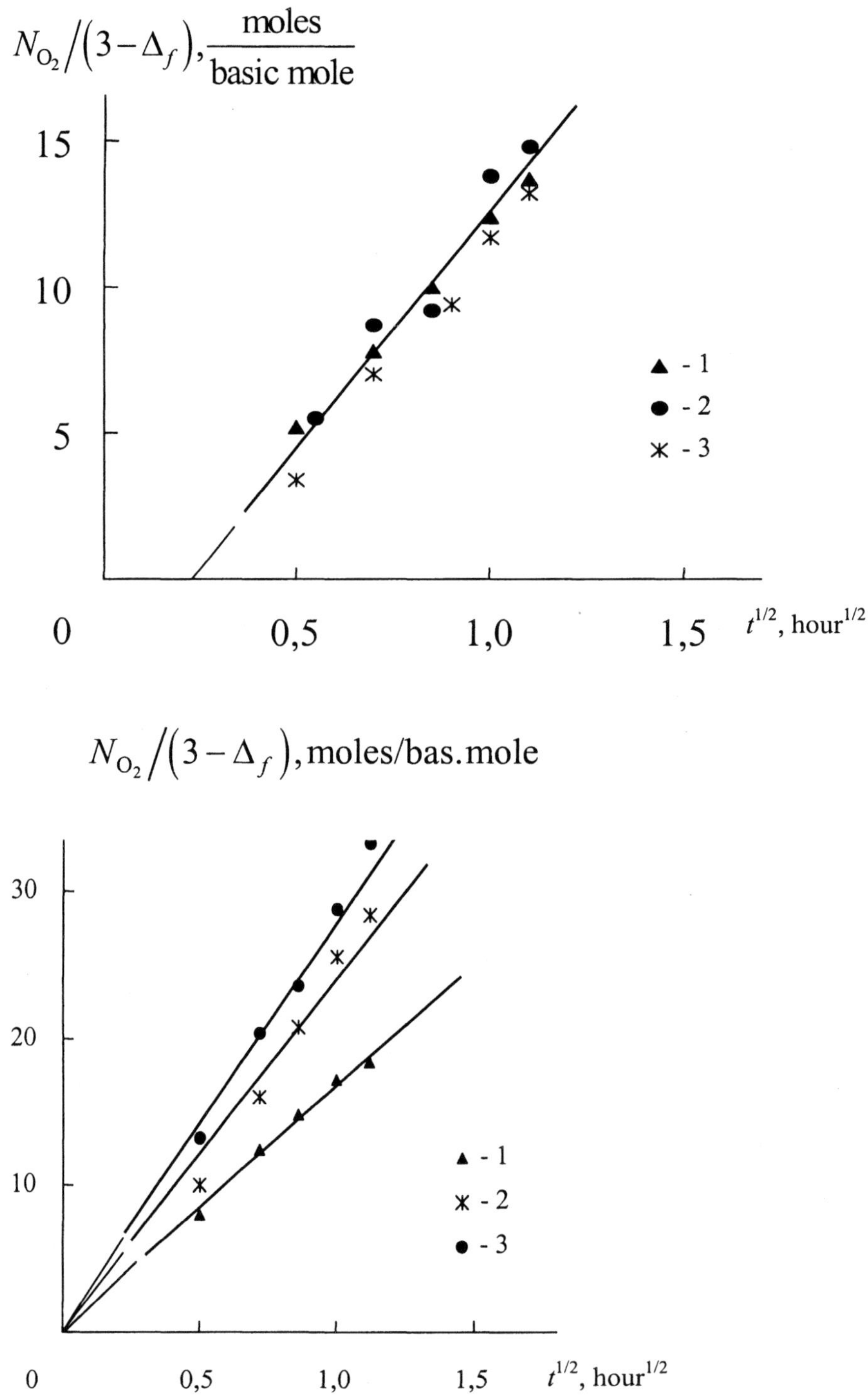

Figure 3. Dependences of the normalized amount of consumed oxygen $N_{O_2}/(3-\Delta_f)$ on time $t^{1/2}$ for PAr (a) and PAASO (b). Testing temperature (K): a) 1- 623 (PAr-1), 2 - 673 (PAr-3), 3 – 723 (PAr-3); b) – 623 (PAASO-1), 2 - 673 (PAASO-2), 3 - 723 (PAASO-3) [23].

Between the plots of Fig. 3a and 3b there is an important difference. The straight plots for PAr pass through origin, whereas straight plot for PAASO is displaced on the axis of absciss. Identical effect is observed for atactic and isotactic polypropylene in paper [9]. The latter straight line is displaced on some interval of time t_0. This displacement was explained by the linear termination of chain on the elements of a crystalline phase, which plays an essential role in the very beginning of reaction, when free radicals participating in oxidation reaction are trapped by crystalline formations, in which oxygen is completely absent or its concentration is nonessential. The too small and badly formatted crystallites can not keep free radicals. However, at the increase of sizes and growth of ordering of crystallites their role as free radicals' traps is increased that results the reduction of oxygen consumption rate and the decrease of induction period of polymer oxidation [9]. For studied polymers this difference will be explained below.

For PAr and PAASO, produced by the different methods of polycondensation, the different values of activation energy E_{act} of a thermooxidative degradation in a rather wide interval $E_{act} = 71.2 \div 109$ kJ/mole are observed. As the chemical constitution both of PAr and PAASO does not depend on a method of polycondensation, it is necessary to assume that the differences E_{act} are defined by the differences of melt structure of the mentioned polymers [24].

The plotting of dependences $E_{act}(\Delta_f)$ has shown that the increase of Δ_f or the increase of a compactness degree of a macromolecular coil in a melt results in the linear increase E_{act} for both studied polymers. However, the slope of dependence $E_{act}(\Delta_f)$ for PAr is less that for PAASO. Besides, the values E_{act} are identical for the less compact coils (at $\Delta_f = 2{,}5$) for PAr and PAASO. Such course of dependences E_{act} (Δ_f) assumes that except the structure of a macromolecular coil that is characterized by value Δ_f, there exists at least one more factor influencing on value E_{act}, and the effect of this factor increases at growth Δ_f. Or else, the contribution of the assumed factor also depends on Δ_f. There are all reasons to assume that the mentioned factor is defined by the steric hindrances due to the presence of the substituents of a different type, branching, substituents in different positions (orto-, para-, metha-) etc. In this case, the degree of the influence of the mentioned factor can be described with the help of a Gammet constant σ [25]. The simplest variant of calculation with the use of the following equation was chosen [24]:

$$\log k_d = -2.150 + 0.337\,\sigma \tag{14}$$

The plotting of dependence $\sigma(\Delta_f)$ for PAr and PAASO has shown that, as well as it was assumed the increase of an absolute value of a Gammet constant is observed at increase Δ_f. It means that the increase Δ_f or the compactness degree of a macromolecular coil strengthens a steric hindrance to the penetration of oxygen into a melt of polymers. Analytically, the relationship between σ and Δ_f can be expressed as follows [24]:

$$\sigma = -6.38 - 5.70\,(\Delta_f - 2.50) \tag{15}$$

Thus, the increase of both σ and Δ_f also weakens the access of oxygen to the reactivity centres of polymer macromolecules, decelerates the thermooxidative degradation process and, hence, increases the value of E_{act}. The plotting of the dependence $E_{act}(\Delta_f|\sigma|)$ confirms this statement and allows to obtain the following analytical relationship between E_{act} and product $\Delta_f|\sigma|$:

$$E_{act} = 4.10\Delta_f|\sigma|,\ \text{kJ/mol} \quad (16)$$

We shall point out that the dependence $E_{act}(\Delta_f|\sigma|)$ is linear and pass through the origin. It means that the condition $E_{act} = 0$ is satisfied in two cases: $\Delta_f = 0$ and $|\sigma| = 0$. The first of the mentioned conditions demonstrates that $E_{act} = 0$ it is possible only for the zero-dimensional low-molecular substances. The second of these conditions allows to estimate the maximal value k_d from the equation (14): at $\sigma = 0$ $k_d = 70.8 \times 10^{-4}$ s^{-1}, i.e., approximately three orders of magnitude higher than the experimentally observed for PAr and PAASO of values k_d. The minimal value k_d can be estimated as follows. From equation (15) we determine value of σ corresponding to the maximal value $\Delta_f = d = 3$ and then from the equation (14) – the required value k_d, equal to 0.55×10^{-5} s^{-1} that is close to the experimental value k_d for PAASO, obtained by the interfacial polycondensation (see table 1). Thus, the value of the activation energy of a thermooxidative degradation for PAr and PAASO melts is defined by two factors, namely, by the macromolecular coil structure, characterized by its fractal dimension Δ_f, and by the steric hindrances of a chain characterized by a Gammet constant [24]. The mentioned above steric hindrances can be a traps of free radicals that decreases consumption oxygen rate and increases an induction period of melts PAr and PAASO oxidation (see Fig. 3a).

Now the processes of thermal and thermooxidative degradation from the point of view of proceeding chemical reactions, as a rule, are considered separately [10, 26], even if the same polymer is considered. Nevertheless, it is known [10, 26] that the general increase of resistance to the thermal degradation is accompanied by the increase of the thermooxidative stability of polymers. Therefore it is possible to assume the existence of certain interdependence between the mentioned types of polymer degradation. This statement proves to be true by the data of paper [27], in which the relation between the activation energies of these processes is found. As it is shown [27], between values of activation energies of thermooxidative E_{act}^{therm} and thermal $E_{act}^{T_0}$ degradation there is a linear correlation pass through the origin, which is analytically expressed as follows [27]:

$$E_{act}^{T_0} \approx 1{,}42\ E_a^{therm} \quad (17)$$

The relationship (17) assumes that the role of oxidation (oxygen) consist in the reduction of an energetic barrier of the thermooxidative degradation in comparison with the thermal degradation.

In Fig. 4 the dependence of values Δ_f, averaged for each testing temperature T, on T for PAr and PAASO is shown. As it is possible to see, the essential reduction of the fractal dimension of macromolecular coil at the increase T is observed. As mentioned above, the minimal value Δ_f at $d_s = 1$ should be 2.5 (the horizontal broken line in Fig. 4). From equation (13) we can see that the condition $\Delta_f < 2.5$ is an equivalent to condition $d_s < 1$, i.e., the infringement of connectivity of a macromolecular coil or its breakage. At it is known [27], the intensive thermal degradation of PAr and PAASO begins at a temperature range $T = 665 \div$

693 K. This range T is shown in Fig. 4 by the shaded area. As it is possible to see, the decrease Δ_f lower 2.5 coincides with the beginning of the intensive thermal degradation. In its turn, the decrease Δ_f gives the increase of the consumed oxygen amount and, hence, the intensification of thermooxidative degradation.

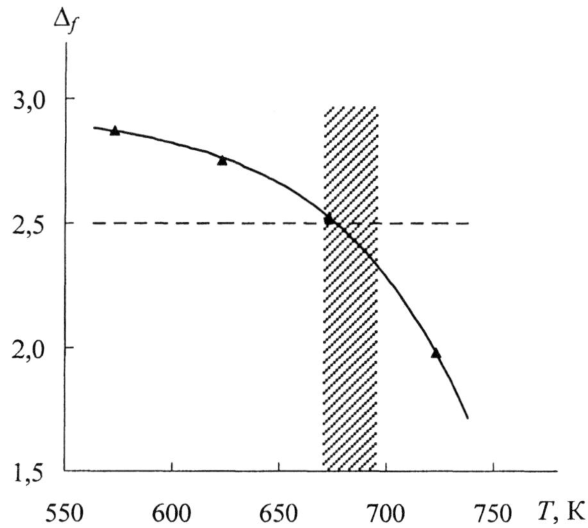

Figure 4. Dependence of the average fractal dimension Δ_f of a macromolecular coil on testing temperature T for PAr and PAASO. The horizontal broken line points out the minimal value Δ_f, the shaded area – the temperature interval of the beginning on intensive thermal degradation [27].

And at last, it is possible to assume that the polymer mass residue m_{res}, maintained during the thermal degradation, will be equal (or proportional), to fractional exponent ν, which characterizes the fraction of a fractal (macromolecular coil), unchanged during the degradation process [19]. Really, the dependence $m_{res}(\nu)$ obtained in paper [27], is linear and pass through the origin. From this dependence the approximate equality $m_{res} \approx \nu$ follows [27].

3. The Physical Sense of Non-Homogeneity of a Medium in Fractal Kinetics of Reactions

The reactions' occurrence in heterogeneous media, to which structure of polymers condensed state is referred [28], does not obey the classic rules of chemical reactions' description [20, 29]. This difference is due to structural features of the mentioned polymers state [30]. So, in the most simple treatment a thermooxidative degradation can be represented by bimolecular reaction [20]:

$$\boldsymbol{A} + \boldsymbol{B} \rightarrow \text{products of oxidation} \tag{18}$$

where A is polymer macromolecule, B is oxygen molecule.

The rate k of such reaction in heterogeneous (fractal) medium is described by the following relationship [20, 29]:

$$k \sim t^{-h}, \tag{19}$$

where t is reaction duration, h is the heterogeneity exponent ($0 < h < 1$), which becomes equal to zero in the case of classic behavior (reactions in homogeneous or Euclidean mediums) and then $k = \text{const}$.

The exponent h is connected with an effective spectral dimension d'_s of polymers structure by the following equation [29]:

$$d'_s = 2(1 - h) \tag{20}$$

that according to the theorem on subordination is connected to a spectral dimension d_s as follows [29]:

$$d'_s = \beta' d_s, \tag{21}$$

where β' is the parameter characterizing a distribution of jump times (for example, molecules of oxidant) [29].

It follows that for prediction of rates of chemical reactions in general and thermooxidative degradation in particular it is necessary to be able to predict the values of d'_s and h as a function of structural parameters of polymers condensed state. For solution of this problem in the first place it is necessary to clarify the physical sense of parameter h. The solution of this task was considered in [31, 32].

The study of chemical reactions on fractal objects corrections for the existence in system small clusters are necessary [20]. Namely, these corrections require the usage in theoretical calculations of not commonly accepted spectral (fraction) dimension d_s [21], but its effective value d'_s. For percolation clusters two cases are possible [33]:

(a) The random walk is located on the largest percolation cluster of system, which is characterized by the dimension d_s;
(b) The random walk can get into any cluster including a small size cluster. The set of such clusters is characterized by the parameter d'_s.

The structure of amorphous polymers in glassy state is a percolation cluster has to be considered [34]. The percolation threshold on a temperature scale coincides with the glass transition temperature T_g. The formation of such percolation cluster is defined by the existence in polymers at temperatures $T \leq T_g$ of local order regions. At $T > T_g$ the set of these regions is decayed [35] and the structure of polymer is no longer a percolation cluster. As it is shown above [11], a polymer melt structure can be treated as a set of a large number of separate clusters (macromolecular coils), and the trajectory of oxygen molecule (atom) on such structure is simulated by random walk [30]. In this case for estimation of d'_s is applicable the equation, obtained in paper [33]:

$$d'_s = d_s\left(2 - \frac{d}{d - \beta_p/\nu_p}\right), \tag{22}$$

where β_p and ν_p are static percolation indexes.

As it is known [36], the fractal (Hausdorff) dimension Δ_f can be expressed as follows:

$$\Delta_f = d - \frac{\beta_p}{\nu_p}. \tag{23}$$

The combination of the equations (13), (22) and (23) allows to obtain the final formula assuming the calculation d'_s on known values Δ_f [31]:

$$d'_s = \frac{2(2\Delta_f - d)}{d+2}. \tag{24}$$

And finally from the equations (20) and (24) will be obtained:

$$h = \frac{2(d+1-\Delta_f)}{d+2}. \tag{25}$$

For three-dimensional Euclidean space the formula (25) is simplified as follows [32]:

$$h = 0{,}4(4 - \Delta_f). \tag{26}$$

In Fig. 5 the dependence h on fractional exponent ν for PAr and PAASO is shown, from which can be observed the linear correlation between these parameters. Therefore the physical sense of a heterogeneity exponent h can be defined this way: a heterogeneity of macromolecular coil structure is defined by the fraction of this coil keeping in a process of a thermooxidative degradation. It means that a degradation process of the fractal object includes the memory effects [37]. From the data of Fig. 5, an analytical relationship between h and ν can be obtained [32]:

$$h = 0.2 + 0.4\,\nu \tag{27}$$

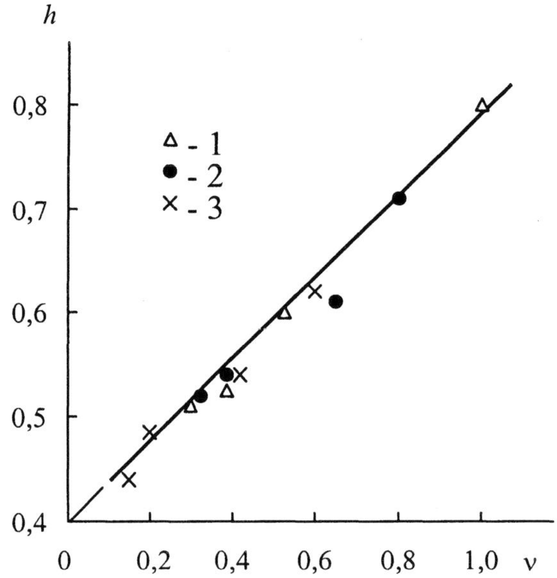

Figure 5. Dependence of heterogeneity exponent h on fractional exponent ν for PAr (1), PAASO-1 (2) and PAASO-2 (3) [32].

Let us consider the limiting cases for h. At $h = 0$ $\nu = -0.5$ or, as follows from equation (6), $\Delta_f = 1.5$. The last value of Δ_f defines the so called "transparent" macromolecular coil, completely open for a diffusion of various diffusates including identical macromolecular coils [14]. As it is mentioned above, this case corresponds to classical behavior ($h = 0$, $k =$ const) [29]. At h = 1 and ν = 2; $\Delta_f = 4$ and there is a upper critical dimension for separate macromolecular coil. In the last case the coil is Gaussian's, i.e., the effects of the excluded volume are absent [5].

Equation (25) allows to calculate the limiting values Δ_f, i.e., Δ_f^0 for $h = 0$ and Δ_f^1 for $h = 1$ in the case of Euclidean spaces with any dimension d. In table 2 the limiting values Δ_f for $d = 1, 2, 3, 4, 5, 6$ and 12 are listed. As follows from the data of this table, the values Δ_f^0 and Δ_f^0 ate the function d and analytically these dependences can be written as follows [32]:

$$\Delta_f^0 = d + 1, \tag{28}$$

$$\Delta_f^1 = \frac{d}{2}. \tag{29}$$

Table 2. Values of the limiting fractal dimension Δ_f^0 and Δ_f^1 of a macromolecular coil as a function of the Euclidean space dimension d [32]

D	Δ_f^0	Δ_f^1
1	2	0.5
2	3	1.0
3	4	1.5
4	5	2.0
5	6	2.5
6	7	3.0
12	13	6.0

4. The Structural Analysis of a Kinetic Curves Type Change at the Polymer Melts Oxidation

A scaling approach in the chemical reactions analysis allows to determine the type and dimension of space, in which these reactions occur [38]. Djordjevic [39] considers the reaction, in which particles ***P*** of a chemical substance diffuse in medium containing randomly located static nonsaturated traps ***T***. At contact of a particle ***P*** with a trap ***T*** the particle disappears. Nonsaturation of a traps means that the reaction

$$\boldsymbol{P} + \boldsymbol{T} \rightarrow \boldsymbol{T} \tag{30}$$

can repeat itself infinite number of times.

It is usually considered that if the concentration of particles and traps is large or the reaction occurs at intensive stirring the process can be considered as the classical first order reaction. However, if the concentration of the randomly located traps is small, with necessity there exist areas of space, practically free from traps. The particles getting into these areas can reach the traps only during rather long time and hence, the decrease of their number in the course of reaction will be slower. The formal analysis of this problem shows that the concentration of particles c falls down under the law [40]:

$$c(t) \approx \exp\left(-Bt^{d/(d+2)}\right), \tag{31}$$

being dependent on the dimension of space *d* (*B* is constant, *t* is the reaction duration).

As it is known [41], the exponent for a time t is always connected to the spectral dimension d_s of space, in which reaction occurs, independently on the space type, euclidean or fractal. The exponent in equation (31) can be written as follows [5]:

$$\frac{d}{d+2}=\frac{d_s}{2}, \tag{32}$$

This is correct for phantom (not allowing for the excluded volume effects) objects. Apparently, this fractal object can create the walk trajectory of low-molecular particles (oxygen molecules, radicals etc.), which can cross it infinite number of times. At this treatment the value d can adopt any magnitudes.

In Fig. 6 kinetic curves s(t) (where s is breakage number on an initial macromolecule [9]) for films of polycarbonate on the basis of bisphenol A, obtained from the solutions in four solvents are shown. As follows from these curves comparison, the obtaining of films PC from different solvents gives not only a quantitative, but also qualitative differences of oxidation kinetics. For films, obtained from solutions PC in methylene chloride and chloroform the sigmoidal curves $s(t)$ are observed and for films, obtained from solutions in 1,4-dioxane and tetrahydrofuran the curves s(t) of autoaccelerated type are obtained [8]. Different types of curves with various chemical mechanisms of PC oxidation are assumed. This difference was explained earlier by various chemical constitution of oxidizing polymers and different testing temperatures [8]. However in paper [42] different types of kinetic curves are obtained at the same factors. Therefore the difference of curves $s(t)$ should be explained by the different structure of the same polymer obtained from different solvents [43].

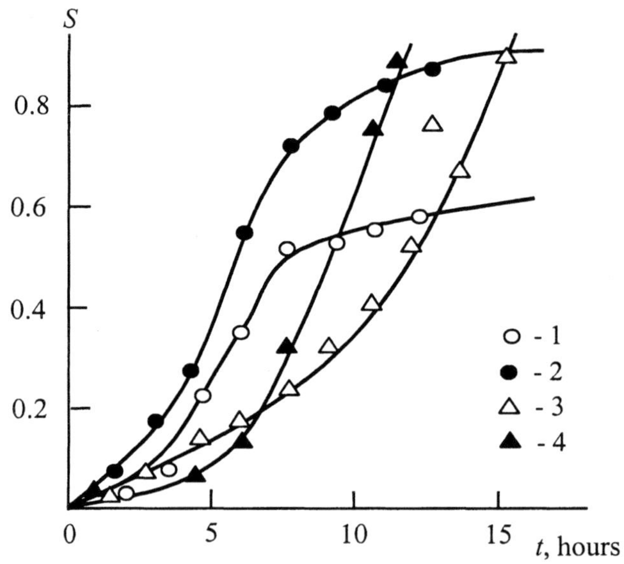

Figure 6. Dependences of breakups number S on one macromolecule on time t at $T = 513$ K for films PC obtained from solutions in methylene chloride (1), chloroform (2), 1,4-dioxine (3) and tetrahydrofuran (4) [49].

For the analysis of curves $s(t)$ within the framework of the scaling relationship (31) a determination of parameter $c(t)$ is required. The value c is considered as the number of "living" in reaction process particles [39 – 41]. In the case of thermooxidative degradation this parameter should be considered as the number of macromolecules, which has no breakages in degradation process. That can be written as follows [42]:

$$c = S_{\lim} - S, \tag{33}$$

where $S_{\lim}$ is a limiting number of breakages on one macromolecule.

The value of $S_{\lim}$ can be determined by different methods. The authors [42] assumed that $S_{\lim}$ is reached in the case when an oxidizing PC loses their polymeric properties. As it is shown [44], this happens in the case of reduction of polymer molecular weight M up to the value M_0, at which in the polymer a molecular entanglements network can not be formed. The value M_0 is estimated as follows [44]:

$$M_0 \approx 2M_e, \tag{34}$$

where M_e is the molecular weight of a chain portion between entanglements nodes, equal to ~ 1780 for PC [44].

The calculation of $S_{\lim}$ according to the technique [9] at $M_0 \approx 3560$ gives a value ~ 3.40. The authors [42] considered three possible structural variants of PC thermooxidative degradation: degradation on a macromolecular coil surface, in this case d in relationship (31) is equal to the dimension of a coil surface Δ_s; degradation in coil bulk and then $d = \Delta_f$; degradation in Euclidean space with $d = 3$. The value Δ_s can be determined as follows [45]:

$$\Delta_s = \Delta_f - 1 \tag{35}$$

In Fig. 7 the dependences $\ln(S_{\lim} - S)$ as the function of t^x, corresponding to the relationship (31), where as x exponents $\Delta_s/(\Delta_s + 2)$ and $d/(d + 2)$ for PC film, obtained from solution in tetrahydrofuran, are adopted. As follows from the data of Fig. 7, on initial oxidation portion (degradation time $t_d \leq 6$ hours) the dependence $\ln(S_{\lim} - S)$ on t^x is linearized at $x = \Delta_s/(\Delta_s + 2) \approx 0{,}46$ and for $t_d > 6$ hours – at $x = d/(d + 2) = =0.6$. This means that on the initial part of the kinetic curve $s(t)$ which is shown in Fig. 6, the oxidation of macromolecular coil surface is realized, as the consequence of which mobile low-molecular radicals are formed [9], and then an oxidation reaction in Euclidean space with dimension $d = 3$ occurs. Values Δ_f for studied films were adopted according to the data [46]. In both cases an oxidation occurs in medium with large density fluctuations [39] and the reaction rate in Euclidean space is much larger, than in fractal space (Fig. 6).

For PC films obtained from solution in chloroform analogous dependences of the portion of an oxidation acceleration ($t_d < 6$ hours) are linearized at $x = \Delta_s/(\Delta_s + 2) \approx 0.42$, and at $x = \Delta_f/(\Delta_f + 2) \approx 0.55$ (and at $d/(d + 2) = 0.6$) it is curvilinear [42]. Such dependences for a portion of an oxidation deceleration ($t_d = 7.5 \div 12$ hours) (Fig. 6) demonstrated the opposite pattern: a linear scaling is obtained at $x = \Delta_f/(\Delta_f + 2) \approx 0.55$ and curvilinear dependence is obtained at $x = \Delta_s/(\Delta_f + 2) \approx 0.42$. Therefore, for sigmoidal curves of oxidation an initial portion of autoacceleration means that the oxidation of a macromolecular coil surface and then (at $t_d \geq 7.5$ hours) an oxidation of this coil bulk happens. Then, the oxidation reaction in both portions in the fractal space occurs: on a portion $t_d = 0 \div 6$ hours – in a space with a dimension $\Delta_s = 1.54$ and on a portion $t_d \geq 7.5$ hours – with a dimension $\Delta_f = 2.54$. In this case the change of a space dimension results in a decreasing of the thermooxidative degradation rate.

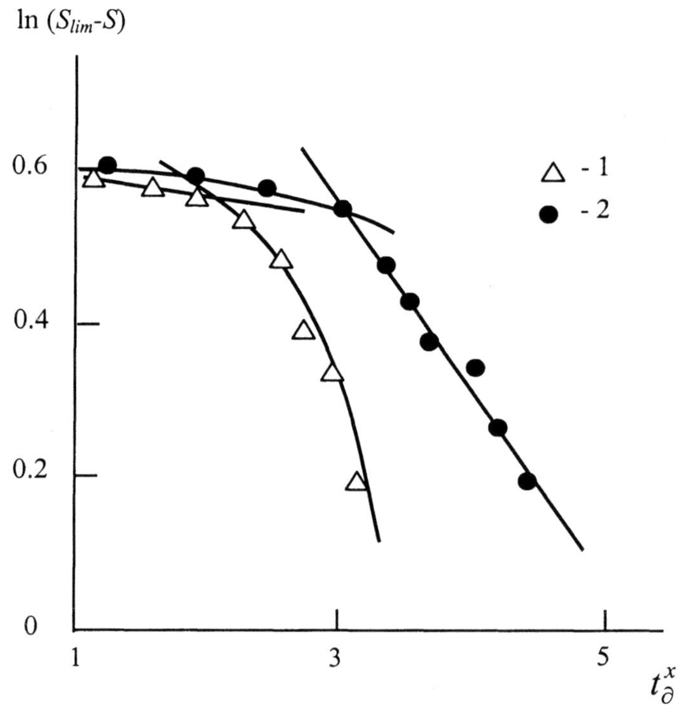

Figure 7. Dependences ($S_{\text{lim}} - S$) on t^x in double log-log coordinates corresponding to relationship (31) for PC films obtained from solution in tetrahydrofuran, at $x = \Delta_s/(\Delta_s + 2)$ (1) and $x = d/(d + 2)$ (2) [42].

We can consider the analytical expression of the criterion of the mentioned above transition for the oxidation kinetic curves type. As the comparison of curves $s(t)$ and values Δ_f for studied polymers (PAASO and PC) [47], the mentioned transition associates with the increase of fractal dimension Δ_f of a macromolecular coil on a melt that supposes its only structural nature. As mentioned above, the increase of Δ_f means the increase of a macromolecular coil compactness (see the equations (10) and (11)) and, therefore, weakening of an oxygen diffusion in a coil. At a certain value Δ_f(Δ_f= 2.54 ÷ 2.69 for PC and 2.72 ÷ 2.84 for PAASO) there occurs the change of the kinetic curve type and, therefore, of the chemical mechanism of a polymer oxidation [8]. On the basis of the described above scaling analysis it can be assumed that the change of the kinetic curve type happens in that case, when the number of reactive sites of a macromolecule in a coil surface N_{sur} and in its bulk N_{b} becomes equal [47]:

$$N_{\text{sur}} = N_{\text{b}}. \tag{36}$$

If we consider equations (8) and (9) the real number of reactive sites N_{b} in a macromolecular coil bulk can be written as follows [47]:

$$N_{\text{b}} = N_{\text{m}}(d - \Delta_f) - N_{\text{sur}}, \tag{37}$$

where N_{m} are the reactive sites number per a macromolecule under condition of their full accessibility. Apparently, the value N_{m} is defined by chemical constitution of a polymer.

The relation of parameters N_b and N_{sur} is defined by the ratio of volume V_{fr} and surface S_{fr} of the fractal object, which is equal to [13]:

$$\frac{V_{fr}}{S_{fr}} = \frac{R}{\Delta_f}, \tag{38}$$

where R is the radius of the fractal object, in our case equal to gyration radius R_g of a macromolecular coil.

The combination of equations (6) ÷ (8) and (36) ÷ (38) allows to obtain structural criterion of transition of oxidation kinetic curves from autodecelerated (sigmoidal) to the autoaccelerated mode [47]:

$$\frac{\Delta_f^{cr}}{d - \Delta_f^{cr}} = \frac{R_g}{2}, \tag{39}$$

where Δ_f^{cr} is the critical value Δ_f at the indicated transition and R_g is expressed in nm.

Let us mark two important features of equation (39). At first, in this equation a parameter N_m is absent, i.e., the value Δ_f^{cr} does not depend on the chemical constitution of the polymer. Secondly, the increase of R_g leads to increase Δ_f^{cr}. It is completely agreed with the assumption serving a basis for derivation of the equation (39): the value N_b increases proportionally to R_g^3, whereas N_{sur} – to R_g^2, i.e., the increase of R_g leads to the raising of the ration V_{fr}/S_{fr}.

Let us consider boundary conditions for the equation (39). For $\Delta_f = 0$, i.e., for the doted zero-dimensional object, $R_g = 0$ and the criterion (39) is correct for such an object. For $\Delta_f = 3$ then $R_g \to \infty$ or, as well as it was necessary to expect, for the Euclidean object the measurement scale does not play a role.

Values of Δ_f^{cr} calculated with the equation (39) are 2.76 for PC and 2.78 for PAASO Those values excellently corresponded with the mentioned above experimental values Δ_f for this transition [47].

If we consider the effect of a macromolecular coil structure on the regime of a thermooxidative degradation autoacceleration [9], the product which is responsible for the autoaccelerated mode of curves $N_{O_2}(t)$, can be the aldehydic groups formed from the methyl groups (which are present in PAASO and PC) according to the scheme:

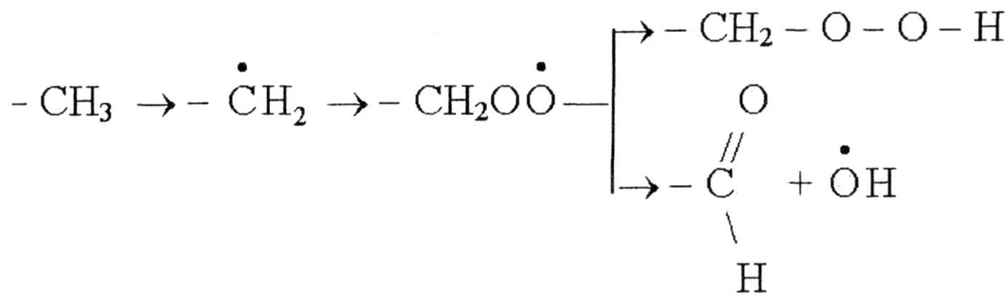

(I)

The oxidation of the aldehyde groups occurring on the scheme:

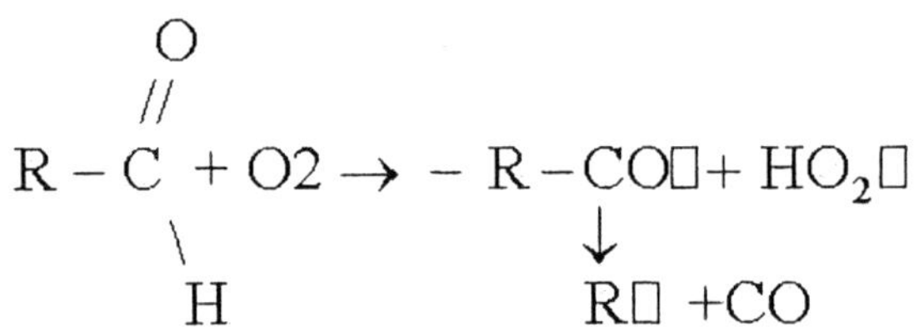

(II)

results in the formation of active free radicals $R\square$ and low-molecular radicals $HO_2\square$. The latter are the mobile radicals, and it allows to consider them as the particles making random walks and to use for their description the reaction of the type [48]:

A + **A** → products of reaction.

The standard classical reaction of order ½ is described by relationship [48]:

$$-\frac{d\rho_W}{dt} \sim \rho_W^{1/2}, \tag{40}$$

where ρ_W is the density of random walks.

For the microscopically heterogeneous (fractal) medium the relationship (40) is written as follows [48]:

$$\frac{d\rho_W}{dt} \sim t^{1-h}\rho_W^{1/2}, \tag{41}$$

and the integrated equation for the reaction rate can be written as follows (with the allowance of quadratic dependence of N_{O_2} or S on t [8]):

$$\rho_W^{-1} - \rho_{W0}^{-1} \sim t^{2(1-h)}, \tag{42}$$

where ρ_{W0} is the initial density of random walks.

As above, for PC in paper [49] $\rho_{W0} = S_{\lim}$ and $\rho_W = (S_{\lim} - S)$ were adopted. The dependences of $\left(\rho_{W0}^{1/2} - \rho_W^{1/2}\right)$ on the time t in double log-log coordinates for PC are shown in Fig.8 and analogous dependences for PAASO were shown [50, 51]. As it is possible to see, at small *t*, corresponding to induction period, the dependences are linear, have small slope, from which can be determined the value $2(1 - h) = d'_s \approx 0.22$ or $h \approx 0.89$. These values correspond to a thermooxidative degradation in fractal space [20, 48]. In addition, according to equation (24) on the basis of the known value of d'_s can be determined a magnitude Δ_f, which is equal to ~ 1.78. This is a typical value of fractal dimension Δ_s for a macromolecular coil surface. This circumstance is one more proof of the assumption about occurrence of the oxidation reaction on a coil surface in case of kinetic curves of plots on Fig. 8 the sharp transition to a portion with much higher slope corresponding to $d'_s \approx 2$ or $h \approx 0$ is observed. The latter means a passage of the reaction in a Euclidean space [20]. Thus, the thermooxidative degradation rate is largely defined by the type of space, in which it is occurring. In fractal space with small connectivity ($d'_s \approx 0.22$) the reaction rate is insignificant (induction period). The increase of d'_s from ~ 0.22 up to ~ 2.0 means a transition to a Euclidean space that gives practically the linear part of kinetic curves with a constant and a very higher rate of oxidation [49 – 51].

The data of papers [49 – 51] agree to the results of a computer simulation. Argirakis and Kopelman [52] have shown that the effective spectral dimension d'_s is increased with time from ~ 1.3 up to ~ 1.9 for two-dimensional Euclidean space and approaches hearer to 2 much faster for a three dimensional space. This circumstance is due to the existence in melts of real polymers of clusters (macromolecular coils) of various sizes. The existence of clusters with small sizes leads to lowering d'_s that is taken in account by introduction of different kinds of corrections. However, such corrections are true only for small times, and for enough larger t the value d'_s begins to increase, as shown on plots of Fig. 8.

Authors [53, 54] have considered another aspect of this transition. In the framework of the fractal analysis, the diffusion of reagent (oxidant molecule, radical, etc.) on the fractal polymer structure can be represented as the walk of the reagent [30]. There are two basic types of walks: random walks (RW) and the random walks with continuous time (CTRW) [55]. If in case of RW, there is no dependence on time between two consecutive walks, then in case of CTRW, the consecutive walks can be realized only through a certain time interval after the previous one. Thus, in case of CTRW, the fractal set of the event times is introduced [55]. For the process of the thermooxidative degradation, this means that the acts of the chemical reaction (chain breakage, radical formation, annihilation or recombination, etc.) are independent from each other for RW, but they are interdependent in time for CTRW. The obtained good correlation of the theory and experiment was achieved by using the following equations for PAASO: for autodecceleration regime [53]:

$$N_{O_2} = 0,9t^{d_s/2}, \tag{43}$$

and for autoacceleration regime [53]:

$$N_{O_2} = 0,087\exp\left(t^{0,78d_s/2}\right). \tag{44}$$

Equations (43) and (44) allow to determine the type of reaction in the process of the thermooxidative degradation. Thus, in the regime of autodecceleration, the bimolecular reaction (the macromolecule reactive center + oxygen) takes place with the help of RW [55]. In the regime of autoacceleration, the pseudo-monomolecular reaction (for example, the radical recombination) takes place with the help of the CTRW [55].

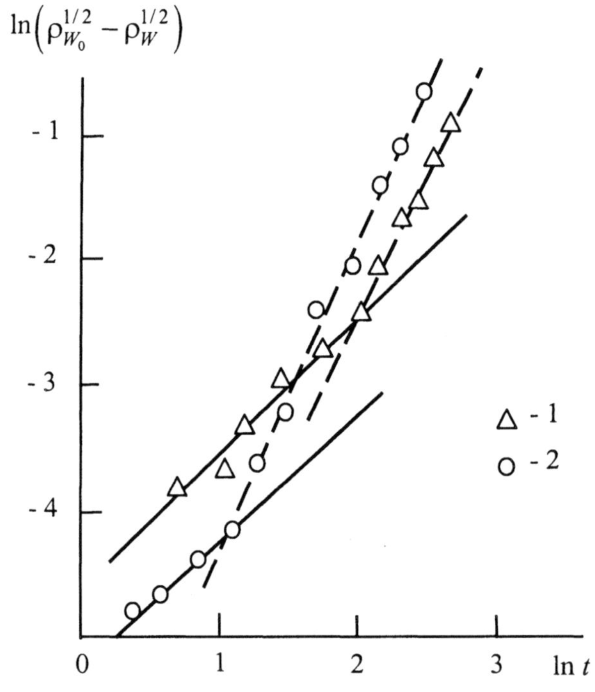

Figure 8. Dependences of the parameter $\left(\rho_{W_0}^{1/2} - \rho_W^{1/2}\right)$ on time t in double log-log coordinates for PC films obtained from solutions in 1,4-dioxane (1) and tetrahydrofuran (2) [49].

The data in Fig. 9 show the dependences $\Delta_f(T)$ for PAASO-1 and PAASO-4 (table 1). As it is seen, for both copolymers, the monotone decrease of Δ_f with temperature is observed. On Fig. 9, there are also the boundaries of the three described above regime of oxidation realization. Above the line I at $\Delta_f \geq 2.84$, the regime of autoacceleration is observed, between the lines I and II at $2.72 \leq \Delta_f \leq 2.84$, the sigmoidal kinetic curves are observed, and below the line II at $\Delta_f < 2.72$ the autodecceleration regime is observed. Hence, at large Δ_f (above the line I in Fig. 9), the density of the macromolecular coil is large enough, the oxidant (oxygen) access is limited and reactions which require less amount of oxygen, for example, the radical recombination, are observed. At small values of Δ_f (below the line II in Fig. 9, where the value ρ is less than 20 % of the density of the Euclidean object), the oxygen access is significantly lightened, what allows the direct occurrence of the bimolecular reaction. Apparently, in the first case, the radical recombination can occur only through some time after their formation and, therefore, the process is modeled with CTRW. In the second case, the acts of oxygen molecules diffusion into polymer are independent from each other, and the process is modeled with the RW. The sigmoidal kinetic curve in such treatment is the intermediate case and its realization is limited by lines I and II in Fig. 9.

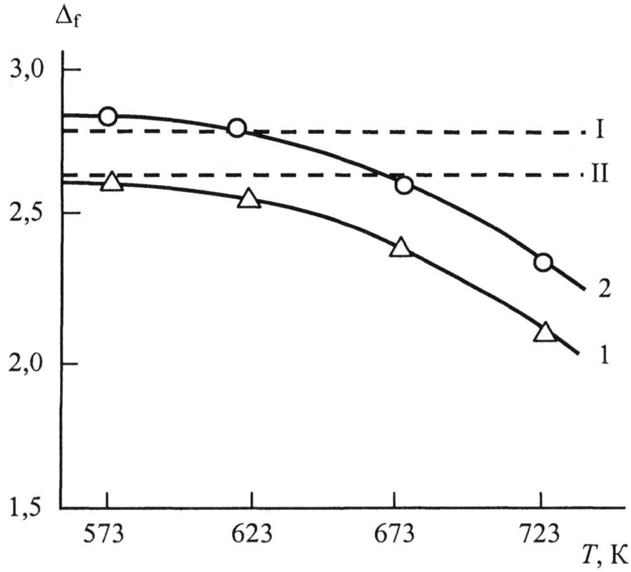

Figure 9. Dependences of the fractal dimension Δ_f of a macromolecular coil on the testing temperature T for PAASO-1 (1) and PAASO-4 (2). The horizontal lines I and II indicate the regime boundaries [53].

The reasons of the slower oxidation of the PAASO melt in the regime of autoacceleration as compared with autodeccelerated mode comes from the number of sites (the reactive centres of macromolecules) $\langle S \rangle$, visited by the walk (RW or CTRW) as the function of time t, determined according to the relationship [55]:

$$\langle S \rangle \sim t^{\gamma d_s/2}, \qquad (45)$$

where γ is the coefficient.

It follows from equations (43) and (44) that for the autoaccelerated regime γ = 0.78, and for the autodeccelerated regime γ = 1.0. As it is shown in [53, 54], the value of $\langle S \rangle$ for CTRW (the autoaccelerated regime) is significantly (about three times) lower as compared with the value for RW (the autodeccelerated regime).

The data in Fig. 10 show the theoretical dependences $N_{O_2}(t)$ for regimes of autoacceleration and autodecceleration (curves 1 and 2, respectively) for PAASO-4 at 673 K.

The experimental curve $N_{O_2}(t)$ has the sigmoidal shape. These curves were plotted according to the equations (43) and (44) and the constant coefficients in them were obtained by using the method of the best fitting. The absolute values of the coefficients are larger as compared with the ones obtained at $T = 573$ K and equal to 4.07 and 0.766, respectively [53, 54]. The points on Fig. 10 show the experimental data $N_{O_2}(t)$. As it can be seen, at certain t value there is a transition from the regime of autoacceleration to the regime of the autodeceleration, what confirms the intermediate character of the sigmoidal kinetic curves. It can be assumed that this transition occurs when in the coils the amount of accumulated oxygen is enough for the bimolecular oxidation reaction occurrence.

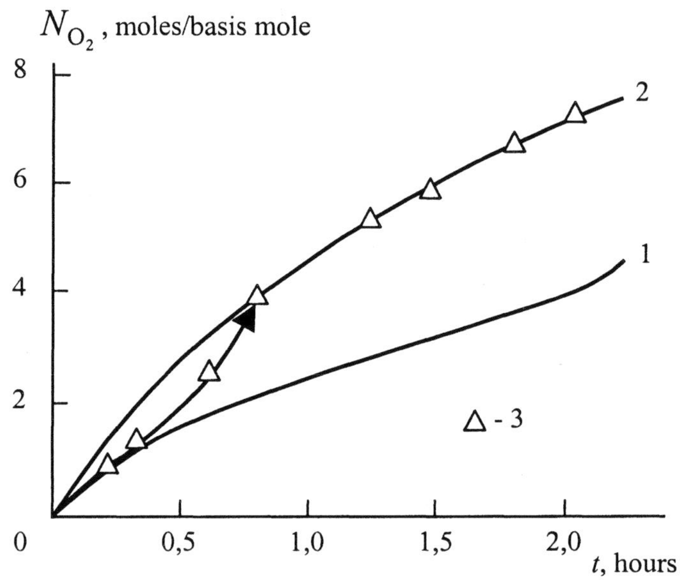

Figure 10. Theoretical curves N_{O_2} (t) for regimes of autoacceleration (1) and autodecceleration (2) for PAASO-4 at $T = 673$ K. 3 – experimental data [54].

Thus, the change of the walks type from random walks (RW) to the random walks with a continuous time (CTRW) sharply retards the process of the thermooxidative degradation. In its turn, the walks type is controled by the structure of the macromolecular coil, which is characterized by its fractal dimension [53, 54].

5. The Effect of a Polymer Melt Structure on Chemical Mechanisms of a Thermooxidative Degradation

As it is assumed [8], the main types of kinetic curves are connected both with temperature regime, and with the chemical mechanisms of a thermooxidative degradation. So, curves $N_{O_2}(t)$ or s(t) of autoaccelerated mode are typical for polymers containing C–H bonds at temperatures less than 473K. The oxidation of such polymers proceeds on the radical-chain mechanism with degenerate branching. The main reaction of chain propagation for them is the following [9]:

$$RO_2^{\bullet} + RH \rightarrow ROOH + R^{\bullet}, \tag{III}$$

and curves themselves $N_{O_2}(t)$ are described by the equation [9]:

$$N_{O_2} = a\left(t - t_0\right)^2, \tag{46}$$

where a is constant, t_0 is the time beginning from which the equation (46) is satisfied, i.e. a process goes in an autooxidation regime.

Curves $N_{O_2}(t)$ or s(t) of autodeccelerated (sigmoidal) type are observed, as a rule, for various carbochain and heterochain polymers at temperatures larger 473 K. The main reaction of chain propagation becomes the reaction of the peroxide radical decomposition [9]:

$$RO_2^{\bullet} \rightarrow R'COH + R''^{\bullet} \qquad RO_2^{\bullet} \rightarrow R'''OR + r^{\bullet} \tag{IV}$$

where $r^{\bullet}$ is a low-molecular radical.

These curves are described according to equation (1).

For PAASO by the analogue with a thermooxidative degradation of another heterochain polyether PC the following scheme of this process can be offered:

$$RH + O_2 \xrightarrow{k_0} R^{\bullet} + HO_2^{\bullet} \text{ (chain initiation)} \tag{V}$$

$$R^{\bullet} + O_2 \xrightarrow{k_1} RO_2^{\bullet} \text{ (chain propagation)} \tag{VI}$$

$$RO_2^{\bullet} + RO_2 \xrightarrow{k_6} ROOR + O_2 \text{ (chain termination)} \tag{VII}$$

$$R^{\bullet} + RO_2^{\bullet} \xrightarrow{k_7} ROOR \text{ (chain termination)} \tag{VIII}$$

Curves of the main gaseous products conversion for PAASO degradation (oxide and dioxide of carbon) at $T = 623$ K follow that the main product is CO as its concentration about 20 times larger than concentration of CO_2 [56]. As it is shown in [8] for PCCO is formed only as a result of methyl groups oxidation, CO_2 is formed both at decomposition of compound ether groups and at oxidation of methyl groups. These observations allow to suppose that at oxidation of PAASO the main radical will be $CH_2\square$ and then a scheme (V) ÷ (VIII) in simplest form can be concretized as follows [56]:

$$-CH_2H+O_2 \rightarrow -CH_2\square + HO_2^{\bullet} \text{ (chain initiation)} \quad \text{(IX)}$$

$$-CH_2\square + O_2 \rightarrow -CH_2O_2\square \text{ (chain propagation)} \quad \text{(X)}$$

$$-CH_2O_2\square + -CH_2O_2 \rightarrow 2CO+2H_2O \text{ (chain termination)} \quad \text{(XI)}$$

$$-CH_2\square + -CH_2O_2\square \rightarrow 2CO+2H_2 \text{ (chain termination)} \quad \text{(XII)}$$

The reaction of chain propagation (III) was excluded from consideration because at $T > 523$ K a bimolecular reaction of hydroxide formation not probable [10]. Secondly, neither breakage of hydroperoxide groups, nor thermal decomposition of hydroperoxide according to [9] gives those main gaseous products of degradation [56]. In Fig. 11 the dependences of conversion CO(N_{CO}) and CO_2 $\left(N_{CO_2}\right)$ on N_{O_2} for both oxidation regimes are shown. In both cases linear correlations passing through origin are observed. This means that at CO formation in an oxidation process of methyl groups oxygen from air takes part. Theoretical relation (in moles) CO: O_2 is 2: 1, whereas from plots of Fig. 11 can be obtained: 2: 2.6 for autodeccelerated and 2: 4.2 for autoaccelerated regimes. Apparently, extra oxygen, as in the case of PC [10], reacts with the polymer. Besides the water forming according to reaction (XI) can lead to hydrolytic decomposition of ether bonds [10].

As mentioned above, the permeability of a macromolecular coil for oxygen can be estimated by its compactness degree (density value ρ): the compacter (the larger ρ) the coil, the less oxygen can permeate in it during a time unit. The value ρ is determined according to the relationship (10), where as proportionality factor of the density of polymer in the case if its dense packing is used. In [56] it was shown that the dependence N_{O_2} on ρ^{-1} for PAASO at three testing temperatures (623, 673 and 723 K) is well approximated by a linear correlation, which can be expressed analytically as follows:

$$N_{O_2} \approx 0{,}55\left(\rho^{-1} - 1{,}4\right). \quad (47)$$

This relationship allows to assume that for macromolecular coils in melt the diffusivity on oxygen D_{O_2} is proportional to ρ^{-1}. Further, the oxidation rate constant k and D_{O_2} are connected by following relationship [1]:

$$\left(k/D_{O_2}\right)^{1/2} = 2{,}10 \times 10^2 \text{ cm}^{-1}. \quad (48)$$

Assuming that at average value $\rho^{-1} \approx 15$ [56] the value $D_{O_2} \approx 5 \times 10^{-5}$ cm^2/s, the value k for both types of curves – with autoacceleration and autodecceleration – can be calculated. It is found that for the first value *k* is about 4 times less, than for the second. Then the following relationship can be used [9]:

$$\frac{dN_{O_2}}{dt} = k[RO_2\square][RH], \qquad (49)$$

where $[RO_2\square]$ is the concentration of radicals $CHO_2\square$, [RH] is concentration of polymer monomer links.

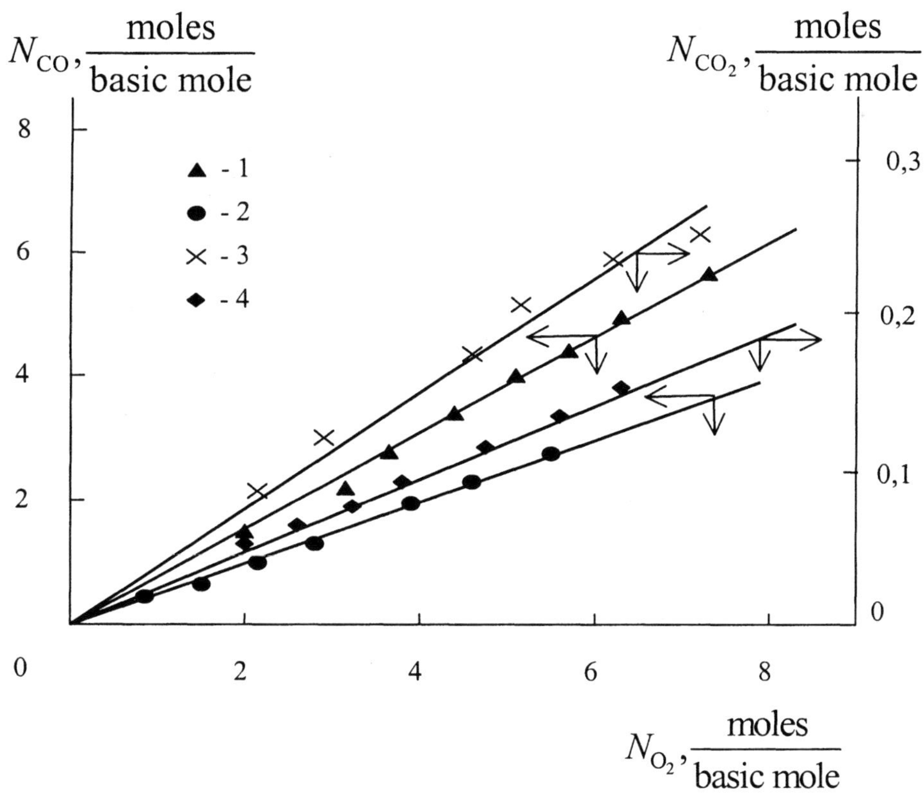

Figure 11. Relation of conversion of carbon oxide N_{CO} (1, 2), carbon dioxide N_{CO_2} (3, 4) and consumed oxygen amount N_{O_2} at $T = 623$ K for PAASO–1(1, 3) and PAASO– 4(2, 4).

Having determined the value dN_{O_2}/dt on curves $N_{O_2}(t)$ [11, 56], the value $[RO_2\square]$ for both types of curves can be calculated. It is found that the concentration

$RO_2^{\bullet}$ is more than three times larger in autoaccelerated regime, than in autodeccelerated. Summarizing all the said above, it can be assumed that in the case PAASO, autoaccelerated and autodeccelerated regimes are differentiated by a chemical mechanism on the stage of chain termination: for the first case is true scheme (VII)m for the second – scheme (VIII). This conclusion is due to the following reasons:

1) According to reaction (XI) conversion CO per mole O_2 is essentially lower, than in a reaction (XII). The analogous relation is observed for curves of autoaccelerated regime in comparison, with autodeccelerated [56];
2) Much larger concentration of radicals $RO_2^{\bullet}$(or $CH_2O_2^{\bullet}$) assumes high probability of an autocatalytic reaction between them [1, 9];
3) The existence of H_2O in reaction (XI) assumes a hydrolytic decomposition of compound ether bonds that also should lead to the acceleration of reaction.

Besides, as marked above, autoaccelerated regime is typical for lower temperatures, autodecelerated – for higher temperatures [8]. Let us consider the problem of equivalency of a testing temperature and structure changes (that can be named as temperature – structural superposition). Authors [56] found no temperature dependence D_{O_2} for PAASO, but it is known [1] that the microdiffusion activation energy for O_2 makes up a value ~ 20 ÷ 40 kJ/mole. Then an analogue with polyethylene can be written [1]:

$$D_{O_2} = 0{,}4\exp\left(-32900/RT\right),\ \text{cm}^2/\text{s}, \tag{50}$$

where R is universal gas constant.

The simple estimations according to the equation (50) showed that assuming $T = 373$ K $D_{O_2} = 5 \times 10^{-5}$ cm^2/s [1], then an increase of D_{O_2} in 4 times is equivalent to growth T up to 428 K, i.e., per 55 K. The change of a macromolecular coil structure, characterized by a decreasing of the fractal dimension Δ_f from 2.90 up to 2.60, is equivalent to a temperature increase per 55K (see Fig. 9) that in itself can change the oxidation regime from autoaccelerated up to autodeccelerated [8].

One more chemical mechanism responsible for autoacceleration at a thermooxidative degradation PAASO is the formation of aldehydic groups from methyl groups according to schemes (I) and (II). Aldehydic groups oxidation, occurring on the scheme (II), where $R^{\bullet}$ is alkyl radical, leads to the formation of free active radicals $R^{\bullet}$ and low-molecular radicals $HO_2^{\bullet}$. This variant coincides with reaction (V) and has the same oxidation products (CO and $HO_2^{\bullet}$) [56].

The most general scheme of transition from autoaccelerated regime up to autodeccelerated is the analysis of branched chain reactions in the form of generalized formula [9]:

$$\varphi = \frac{\nu_k \delta - 1}{\theta} \tag{51}$$

where φ is the factor of a branched degenerated chain reaction autoacceleration, ν_k is the length of kinetic chain, δ is the probability of a degenerated branching of a chain, θ is the time of branched product life.

In turn, the value δ is determined as a product [9]:

$$\delta = \alpha\sigma \tag{52}$$

where α is the probability of formation of a branched product in one link of chain, σ is an average conversion of free radicals at decomposition of this product.

According to equation (51), if $\varphi > 0$, then the oxidation process will occur with autoacceleration, at $\varphi < 0$ a process rate will be limited, after some time the concentration of branched product will reach some limited value, i.e., oxidation process will occur in autodecccelerated regime. From equation (51) it can be seen that the defining factor for this transition is δ. The decreasing δ leads to the realization of the condition $\varphi < 0$ (at $\nu_k\delta < 1$) and oxidation process will occur in autodeccelerated regime. In its turn, from equation (52) it follows that the main contribution in the variation of δ makes up parameter σ, which can be changed in limits – from 10^{-4} up to 1 [9]. The small values of σ are due to decomposition of initial radicals as a result of recombination inside a cell [9]. In the framework of the cellular model a rate of this process k_r is connected with a diffusivity D as follows [57]:

$$k_r = 4\pi N_A D\lambda \tag{53}$$

where N_A is the Avogadro number, λ is the length of diffusive jump.

Therefore, it follows such tendency. An increase of a compactness degree of a macromolecular coil in melt characterized by growth of Δ_f, is defined a diffusivity decrease that leads to a rate reduction for a radicals recombination, an increase σ and growth φ. At reaching a criterion $\varphi = 0$ the type of kinetic curves $N_{O_2}(t)$ is changed from autodeccelerated up to autoaccelerated regime [56].

Another variant of the interdependence of a melt structure and chemical mechanisms of an oxidation in paper [58] is considered. As it is known [9], for autoaccelerated regime of an oxidation can be written a variant of the equation (46):

$$N_{O_2}(t) \sim At^2, \tag{54}$$

$$A = \frac{W_0}{\gamma_r k_H [RH]}, \tag{55}$$

where W_0 is a chain initiation rate, γ_r is probability of exit of free radicals from the "cell", k_H is the rate constant of polymer hydroperoxide decomposition reaction.

As it is shown in paper [58], from a comparison of the parameters $k_d t/\rho$ it follows that an increase T and growth k_d should lead to the increase of initiation chain rate, and decreasing ρ at reduction Δ_f to decrease k_H and/or γ_2.This question can be precised by the following method [58]. The autoaccelerated course of an oxidation process will be explained by the collection of hydroperoxide groups in oxidizing polymer, decomposition of which leads to additional initiation of free radicals – degenerate branching of chain [9]. Relationship between the concentration of branched product [A] and t will be as follows [9]:

$$[A] = \frac{W}{k_a\left(1 - e^{-\text{kat}}\right)}, \tag{56}$$

where W is A formation rate, k_a is rate constant of an autoaccelerated reaction.

Assuming [A] = $N_{O_2}(t)$, W = $dN_{O_2}(t)/dt$ and neglecting the member in brackets because of its low value, authors [59] calculated the magnitude k_a according to the equation (56). It is found that k_a is decreasing sharply at decrease ρ that is shown on the plot of Fig. 12. Therefore, the decrease of compactness degree of a macromolecular coil, characterized by reduction ρ, leads to a fast decrease of k_d and autoaccelerated reaction stopping. As it is shown above, for PAASO an autoaccelerated oxidation type is observed only at $\Delta_f \geq 2.72$ or $\rho \geq 0.25$ [58]. At $\Delta_f = 2.60$, when for PAASO an oxidation of autodeccelerated type (at $T = 673$ and 723 K) is observed, the value ρ is reduced up to ~ 0.11 and k_a – up to ~ 10^{-3} s^{-1}that leads to a corresponding decrease in $dN_{O_2}(t)/dt$ and practically to stop of oxygen consumption [58].

6. A Physical Aspects of a Stabilization Process of Polymer Melts

Modern ideas about raising of polymers thermostability together with many attempts of new thermostable polymers synthesis give large attention to the stabilization of industrially produced polymeric materials by different organic and nonorganic stabilizing additives. The importance of this problem has determined many studies of chemical aspects of polymers stabilization systematized in a number of monographs [1, 9, 10, 57, 59]. However physical aspects of this problem, as a rule, are not enough studied. One of the possible (and most real) directions of the mentioned question research is the usage of the fractal analysis methods [6, 15, 17].

In Fig. 13 kinetic curves $N_{O_2}(t)$ for initial and stabilized by industrial stabilizer for PAASO are shown. As can be seen, curves $N_{O_2}(t)$ are identical, but the amount of consumed O_2 is essentially less for stabilized block-copolymer. Now there is a number of models describing reactions in non-ordered fractal medium and allowing to define these reaction types [55]. The reaction of oxygen A and PAASO chain (or stabilizer) B is described according to the equation (1). As the mobility of reagent B should be accepted zero, then the reaction (1) is described in the framework of the task on traps [39, 53]. In this case atoms (molecules) of oxygen are considered as particles made walks on polymer structure, which can be of two main types: random walks (RW) and continuous time random walks (CTRW) [55]. The difference of these types of walks is described in detail in chapter 4 above.

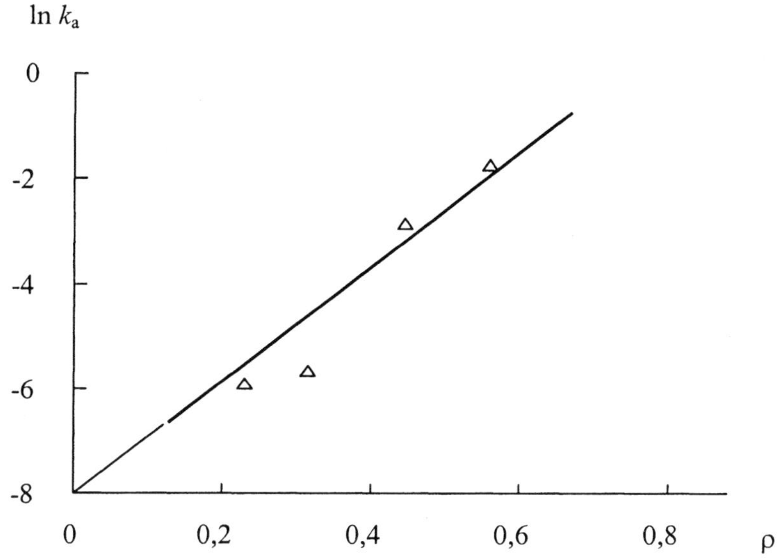

Figure 12. Dependence of autoaccelerated oxidation rate constant K_a on density ρ of a macromolecular coil for PAASO [58].

As it is shown in paper [60], for description of shown in Fig. 12 curves $N_{O_2}(t)$ is a power relationship, identical to equation (43) with exponent $\gamma = 0.52$ for initial PAASO and $\gamma = 0.29$ – for stabilized PAASO. Then by virtue of a fractional exponent the existence of a trajectory of oxygen atoms (molecules) walk can be simulated by CTRW both for initial, and stabilized PAASO [60]. This circumstance allows to consider the physical aspects of PAASO stabilization in the framework of the mentioned model. For CTRW the important parameter of process is probability $\psi(t_b)$ that next event happens after interval of time t_b after realization of previous event. In terms of the simplest example (Poisson's process) it can be written [55]:

$$\psi(t_b) \sim \frac{1}{t_b^{\gamma+1}}, \tag{57}$$

where

$$\gamma = \frac{\ln N}{\ln b} \tag{58}$$

In equation (58), N is a parameter, b is characteristic of Poisson's process. As in [55], authors [60] assumed $N < 1$ ($N = 0.5$) and then from the equation (57) obtained $b = 0.264$ for initial

PAASO and b = 0.092 for stabilized PAASO. The value d can be expressed through the activation energy E_{act} as follows [55]:

$$b = \exp\left(-\frac{E_{act}}{RT}\right) \quad (59)$$

From the equation (59) it follows the physical sense of parameter b: it is proportional to the steric factor p, which characterizes the achievement of difficulty degree by oxidant of macromolecule reactive centers [61]. As follows from the quoted above estimation b, the access of oxidant is much more difficult in case of stabilized PAASO. The equation (59) allows also to make the estimation E_{act} in relative units by virtue of an arbitrary value N in the equation (58). This estimation gives the value E_{act} = 29.6 for initial PAASO and 51.0 – for stabilized PAASOthat agreed well with experimentally determined values E_{act} = 71 and 105 kJ/mole, respectively [60].

In the framework of the CTRW model it can be expected that the increase $\psi(t_b)$ will lead to the increase of oxygen consumption rate k, which can be calculated as follows [62]:

$$k = \frac{N_{O_2}^{i+1} - N_{O_2}^{i}}{\Delta t_i}, \quad (60)$$

where $N_{O_2}^{i+1}$ and $N_{O_2}^{i}$ are values N_{O_2} corresponding to times t_{i+1} and t_i, $\Delta t_i = t_{i+1} - t_i$.

The plotting of the dependence k on $\psi(t_b)$ demonstrates its curvilinearity approximately corresponding to a quadratic law. Therefore for linearization of the mentioned correlation the dependence k on $[\psi(t_b)]^{1/2}$ shown in Fig. 14 was plotted. This dependence is linear and passes through origin. Then the increase t_b, i.e., interval of time between oxygen diffusion and oxidation reaction leads to decrease k. The quadratic law of relation between k and $\psi(t_b)$ assumes bimolecular reaction of oxidation that corresponds to chemical mechanism for kinetic curves of autodecelerated type (Fig. 13) [8].

Let us consider the effect γ on value t_b according to a relationship (57). Assuming proportionality coefficient in this relationship equal to 10^3, authors [60] obtain for $\psi(t_b) = 1$ t_b = 94,2 for initial PAACO and t_b = 211 relative units for stabilized PAASO. Then incorporation of stabilizer in PAASO increases the time between two sequential events (oxygen diffusion and oxidation reaction) approximately in 2.2 times. About so are different the values N_{O_2} for initial and stabilized PAASO (see Fig. 13). Apparently, this effect is realized because of "trapping" oxidant by stabilizer [60].

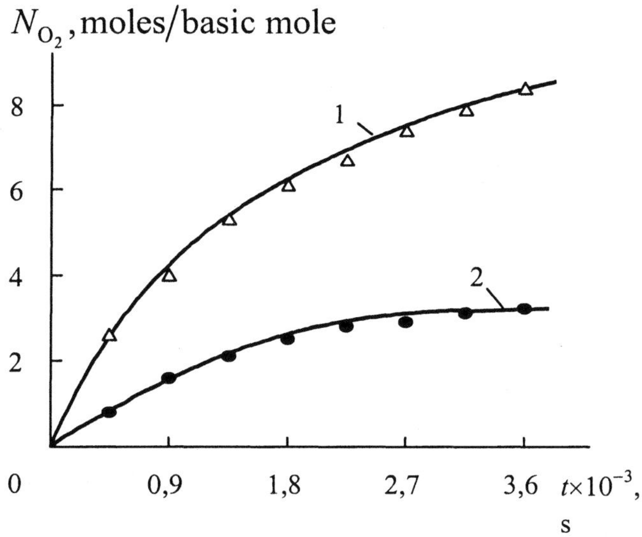

Figure 13. Dependences of the consumed oxygen amount N_{O_2} on time t for samples of initial (1) and stabilized (2) PAASO [60].

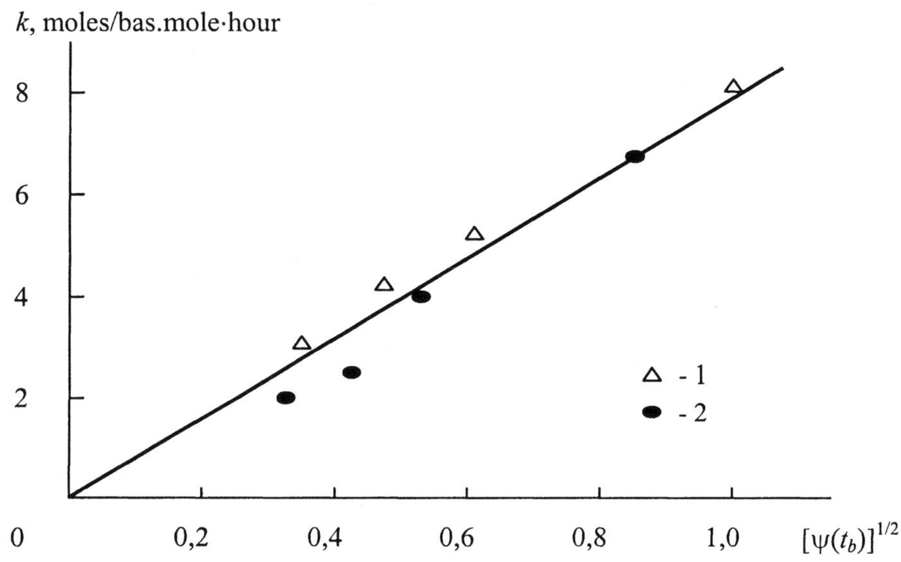

Figure 14. Dependence of oxygen consumption rate K on parameter $[\psi(t_b)]^{1/2}$ for samples of initial (1) and stabilized (2) PAASO [60].

7. CONCLUSIONS

For characterization of a polymer melt structure the fractal dimension of a macromolecular coil is used. It is shown that the oxygen consumption kinetics in a thermooxidative degradation process is defined by chemical constitution of polymer and its structure. The quantitative analysis of kinetic curves in the framework of the fractal analysis is made.

It is demonstrated that the transition of kinetic curves of melts oxidation from autoddecelerated (sigmoidal) up to autoaccelerated regime is defined by the structural factor, namely, by reaching the fractal dimension of a macromolecular coil a critical value, at which a number of reactive sites in bulk and surface becomes equal. The transition from induction period up to sharp acceleration of thermooxidative degradation in case of kinetic curves of an autoaccelerated type is due to a change of space type, in which reaction is occurred, from fractal up to Euclidean.

The effect of melt structure not only on quantitative characteristics of a thermooxidative degradation process, but on qualitative changes in this process, in particular, on chemical mechanisms of reaction is shown.

REFERENCES

[1] Emanuel N.M., Buchachenko A.L. *The Chemical Physics of Polymers Aging and Stabilization* (in Russian) Moscow. Nauka. 1982. 359 p.

[2] Monakhova T.V., Bogaevskaya T.A., Shlyapnikov Yu.S. *Vysokomol. Soed. B*. 1985. V. 37. № 1. P. 160-162.

[3] Shlyapnikov Yu.S., Kolesnikova N.N. In book: *Aging of Polymers, Polymer Blends and Polymer Composites*. Ed. Zaikov G., Buchachenko A., Ivanov V., v. 2. New York, Nova Science Publishers, Inc. 2002. P. 123-131.

[4] Vilgis T.A. *Phys. Rew. A*. 1987. V. 36. № 3. P. 1506-1508.

[5] Vilgis T.A. *Physica A*. 1988. V. 153. № 2. P. 341-354.

[6] Mandelbrot B.B. *The Fractal Geometry of Nature.* San-Francisco. W.H.Freeman and Comp. 1982. 459 p.

[7] Rammal R., Toulouse G. *J. Phys. Lettr.* (Paris). 1983. V. 44. № 1. P. L13-L22.

[8] Emanuel N.M. *Vysokomol. Soed. A*. 1985. V. 27. V. 7. P. 1347-1363.

[9] Shlyapnikov Yu.A., Kiryushin S.G., Mar'in A.P. *Antioxidative Stabilization of Polymers.* London. Taylor and Francis. 1996. 259 p.

[10] Kovarskaya B.M., Blyumenfeld A.B., Levantovskaya I.I. *Thermal Stability of Heterochain Polymers* (in Russian). Moscow. Khimia. 1977. 276 p.

[11] Kozlov G.V., Shustov G.B., Zaikov G.E. In book: *New Perspectives in Chemistry and Biochemistry*. Ed. Zaikov G. New York. Nova Science Publishers. Inc. 2002. P. 11-17.

[12] Kozlov G.V., Schustov G.B., Zaikov G.E. In book: *Chemistry and Biochemistry on the Leading Edge.* Ed. Zaikov G. New York. Nova Science Publishers. Inc. 2002. P. 21-29.

[13] Lobanov A.M., Frenkel S.Ya. *Vysokomol. Soed. A*. 1980. V. 22. № 5. P. 1045-1057.

[14] Baranov V.G., Frenkel S.Ya., Brestkin Yu.V. *Dokl. AN SSSR*. 1986. V. 290. № 2. P. 369-372.

[15] Kozlov G.V., Dolbin I.V., Batyrova H.M., Zaikov G.E. In *Mater. III All-Russian Conf. "New Chemical Techniques: Production and Application"*. Penza. 2001. P. 61-63.
[16] Novikov V.U., Kozlov G.V. *Russ. Adv. Chem.* 2000. V. 69. № 6. P. 572-599.
[17] Feder E. *Fractals* (in Russian). Moscow. Mir. 1991. 256 p.
[18] Bolotov V.N. *Pisma v ZhTF.* 1995. V. 21. № 10. P. 82-84.
[19] Nigmatullin R.R. *Teoret. I Matemat. Fizika.* 1992. V. 90. № 3. P. 354-362.
[20] Klymko P.W., Kopelman R. *J. Phys. Chem.* 1983. V. 87. № 23. P. 4565-4567.
[21] Alexander S., Orbach R. *J.Phys. Lettr.* (Paris). 1982. V. 43. № 17. P. L625-L631.
[22] Balankin A.S. *Synergetics of Deformable Body* (in Russian) Moscow. MO SSSR. 1991. 404 p.
[23] Kozlov G.V., Shustov G.B., Zaikov G.E. *Zhurnal Prikl. Khimii.* 2002. V. 75. № 3. P. 485-487.
[24] *Kozlov G.V., Dolbin I.V., Shustov G.B. In Proceeding of the 1-st Internat. Sci. Confer. "Modern problems of organic chemistry, ecology and biotechnology"*. Luga, Russia. June. 2001. P. 15-16.
[25] Gammet L. *The Basis of Physical and organic Chemistry: Rates, Equilibriums and Reaction Mechanisms* (in Russian). Moscow. Mir. 1972. 452 p.
[26] Alkenis A.F., Zaikov G.E., Karlivan V.P. *The Chemical Stabilization of Polyesters* (in Russian). Riga. Zinatne. 1978. 218 p.
[27] Kozlov G.V., Shustov G.B., Zaikov G.E. In book: *Aging of Polymers. Polymer Blends and Polymer Composites*. Ed. Zaikov G., Buchachenko A., Ivanov V., v. 2. New York. Nova Science Publishers. Inc. 2001. P. 151-160.
[28] Kozlov G.V., Novikov V.U. *Synergetics and Fractal Analysis of Curves Polymers* (in Russian). Moscow. Klassika. 1998. 112 p.
[29] Kopelman R. In book: *Fractals in Physics*. Ed. Pietronero L., Tosatti E. Amsterdam-Oxford-New York-Tokyo. North-Holland. 1986. P. 524-527.
[30] Afaunov V.V., Kozlov G.V., Mashukov N.I., Zaikov G.E. *Zhurn. Prikl. Khimii.* 2000. V. 73. № 1. P. 136-140.
[31] Dolbin I.V., Kozlov G.V., Zaikov G.E. In *proceeding Internat. Symp. "Fractals and Applied Synergetics"*. Moscow. MOSU. 2603- Nov. 2001. P. 41-42.
[32] Kozlov G.V., Shustov G.B., Dolbin I.V., Zaikov G.E. *Izvestiya KBSC RAN. 2002.* № 1. P. 141-145.
[33] Argirakis P. In book: *Fractals in Physics*. Ed. Pietronero L., Tosatti E. Amsterdam-Oxford-New York-Tokyo. North-Hollad. 1986. P. 513-518.
[34] Kozlov G.V., Gazaev M.A., Novikov V.U., Mikitaev A.K. *Pisma v ZhTF.* 1996. V. 22. № 16. P. 31-38.
[35] Beloshenko V.A., Kozlov G.V., Lipatov Yu.S. *Fizika Tverd. Tela.* 1994. V. 36. № 10. P. 2903-2906.
[36] Sokolov I.M. *Russ. Adv. Phys. Sci.* 1986. V. 150. № 2. P. 221-256.
[37] Meilanov R.P., Sveshnikova D.A., Shabanov O.M. Izvestiya YU *Zov. Severo-Kavkaz. Reg. Estestv. Nauk*i. 2001. № 1. P. 63-66.
[38] Kozlov G.V., Beyev A.A., Lipatov Yu.S. *Dokl. NAN Ukraine.* 2001. № 10. P. 144-147.
[39] Djordjevic Z.B. In book: *Fractals in Physics*. Ed. Pietronero L., Tosatti E. Amsterdam-Oxford-New York-Tokyo, North-Holland, 1986, P. 581-585.
[40] Grassberger P., Procaccia I. *J. Chem. Phys.* 1982. V. 77. № 12. P. 6281-6284.
[41] Meakin P., Stanley H.E. *J. Phys. A.* 1984. V. 17. № 2. P.L173-L177.

[42] Dolbin I.V., Kozlov G.V. *Dokl. Adygsk. (Cherkessk.) Internat. AN.* 2002. V. 6. № 1. P. 72-76.

[43] Shogenov V.N., Beloshenko V.A., Kozlov G.V., Varyukhin V.N. *Fizika i Technika Vysok. Davl.* 1999. V. 9. № 3. P. 3036.

[44] Wu S. *J. Polymer Sci.: Part B: Polymer Phys.* 1989. V. 27. № 4. P. 723-741.

[45] Kozlov G.V., Sozaev V.A. In book: *Fractals and Local order in Polymeric Materials* Ed. Kozlov G., Zaikov G. New York, Nova Science Publishers. Inc. 2001. P. 129-136.

[46] Kozlov G.V., Dolbin I.V., Mashukov N.I., Burmistr M.V., Korenyako V.A. *Voprosy Khimii i Khimich. Technology.* 2002. № 6. P. 71-77.

[47] Dolbin I.V., Kozlov G.V., Mashukov N.I. *Uspekhi Sovrem. Estestvozn.* 2002. № 4. P. 101-102.

[48] Kopelman R., Klymko R.W., Newhouse J.S., Anacker L.W. *Phys. Rev. B.* 1984. V. 29. № 6. P. 3747-3748.

[49] Kozlov G.V., Dolbin I.V., Zaikov G.E. In book: "*Reactions in Condensed Phases. Kinetics and Thermodynamics*". V. 1. Ed. Zaikov G. New York. Nova Science Publishers. Inc. 2003 (in press).

[50] Kozlov G.V., Shustov G.B., Zaikov G.E. *Proceeding All-Russian Conf. "Chemistry in Technology and Medicine".* Machachkala. DSU. 2002. P. 48-51.

[51] Kozlov G.V., Batyrova H.M., Zaikov G.E. In book: *New Perspectives in Chemistry and Biochemistry".* Ed. Zaikov G. New York. Nova Science Publishers. Inc. 2002. P. 49-55.

[52] Argirakis P., Kopelman R. *Phys. Rev. B.* 1984. V. 29. № 1. P. 511-514.

[53] Kozlov G.V., Zaikov G.E., Lipatov Yu.S. *Dokl. NAN Ukraine.* 2002. № 8. P. 130-135.

[54] Kozlov G.V., Zaikov G.E., Lipatov Yu.S. *Russian Polymer News.* 2003. V. 8. № 1. P. 59-63.

[55] Blumen A., Klafter J., Zumofen G. In book: *Fractals in Physics.* Ed. Pietronero L., Tosatti E. Amsterdam-Oxford-New York-Tokyo, North-Holland. 1986. P. 561-574.

[56] Kozlov G.V., Shustov G.B., Zaikov G.E., Burmistr M.V., Korenjako V.A. Voprosy *Khimii i Khimich. Technology.* 2002. № 3. P. 67-72.

[57] Gladyshev G.P., Ershov Yu.A., Shustova O.A. *Stabilization of Thermoresistant Polymers* (in Russian). Moscow. Khimia. 1979. 271 p.

[58] Kozlov G.V., Shustov G.B., Zaikov G.E. *Izvestija VUZov. Severo-Kavkaz. reg. Estestv. Nauki.* 2002. № 3. P. 61-63.

[59] Grassy N.A. *Chemistry of Polymers Degradation Processes* (in Russian). Moscow. Khimia. 1959. 252 p.

[60] Kozlov G.V., Shustov G.B., Zaikov G.E. *Khimich. Promyshlen.* 2002. № 8. P. 1-4.

[61] Kozlov G.V., Dolbin I.V., Shustov G.B. *Proceeding All-Russian Conf. "Chemistry in Technology and Medicine".* Machachkala. DSU. 2001. P. 159-162.

[62] Kozlov G.V., Shogenov V.N., Afaunov V.V., Zaikov G.E. In book: *New Perspectives in Chemistry and Biochemistry*". Ed. Zaikov G. New York. Nova Science Publishers. Inc. 2002. P. 19-26.

In: Homolytic and Heterolytic Reactions: Problems and Solutions ISBN 1-59033-980-0
Editors: G.E. Zaikov, et al., pp. 233-259

Chapter 9

EPOXY-URETHANE COPOLYMERS

Pablo Marcelo Stefani[1], Stella Maris Moschiar[2] and Mirta Inés Aranguren[2*]

(1)Universidad Tecnológica Nacional – Facultad Regional Concepción del Uruguay.
Ing. Pereira 676, E3264BTD Concepción del Uruguay, Argentina.
E-mail: stefanip@frcu.utn.edu.ar

(2) Institute of Materials Science and Technology (INTEMA),
University of Mar del Plata- National Research Council (CONICET),
Av. Juan B. Justo 4302, (7600) Mar del Plata, Argentina
E-mail: marangur@fi.mdp.edu.ar
E-mail: smoschia@fi.mdp.edu.ar

ABSTRACT

The reaction kinetics and the curing process of an epoxy-urethane copolymer in a heated mold were modeled. The phase separation process was studied and used to analyze the final morphologies. The final thermal, mechanical and fracture properties were correlated to the corresponding morphologies. The system selected for the study was an epoxy resin (DGEBA, Araldyt GY9527, Ciba Geigy), co-reacted with an urethane prepolymer (PU, Desmocap 12, Bayer) through an amine that acted as crosslinking agent (mixture of cycloaliphatic amines, Distraltec). The kinetic study focused on the effect of the curing conditions and PU concentration on the reaction rate. The global kinetic parameters included the initial chemical control and further diffusional step as the sample gets close to the glass transition temperature. The copolymerization with PU reduced the activation energies of the chemical and diffusional controlled parts of the reaction and increased the final conversion of the epoxy –amine system. The kinetics model was applied to the analysis of the curing of a plaque, time-temperature profiles measured in the mold and the consequent final morphologies obtained. Phase separation is a function of the conversion and temperature reached in the curing part and was analyzed using experimental data and a mathematical model that predicts temperature and conversion

* To whom all correspondence should be addressed

throughout the thickness of the mold. The size of the dispersed phase increased with the initial PU concentration while there were practically no differences as a function of position in the mold or oven. The superposition of the phase diagrams with the conversion-temperature trajectories during cure allowed to explain the morphologies generated. Moreover, the addition of PU proved to lead to the usual trend of improved toughening and reduced modulus and compression yield stress. This result is correlated to a morphology consisting in a fine rubber particle dispersion, but also to the ductilization effect of the flexible elastomer copolymerized to the epoxy amine system.

KeyWords: Urethane–epoxy copolymers, curing kinetics, diffusion control, phase separation, mechanical properties.

1. INTRODUCTION

Amine-cured epoxy resins have been frequently combined with elastomeric second phases to improve their intrinsic low impact resistance [1-9]. Usually, a liquid elastomer is added to the amine/epoxy mixture, and it becomes phase separated during the polymerization.

Different approaches have been used to model the reaction of neat epoxy-amine networks. Some of them have included the effect of vitrification that can be reached if cure is carried out at temperatures below the ultimate glass transition temperature of the system. This has been done using a fictitious advance of reaction $\zeta = x/x_{max}$, where x is the conversion and x_{max}, is a constant that depends on the curing temperature [10]. Other approaches require the inclusion of diffusion control at high conversions in the overall kinetic constant. [11-15]. However, there are not many publications indicating that the same kinetic parameters used for isothermal runs can also be satisfactorily applied to predict non isothermal runs. This is of the utmost importance for the modelling of reactive processes, where usually temperature profiles are developed in a piece. In the present case, we have undertaken the last approach by considering a chemical and diffusional controlled steps in the reaction of the copolymerization of urethane with epoxy-amine. The effect of the copolymerization was also satisfactorily addressed.

The reactive PU-epoxy- amine mixtures remain homogeneous until a certain extent of reaction is reached (cloud-point conversion). At this point a modifier-rich phase is segregated in form of particles of a few micrometers in size and finally the phase separation is arrested by gelation [16-19]. The competence between the phase separation process and the chemical reaction determines the morphology and properties of the final thermoset. This balance is affected by solubility, initial concentration and reactivity of the elastomer, as well as by the cure conditions. As it has been reported in the literature, the greater the initial concentration of elastomer [17], the lower the miscibility of the system [20], the greater the volume fraction of dispersed phase that is obtained.

When these modified systems are cured in a heated mold, phase separation profiles may be developed, due to differences in the conversion-temperature-time histories, which are functions of the position in the mold [21]. The kinetic model developed earlier as well as the experimental results obtained from the phase separation study were used to predict the final morphology of the different copolymers under different curing conditions. The morphologies observed by SEM were in perfect correlation to the expected results.

The introduction of a second elastomeric phase increases the toughness of a brittle matrix. Different studies have been published related to the deformation mechanisms associated with this effect. [1, 22-24]. The improvement in toughening increases with the increment of the volume fraction of the dispersed phase, and with the flexibility of the matrix, since the deformation mechanisms are related to the matrix characteristics [25]. The copolymerization of reactive elastomers with the epoxy-amine system produces a fine dispersion of a second phase and the ductilization of the matrix, as has been previously discussed by Bussi and Ishida, and similarly by Mulhaupt and Buchholz [2, 26]. In the present study both effects are expected to affect the final properties of the copolymer networks.

2. EXPERIMENTAL

2.1. Materials

The epoxy resin used is a DGEBA (diglycidyl ether of bisphenol A; weight by epoxy equivalent=189.8 g) ARALDIT GY 9527 from Ciba Geigy Co. The crosslinker is a mixture of cycloaliphatic amines (weight per amine equivalent = 59.5 g, Distraltec). The modifier is a commercial elastomer based on a linear polyurethane, with terminal isocyanate groups blocked by an alkylphenol (Desmocap 12, Bayer; weight by isocyanate (NCO) equivalent 2470 g).

2.2. Testing Methods

2.2.1. Differential Scanning Calorimeter

The heat evolved during the copolymerization reaction, as well as the glass transition temperatures of the final materials taken as the onset of the transition were determined using a differential scanning calorimeter (Shimadzu DSC 50) at a heating rate of 10ºC/min.

2.2.2. Gel Permeation Chromatography

Gel permeation chromatography (GPC) was used to determine the molecular weight distribution of urethane prepolymer. GPC was performed in a Waters 244 device provided with a refraction index detector. THF was used as a solvent at a 1 ml/min flowing rate. Columns of Styragel of 500, 1000, 10000 and 100000 Å were used.

2.2.3. Gelation Time

A set of thin tubes containing modified and pure epoxy-amine reactive mixtures, was immersed in an oil bath kept at constant temperature. Gelation times, t_{GEL}, were measured by gently pulling a thin wire, immersed in the sample, and taking t_{GEL} as the time at which the whole tube was lifted by pulling the wire

2.2.4. Cloud-Point Time

Transmission optical microscopy (TOM) measurements were performed with an Olympus BHT-M microscope equipped with a photo electric cell. The time at which phase separation began (i.e. cloud point time for a particular sample and curing temperature), t_{CP}, and the interval of time for phase separation to be completed, Δt_{CP}, were determined from the light transmission recorder at different constant cure temperatures. The cloud-point time, t_{CP}, was determined at the onset of the light transmission decrease.

2.2.5. Kinetic Measurements

Differential scanning calorimetry (DSC) was used to investigate the rate of the reaction. This technique is based on the implicit assumption that there exists a proportionality between the heat evolved during cure, ΔH_i, and the extent of the reaction, x.

$$x = \frac{\Delta H_i}{\Delta H_T} \tag{1}$$

whereΔH_T is the total heat evolved during a dynamic run to reach complete conversion.

The initial mixtures are completely miscible, but very viscous. The epoxy and PU elastomer are mixed manually at 80°C during 30 min. Then, the mixture is degassed under vacuum for two hours. Finally, the amine is added and mixed slowly to avoid mechanical heating of the reactive mixture. All samples were prepared in stoichiometric conditions (n° of epoxy groups+ n° of isocyanate groups = n° of amine groups) and run at constant temperatures (isothermal runs at 70, 85 and 100°C) or at a constant heating rate of 10°C/min (dynamic runs). Samples smaller than 10 to 15 mg were used for the DSC measurements (Shimadzu DSC-50).

2.2.6. Determination of Temperature Profiles during the Cure in Mold

The reactive mixture was cast at room temperature into a glass mold (thickness = 1 or 2 cm). Then, the mold was placed inside a programmable oven (Memert ULP 500) at a selected constant temperature. Alumel-chromel thermocouples were used to monitor the temperature evolution, at different positions of the sample thickness.

2.2.7. Bending and Compression Tests

Bending and compressive tests were performed in a Shimadzu SC 500 universal testing machine. Bending tests were run following the procedures ASTM D790-86 (method 1, procedure A) at a crosshead speed of 12 mm/min. The compression samples were deformed between polished steel plates following the test procedure ASTM D695-91 at a crosshead speed of 0.5mm/min. The displacements were calculated from the readings obtained with a linear variable differential transducer (LVDT).

The bending and compressive tests specimens were machined to achieve the following dimensions: Bending specimens: 3×12×120 mm, compression cylindrical specimens: 5×7.5 (in mm, diameter and height, respectively).

2.2.8. Impact Test

The impact tests were conducted using a pendulum-striker (Wolpert, PW5). Precraked test specimens were used to determine the critical strain energy release rate, G_{IC}. Sharp initial cracks were obtained by first machining a V-notch of 1mm and then generating a natural crack by carefully tapping on a new razor blade placed in the notch of the pre-compressed specimen [27-29]. The length of the initial crack was determined after performing the test, using a profile projector (10×) to observe the surface of the broken samples. A 5-point average was used to calculate the initial crack length.

2.2.9. Morphology

The SEM photographs of the fracture surface of the different copolymers were taken with a scanning electron microscope Philips model SEM 505. The samples were previously coated with gold. Micrographs were magnified and regions containing about 100 particles (PU inclusions in the epoxy-amine phase) of dispersed phase were analyzed. The average diameter of the particles, Dp, and volume fraction, V_D, of the dispersed phase were calculated from the particle-size distribution, as *D* (diameter) versus *n* (number of particles) for each formulation, using with eqs. 4 an 5 respectively [30]

$$Dp = \frac{\sum nD}{\sum n} \tag{4}$$

$$V_D = (\pi / 4) \sum nD^2 / A_T \tag{5}$$

where A_T is the area of the micrograph region under analysis. Equation (5) assumes that the volume fraction is an isotropic property. Hence, the values measured in the plane are the same as in the volume.

3. Results and Discussion

3.1. Characterization of PU Elastomer

The glass transition temperature of PU was -60°C as determined by DSC. The low Tg of PU is consequence of the higher flexibility of the chains of this prepolymer. This is related to the high molecular weight of the reactives used in the synthesis of commercial product, which results in Mn and Mw values of 3477 and 4023, respectively.

3.2. Epoxy-Urethane Copolimerization Reaction

The schematic of the copolymerization reaction is shown in **Figure 1** and has been discussed in a previous publication [31,32]. The amine group reacts with the epoxy groups by ring opening or with isocyanate groups by deblocking of the terminal isocyanate of the PU elastomer and formation of an urea group.

The alkylphenol displaced remains in the reactive mixture and acts as catalyzer of the epoxy-amine reaction. The reaction between amine groups and isocyanates is extremely fast and under the reaction conditions the replacement of the alkylphenol by the amine is favored. Etherification reactions, which are favored at high temperatures, were not considered in the present scheme of reaction.

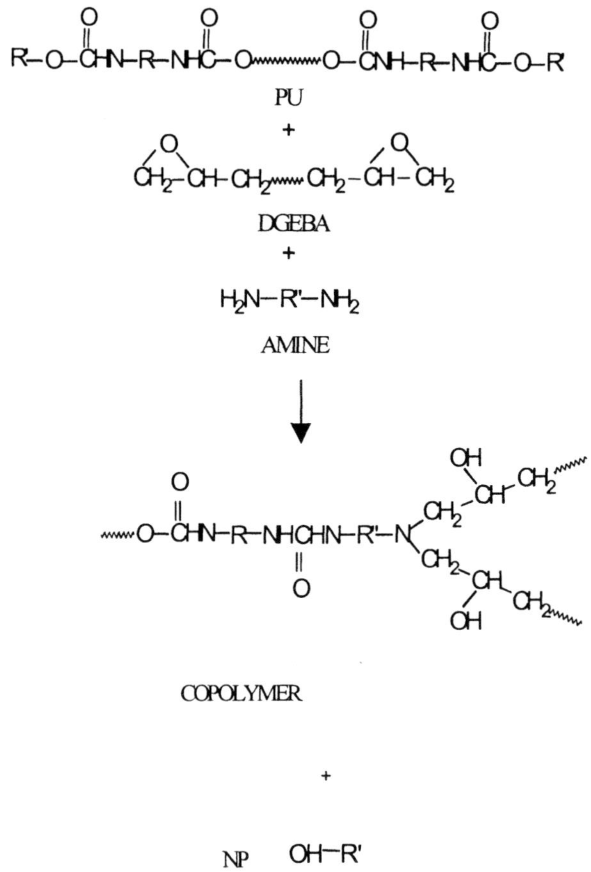

Figure 1: Schematic of the copolymerization reaction

3.3. Kinetics of Copolimerization

3.3.1. Theoretical Background

The curing of epoxy resins with amines has been frequently modeled using Kamal's kinetic expression for the reaction rate, as follows [33,34].

$$\frac{dx}{dt} = \left(k_1 + k_2 x^m\right)\left(1 - x\right)^n \tag{6}$$

This type of equation has been very useful in describing systems where there is a maximum in the isothermal reaction rate at a time larger than zero. This is a characteristic of autocatalytic processes, such as that of the cure of an epoxy resin with an amine. In this case the reaction is being catalyzed by the presence of OH groups, which are generally present in very small amounts at the beginning of the reaction and are further generated during crosslinking. If the non catalyzed path of the reaction is negligible with respect to the autocatalyzed path, the above expression can be simplified to

$$\frac{dx}{dt} = k_c x^m (1-x)^n \tag{7}$$

where the constant k_l has been taken =0. This model requires the use of a "seed" to be numerically solved (an initial conversion), whose size may be of importance depending of the rate of the reaction (it may shift the curve of conversion vs. time on the time scale). In this case the initial conversion ("seed" at time =0) was taken as 10^{-9}. Lower values of initial conversion did not produce changes in the fitting parameters obtained from the non linear regression analysis, neither in the predictions obtained by integration of the expression of the rate of reaction in the complete model.

Another usual simplification of the kinetic expression, when applied to epoxy-amine curing, is the assumption that the sum of the exponents in equation 7 must be equal to 2 [35,36]. Previous calculations applied to the present system indicated that this is a reasonable assumption in the present case [32] and thus the following equation will be used in the rest of the calculations:

$$\frac{dx}{dt} = k_c x^m (1-x)^{2-m} \tag{8}$$

These models are flexible enough to give good fitting curves for the autocatalytic regime of the reaction. Usually, isothermal runs are utilized to obtain the kinetic constants at fixed temperatures and then, an Arrhenius type of equation is used to represent the functionality of k_c with temperature. In the present work, nonlinear regression analysis, based on Marquardt method, was applied to the experimental data, which allows to include non isothermal runs (i.e.: dynamical runs at 10°C/min). With this approach the set of kinetic parameters found can reproduce very efficiently isothermal and nonisothermal curing conditions, if the reaction does not become diffusion controlled at high conversions.

As it has been discussed previously in the literature, epoxy-amine systems cured under isothermal conditions may not reach the complete conversion, because the reactive mixture may reach vitrification at a lower conversion if the curing temperature is lower than $Tg\infty$, the glass transition temperature of the completely cured system. In that case, the reaction becomes diffusion controlled. Different approaches have been proposed to deal with this effect. The Rabinowitch model has the simplicity of considering that the overall time for the reaction is the sum of the time for the diffusion of the reactants and the time required for the chemical reaction. [11, 37]

$$\frac{1}{k_o(T,x)} = \frac{1}{k_c(T)} + \frac{1}{k_d(T,x)} \tag{9}$$

where k_c and k_d are the rate constants of the chemically and diffusion controlled reaction steps, respectively; and k_o is the overall rate constant of the reaction.

This equation shows that the overall rate constant is governed at the beginning of the reaction by the kinetic rate constant (before vitrification) and at the end of the reaction by the diffusion rate constant (after vitrification), when the diffusion of the chemical reactants becomes the limiting step. The constant k_o is then used in equations 7 or 8 replacing the value of k_c, and the expression obtained by this procedure is valid for the entire conversion range:

$$\frac{dx}{dt} = k_o x^m (1-x)^{2-m} \tag{8bis}$$

The Addam-Gibbs theory was selected to represent the temperature dependence of the diffusion rate constant [38]. In this approach the molecular mobility is assumed to be the consequence of a cooperative rearrangement of structural units due to thermal fluctuations, which allows to overcome the energy barrier that separates the initial and final conformation. Their treatment leads to the following expression:

$$\ln k_d = \ln k_{d0} - \frac{s}{T \ln\left(\frac{T}{T_g - 50}\right)} \tag{10}$$

with

$$s = \frac{E_d \ln 2}{\Delta C_P}$$

where E_d is the activation energy of the diffusion mechanism and ΔCp is the change in specific molar heat of the sample at Tg.

3.3.2. Experimental Conversion

As it was mentioned above, the added PU can also copolymerize with the amine crosslinker. However, the elastomer is added in small amounts (10 and 20 % by weight with respect to the epoxy resin), which represents a negligible concentration of reactive groups, since PU is a long linear chain with reactive terminal groups. This feature is reported in Table 1 for one preparation of each system.

Since the amount of isocyanate groups is only a small percentage of the number of epoxy groups (Table 1); thus, the reaction is essentially that of the epoxy-amine. This should not lead to the conclusion that the addition of the elastomers has no effect on the cure reaction. As it will be discussed in detail below, the reaction is accelerated and the vitrification delayed.

The dynamic runs of the reactive mixtures allow to measure the heat of reaction corresponding to complete conversion which is also included in Table 1. If the values of ΔH_T are expressed by weight of the sample, the dilution effect of the PU addition becomes evident. A decrease of about 17% of the total heat of reaction occurs with the 20% PU system with respect to the neat epoxy-amine (EA) reactive mixture.

Figure 2 shows the experimental data of conversion vs. time, calculated as mentioned above, for an isothermal run (T_{cure}= 85°C) of the neat epoxy-amine system and the modified mixtures (10 and 20 % of elastomer). It is clear from the figure that the reaction is faster with the addition of the PU and the ultimate conversion increases with the elastomer concentration.

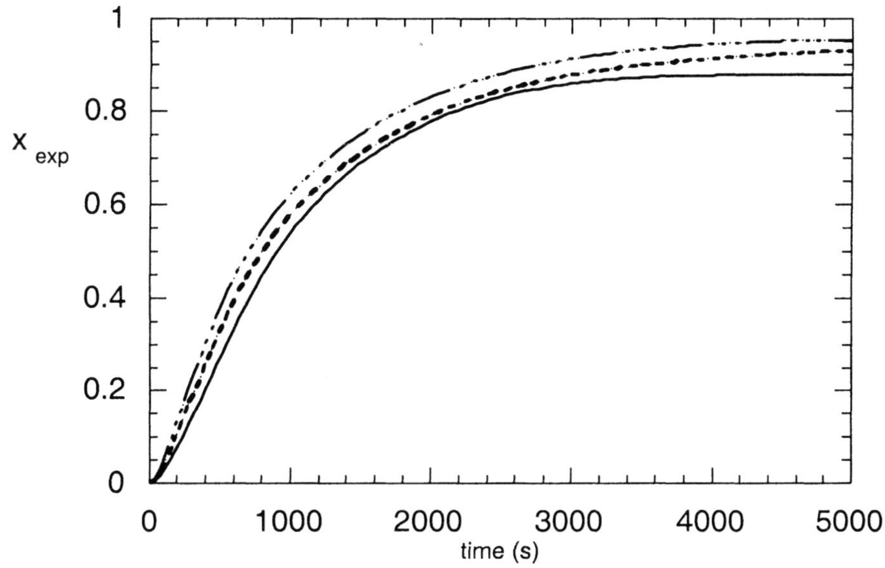

Figure 2. Experimental conversion vs. time at 85°C for the neat epoxy-amine system (continuous line), for the epoxy-amine with 10% of elastomer (- - -) and with 20% of elastomer (—— – ——).

3.3.3. Reaction at Short Times: Chemical Control

Equations 7 and 8 show that the rate of reaction is the product of a kinetic constant and a function of the conversion. Following the reasoning of Wisanrakkit and Gillham, [11] in those conditions, the curves of conversion vs. ln (time) obtained from isothermal runs should have the same functional form, and should only show a displacement in the ln (time) axis. This is only true for the chemically controlled step of the reaction. At those short times the curves should be superposable by simply shifting each curve along the ln (time) axis relative to the curve at the reference temperature by a shift factor $a_{(T)}$. Figure 3 shows the resulting master curve for the epoxy-amine system and that for the system modified with the addition of 20% of elastomer at a reference temperature of 85°C. The superposition is quite good in both cases, which demonstrates that for each system the mechanism of reaction is the same irrespective of the curing temperature. The individual curves separate from the master curve at the point where vitrification sets up.

The master curve obtained by superposition of the data of x vs. ln(time) can give additional information [11]. The shift factors obtained can be written as:

$$a_{(T)} = \ln\,(time) - \ln\,(time_{ref}) = \ln k_{(T)} - \ln k_{(Tref)} = -E/RT + E/RT_{ref} \quad (11)$$

where T_{ref} is the temperature selected as the reference. From the calculated values of $a_{(T)}$ the activation energy of the kinetically controlled part of the reaction can be calculated. The results are also included in Table 1. Although this method does not give a complete set of kinetic parameters, it shows a trend of decreasing activation energies for systems with increasing amounts of elastomer. A nonlinear regression analysis based on Marquardt algorithm was also used to find the best fitting parameters to equation 8 [32, 39]. The values of activation energy found for the epoxy-amine system are in close agreement to those found in the literature for similar systems [40], and the addition of the PU elastomer reduces that value. The results are summarized in Table 1.

Table 1. Stoichiometry of the samples, total heats of reaction (ΔH_T), and values of fitting parameter for chemically and diffusional controlled part of reaction

	Epoxy-amine (EA)	EA + 10% PU	EA + 20% PU
Mass of epoxy (g) [a]	1.9642	1.8597	2.0641
Mass of amine (g) [a]	0.6196	0.5817	0.6687
Mass of PU (g) [a]	---	0.1996	0.5136
r (stoichiometric ratio)[b]	0.994	1.004	1.005
# NCO/ # E .100 (%)	---	0.37	0.85
ΔH_T (J/g)[c]	371.2±20	353.9±15.0	307.8±8.4
ln A (eq. 8)	11.18	10.23	8.16
Ec (kJ/mol) (eq. 8)	52.06	48.88	42.32
m (eq. 8)	0.340	0.310	0.315
n (eq. 8)	1.660	1.690	1.685
Ec(kJ/mol) (master curve)	45.22	44.89	46.39
ln kdo	11.44	13.04	10.37
s	731.04	577.21	401.44
ρ (Kg/m^3)	1140	1135	1127
Cp (J/Kg °C) [d]	2400	2300 (2200) [e]	2100 (2000) [e]
$\alpha \times 10^{-8}$ (m^2/s) [f] (for T< Tmax)	6.7	7.2 (7.6)	7.6 (8.4)
$\alpha \times 10^{-8}$ (m^2/s) [f] (for T> Tmax)	10	10	10

[a] The reported values correspond to one of the different samples prepared for each system.
[b] r = (n° eq. of epoxy + n° eq. of NCO) / n° eq. of amine
[c] The values shown are the average of at least three specimens. The heat expressed as kJ/mol indicate mol of defective reactive groups (ex. amine or (epoxy + isocyanate))
[d] Measured by DSC. A constant Cp value was adopted, averaged in the temperature interval of curing process.
[e] Bracketed Cp values where used in the calculations for oven temperature of 30°C, since the range of temperature during curing is very different (lower) than that of the other higher temperature runs.
[f] α values are best fitting parameters. Values are comparable to literature data for similar systems.

This effect is in agreement with the proposed scheme of the reaction, where the amine reacts with the isocyanate group of the PU, freeing in the reactive mixture the blocking agent, alkylphenol, which catalyzes the reaction epoxy amine. It is interesting to note that the two completely different numerical approaches used to find the activation energies lead to similar values and to the same trend as PU is added.

On the other hand, the nonlinear regression method gives the complete set of kinetic parameters from the simultaneous consideration of isothermal and dynamic DSC runs. Figure

4 shows the excellent fit of the model to the experimental conversion vs. time data. As expected, the kinetic model represents the experimental results up to the point where vitrification sets in.

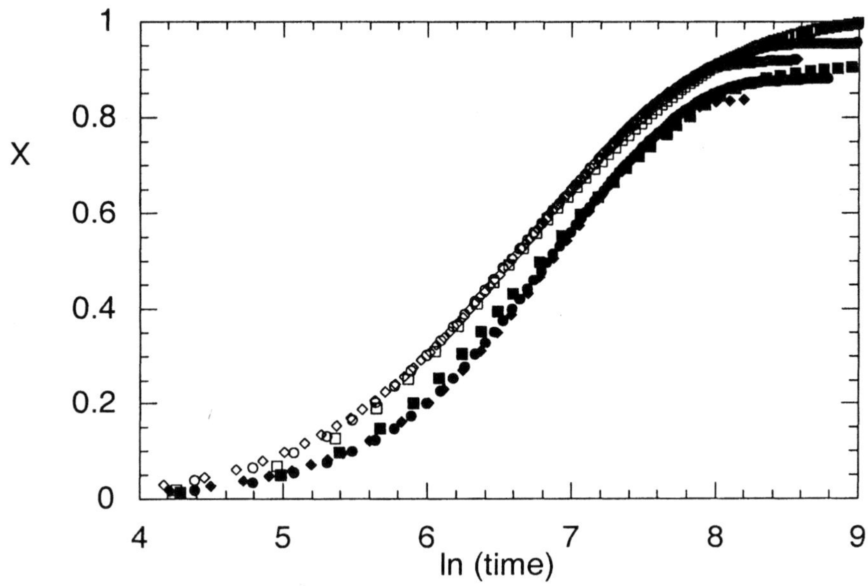

Figure 3. Master curve of the experimental conversion vs. ln (time) in seconds at a reference temperature of 85°C. Open symbols correspond to the epoxy-amine system. Filled symbols to the E-A + 20% PU. Diamonds 70°C; circles 85°C, squares 100°C.

3.3.4. Reaction at Long Times: Diffusion Control

From the previous discussion, it is clear that a purely kinetic model cannot represent the isothermal curing, when the material reaches the glass transition temperature (branching off the master curve shortly after vitrification). The Di Benedetto equation was utilized to model the glass transition evolution of the system as a function of the conversion [41]

$$\frac{T_g - T_{g0}}{T_{g\infty} - T_{g0}} = \frac{\lambda x}{1\text{-}(1\text{-}\lambda)x} \qquad (12)$$

where Tg_0 is the glass transition temperature of the system at the initial time and λ is Tg_0 / Tg_∞ according to the work of Pascault and Williams.[42,43]. This is a "rough approximation" that has also been used in the past in the absence of experimental values for the system [44, 45].

The data of Tg_0 was measured on the neat epoxy resin using dynamic scanning calorimetry and found to be equal to 241°K, in excellent agreement with published data [42]. Experimental values of Tg_∞ are reported in Table 2 and were measured from DSC second runs after a dynamic cure. Using this last equation and replacing the value of Tg by T_{cure}, it is possible to calculate the conversion at which vitrification is reached. The values are reported in Table 2. Figure 3 shows that the rate of reaction is greatly reduced after reaching this conversion, x_{glass}. From the values reported for x_{glass}, it is evident that vitrification occurs at lower conversions for lower temperatures of curing, a feature already expected. It is also seen that an increment in the PU concentration results in an increment of the conversion at which vitrification takes place (delay of the diffusion control of the reaction).

Table 2. Calculated conversions at which vitrification takes place under isothermal curing conditions and glass transition temperatures of completely cured samples (Tg∞)

System	T_{cure} (°C)			Tg∞ (°C)
	70	**85**	**100**	
EA	0.740	0.813	0.880	130
EA+10% PU	0.760	0.835	0.904	124
EA+20% PU	0.777	0.854	0.924	118

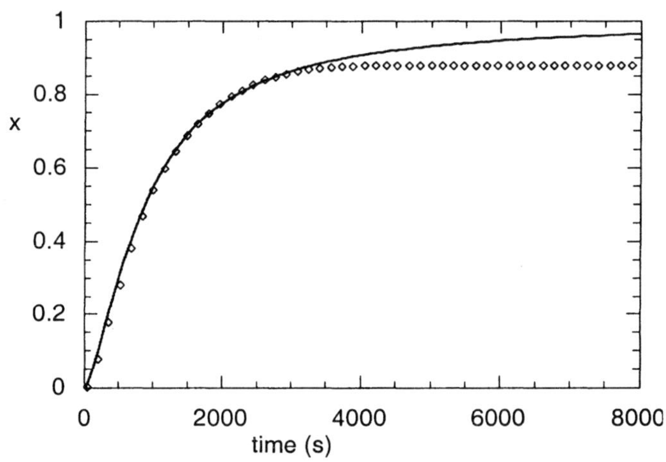

Figure 4. Comparison of experimental and predicted values of conversion vs. time. Calculated values were obtained using only the chemical kinetic constant.

Since the mobility of the segments carrying reactive groups is highly reduced in the last part of the reaction, the calculation of x_{glass} allows to select the range of conversions that gives more information about the diffusion rate constant k_d. The non linear analysis method used in the first part of the work was used again to find the best fitting diffusional parameters of the complete model (eqn. 8 bis). The experimental data of conversion and time, at conversions higher than x_{glass}, were used in this case, keeping constant the already calculated parameters of the chemically controlled part of the reaction. The diffusional parameters are reported in Table 1. The value of the parameter "s" in the table, which is directly proportional to the activation energy for the diffusion process, shows a decreasing trend with the increment of the PU elastomer concentration in the reactive mixture. This is explained by the increased mobility of the segments in the reactive mixture with the addition of the elastomer, which reduces the Tg of the network.

3.3.5. Overall Reaction Rate

At this point, all the parameters that appear in the overall expression for the reaction rate are known and can be utilized to predict rates of reaction and conversion as functions of the time for the complete range of conversions under different curing conditions (i.e. isothermal or dynamic runs). Figure 5 (a,b) show the comparison between experimental and calculated values of x and dx/dt vs. time for the systems with 10% of PU. The figures show an excellent agreement between experimental and calculated data of conversions, as well as reaction rates. Similar results were obtained with the samples prepared with other percentages of PU. The predictions are equally good for the isothermal and dynamic curing conditions. The incomplete final conversion of the systems cured at low temperatures is well reproduced, as well as the position (time) and magnitude of the reaction rates in all the cases.

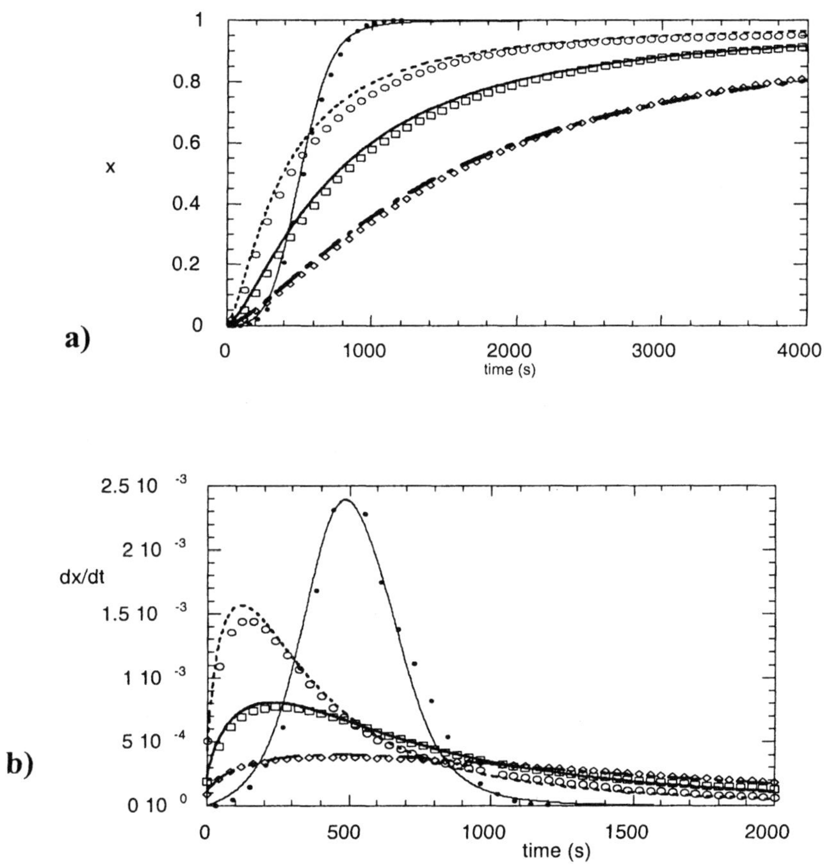

Figure 5. Comparison of experimental and predicted values of conversion (a) and reaction rates (b) vs. time of system with 10% PU. Predictions of the model were obtained using the overall kinetic constant and are shown with lines. Diamonds 70°C, squares 85°C, circles 100°C, filled circles dynamic run (10°C/min).

The complete model can cover the two ends of the reaction controlled by kinetics or by diffusion of the reactants. It reproduces different curing conditions and in this respect it can be very useful to predict results of curing in a mold, as well as other commercial processing conditions (it could reproduce conversion profiles in a piece associated to temperature profiles developed during curing). The use of the Rabinowitch equation allows to find a complete expression than can reproduce quite well the effects of the vitrification on the overall reaction rate, to obtain a sample with final conversion lower than 1.

The addition of the PU elastomer is seen to reduce both the activation energy of the chemically controlled step of the reaction and that of the diffusion controlled step. For the first part of the reaction, the decrease of the energy barrier, E, is explained by the increase in the concentration of OH groups from the alkylphenol released during the copolymerization with amine. For the diffusion controlled part of the reaction, the activation energy for diffusion is reduced because of the increased mobility of the segments containing reactive groups. The presence of the elastomer reduces the Tg of the material and thus, delays the onset for vitrification in the reacting sample.

In agreement with the above reasoning, the final conversion reached by the epoxy-amine system under isothermal conditions increases with the elastomer concentration.

3.4. Curing in a Heated Mold

3.4.1. Mathematical Model

Phase separation as a function of conversion and temperature in the curing part was analyzed using experimental data and a simple mathematical model that predicts temperature and conversion throughout the thickness of the mold. This type of theoretical calculation has been the subject of several publications [21, 46] and thus only a concise description of the procedure will be provided here.

The following assumptions were adopted to solve this model: (a) homogeneus system: there is good mixing at initial time; (b) the diffusion of reactants in the mold is neglected, (c) one-dimensional heat conduction; (d) constant thermal and physical properties (α, ρ, ΔH, Cp).

The mass (reaction rate) and energy equations in the curing polymer must be solved as a function of time.

$$\frac{\partial T}{\partial t} = \alpha \frac{\partial^2 T}{\partial z^2} + \frac{\Delta Hr}{Cp} R \text{ (Energy balance)} \tag{13}$$

$$\frac{dx}{dt} = R \text{ (Reaction rate)} \tag{14}$$

where

$$\alpha = \frac{k}{\rho . Cp} \tag{15}$$

These equations relate conversion (x) and temperature (T), as functions of time (t) and position in the mold thickness (z), for given values of reaction heat (ΔHr), thermal diffusivity

(α), heat capacity (Cp), average density (ρ), and reaction rate (R). Values of the physical properties used in the model are reported in Table 1.

Boundary conditions

$$\frac{dT}{dz} = 0 \text{ at } z = \tfrac{1}{2} \text{ thickness (symmetry at the center of the piece)}$$

$T = T_W$ at $z = 0$ (at the wall)

The values of T_W were obtained from the experimental temperature-time profiles at the wall of the mold.

Initial conditions

$T = T_O\ x = 0$ at $t=0\ \forall z$

3.4.2. Comparison between Mathematical Model and Experimental Results

Samples of epoxy-amine and epoxy-amine-urethane copolymers were cured in heated molds of different thicknesses at fixed oven temperatures and at varied concentrations of PU in the copolymers. Composition, thickness and curing conditions of specimens prepared are summarized in the Table 3.

Figures 6a, 6b and 7 show the temperature evolution at two thickness locations (wall and center), for the epoxy-amine (EA) and epoxy-urethane-amine (EA-PU) copolymers at different oven temperatures.

Three steps can be distinguished during the curing process:

1) Heating of the reactive mixture, when the temperature of reactive mixture is lower than the temperature of the heating air. In this step, the wall temperature is higher than the temperature at the center of the part.
2) Heating of the polymer due to the generated heat of reaction. The rate of heat generated during the curing reaction is larger than the rate of heat conduction towards the mold walls and then, a maximum in temperature occurs at the center of the piece.
3) A cooling period, which follows when the rate of heat generated inside the piece is lower than the conduction rate.

The maximum of temperature in the center of the mold is the result of two competing factors: (a) the rate of heat generated by the exothermic curing reaction and (b) the conductive heat flux towards the walls. The larger the ratio of the (a) factor with respect to (b) the higher the maximum temperature reached by the sample in the mold. Many previous publications have described the effect of the processing conditions on these two factors [47,48]. That is, the maximum temperature in the center of the piece will be higher if the external oven temperature, the heat of reaction, or the thickness of the mold are higher and it will be lower if the thermal conductivity is higher. The effect of the oven temperature for these systems is shown in the Temperature-time curves of Figures 6a and 6b. At a fixed oven temperature of

70°C (Figures 6b, 7), the maximum temperature at the center of the mold decreases with the addition of the PU elastomer (the maximum temperature reached in the center of the plaques are 151, 140 and 128°C for 0, 10, and 20% of PU, respectively). This can be explained by the dilution effect of the modifier on the copolymerization reaction heat, as has been previously explained.

The glass transition temperatures, Tg, measured in the center and the wall of the different plaques are shown in Table 3. In all cases, Tg measured in the center of the piece is higher than at the wall, which is the result of the higher temperature reached in the center of the mold during the cure.

A lower Tg is observed when the amount of modifier increases (for a given position in the mold and for a fixed oven temperature), in complete agreement with the lower temperatures reached during the cure and the elastomer effect on the thermoset transition (PU dilution effect as explained above). Figures 6a, 6b and 7 also show the excellent fit between the results of the model and the experimental temperature-time profiles. The model also allows to calculate the overall calorimetric conversions-time profiles in the part. At short times, the conversion at the wall increases faster than at the center of the mold. As the curing reaction proceeds the conversion at the center overcomes the conversion at the wall. The higher conversion reached at the center of the piece is the direct cause of the higher Tg measured in that position. Besides, this model can effectively predict the vitrification of all the systems studied when the oven temperature is low, as it is shown by the low final conversion reached in Figure 6a.

Table 3: Conditions of curing, thicknesses of the samples and Tg of the plaques for the pure and modifed epoxy-amine system

Sample	To (°C) [a]	Position	Thickness (cm)	Tg (°C)
	50	Center	1	60
	50	Wall	1	60
	70	Center	1	91
Epoxy	70	Wall	1	87
	100	Center	1	122
	100	Wall	1	110
	30	Center	2	53
	30	Wall	2	52
	70	Center	1	97
Epoxy-10 wt% PU	70	Wall	1	86
	100	Center	1	109
	100	Wall	1	103
	30	Center	2	53
	30	Wall	2	54
	70	Center	1	85
Epoxy-20 wt% PU	70	Wall	1	80
	100	Center	1	98
	100	*Wall*	1	99

[a] To: Oven temperature

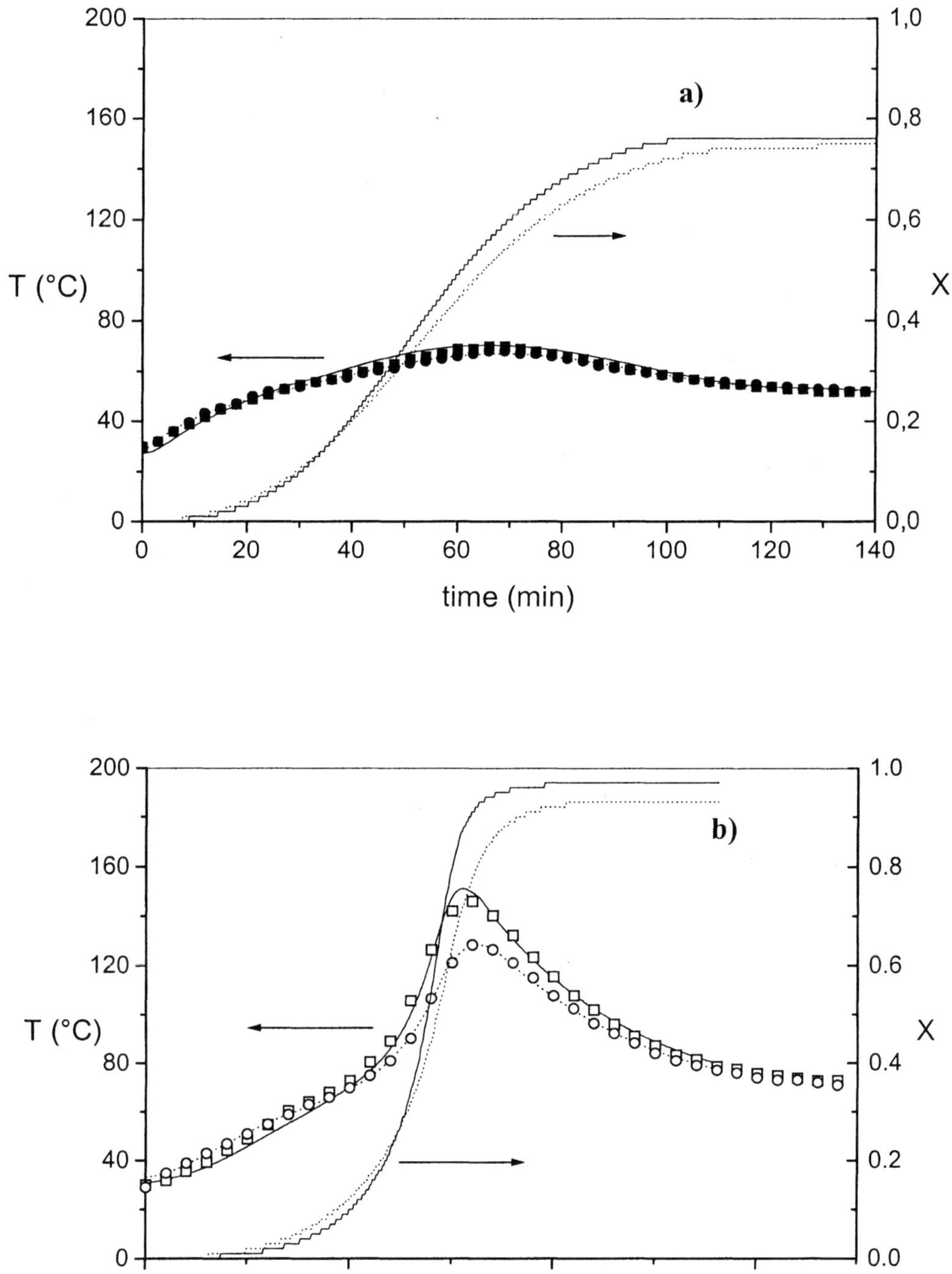

Figure 6: Epoxy-amine system. Thickness of the plaques: 1 cm. The symbols indicate experimental measurements. The lines are the results of the model. Temperature-time curves: (O, ----) wall; (□, —) center. Conversion-time curves: (----) wall; (—) center. Oven temperatures: a) 50°C; b) 70°C,

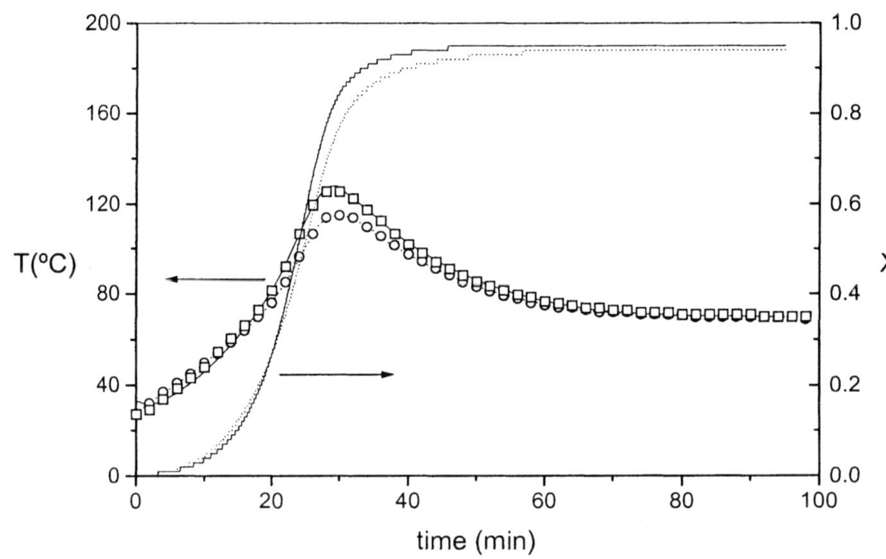

Figure 7: Epoxy-amine-20 wt% Desmocap 12 system. Symbols and lines have the same meaning as in Figure 2. Oven temperature: 70°C, thickness 1 cm

3.4.3. Conversion-Temperature and Phase Separation Diagrams

The formation of a heterogeneous structure and the glass transition of the final copolymers can be explained using a conversion-temperature phase diagram. In that plot the vitrification and gelation curves are shown. $Tg\infty$ is the Tg of the system at complete conversion and $_{gel}Tg$ is the T at which the gelation curve intercepts the vitrification curve. Figure 8 shows such a plot for the epoxy-amine system, including the conversion-temperature trajectories of the curing process (center and wall) indicated at two different conditions: oven temperature = 50 and 100°C. Also, the vitrification conversion (x_V) and gel conversion (x_{GEL}) vs. temperature curves are plotted. In the sample cured at 50°C, there are not important differences between center and wall conversion-temperature trajectories. The low Tg measured in this case (60°C for the center and wall) was a consequence of vitrification taking place at a low conversion of about 0.7.

Table 4: Time (in minutes) and conversion of cloud point, phase-separation interval and gelation

Tc [a]	EA	EA + 10 wt% PU			EA + 20 wt% PU		
(°C)	t_{GEL}	t_{GEL}	t_{CP} (x_{CP})	$\Delta t_{CP}(x_{CP}+\Delta x_{CP})$	t_{GEL}	$t_{CP}(x_{CP})$	$\Delta t_{CP}(x_{CP}+\Delta x_{CP})$
50			91(0.59)	14 (0.61)		61(0.58)	17(0.62)
60			46(0.54)	9 (0.61)		32(0.52)	12.4(0.62)
70	33	31	25(0.49)	7.6 (0.61)	31	21(0.47)	8.4(0.60)
85	19	18	11.2 (0.44)	6.2) (0.61)	16	9.1(0.40)	3.4(0.52)
100	10	10	6.4(0.45)	3.4 (0.61)	9.5	5(0.39)	1.8(0.50)

[a] Cure temperature

The conversion-temperature trajectories of the sample cured at 100ºC (center and wall) intercept the vitrification curve at values of conversion near to one. A Tg of 122ºC measured in the center of the sample, close to Tg∞ (130ºC) confirms that the sample was close to reach complete conversion. The gelation time, cloud point time, and time interval for the phase separation process for the systems epoxy-amine with 10 and 20 % by weight of modifier were measured in small samples at different constant temperatures (Table 4). To relate these times to conversions, the kinetic model already described, was used.

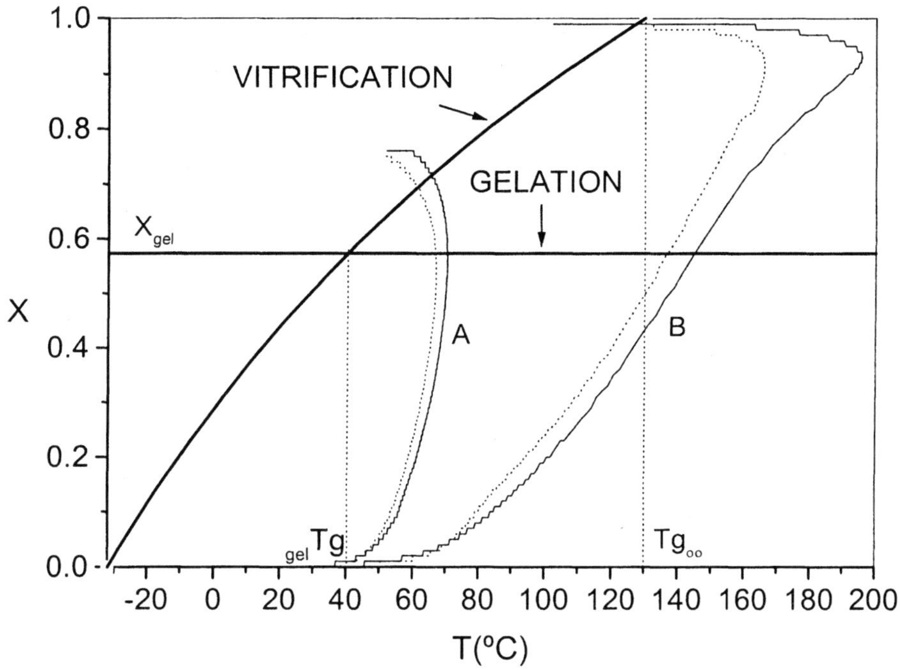

Figure 8: Phase diagrams for epoxy-amine system. Conversion-temperature curves with an oven temperature: A) 50ºC, B) 100ºC (.....) wall of plaque; (—) center of plaque.

Thus, the experimental data (time vs. temperature) were converted to conversion vs. temperature by means of this calculation. It is clear in the Table 4 that the cloud-point conversion decreases with the addition of elastomer for all the cure temperatures.

Figures 9 and 10 show the conversion-temperature diagrams for the system epoxy-amine modified with 10 % and 20 % of PU. Phase separation occurs in the region between the dashed line and x_{GEL} at 10% PU and between the two dashed lines at 20% PU. The curve of x_{CP} vs. curing temperature (lower dashed line in Figures 9 y 10) shows an intercept with the x_{GEL} line at 50°C and around 45°C for the samples with 10% and 20% of PU, respectively. This indicates that the sample with lower concentration of PU can produce a transparent material up to slightly higher temperatures than the 20% PU sample. In both cases, the cloud-point conversion decreases with increasing cure temperature until an approximately constant value is reached at a temperature of about 85ºC. The higher the cure temperature, the faster the reaction rate and then, higher conversions are achieved at shorter times. The kinetic rate shows a stronger dependency with the temperature than the diffusion process. Large molecules do not diffuse fast enough to maintain the system homogeneity during the reaction and phase separation occurs at lower conversion. At higher temperatures this effect is less important (x_{CP} is approximately constant at cure temperatures ≥ 85°C), probably due to the relatively small size of the "structures" present at low conversion, which consequently can diffuse faster. At temperature higher than 80°C, at the end of the phase separation process, the conversion of the sample with 20% of PU is smaller than the gelation conversion. This means that in these conditions, the gelation does not arrest the phase-separation process. However, at lower temperatures it is observed that the phase separation process is arrested because of diffusional restrictions [12] by vitrification or gelation (at $T<_{GEL}Tg$ or $T>_{GEL}Tg$, respectively). This last feature (phase separation arrested by gelation) is observed at all the cure temperatures utilized for the samples with 10% of PU.

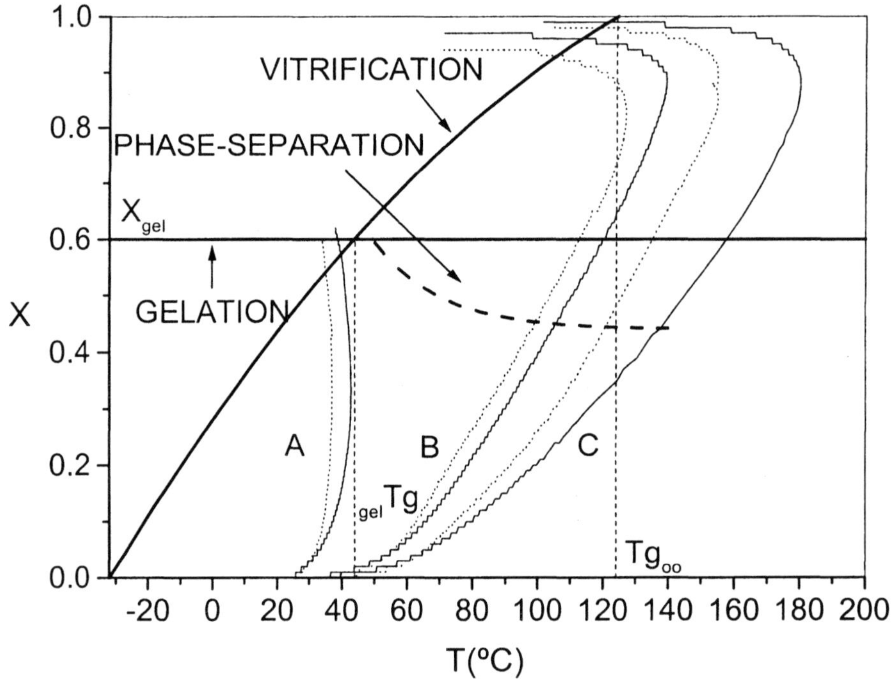

Figure 9: Phase diagrams for epoxy-amine-10 wt% Desmocap 12 system. Conversion-temperature curves with an oven temperature: A) 30°C, B) 70°C, C) 100°C (.....) wall of plaque; (—) center of plaque

The curves conversion –temperature of curing that represent the trajectories followed in a heated mold (Table 3) are also included in Figures 9 and 10. The curve that represents the cure at an oven temperature of 30° C cross the vitrification curve before phase separation or gelation take place for 10 and 20% of PU samples. Thus, the diagrams indicate that the samples should remain as a one-phase material, as it was observed by microscopy (Figure 11) and by simple eye observation (transparent sample).

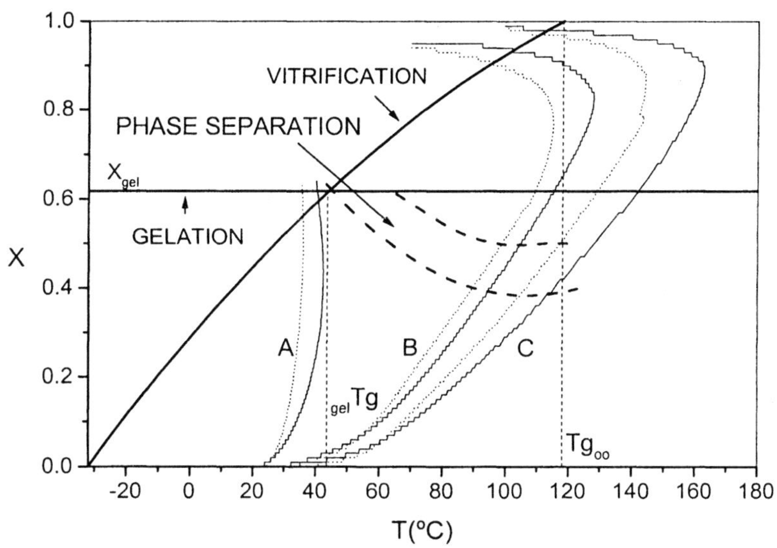

Figure 10: Phase diagrams for epoxy-amine-20 wt% Desmocap 12 system. Conversion-temperature curves with an oven temperature: A) 30°C, B) 70°C, C) 100°C (.....) wall of plaque; (—) center of plaque

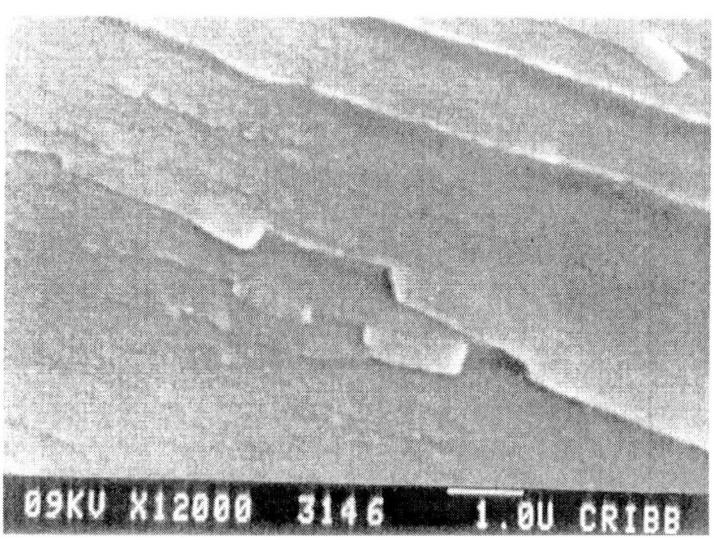

Figure 11: Morphology of the plaques modified with 10 wt % of PU and cured at oven temperature of 30°C (SEM)

The two curing trajectories at the higher oven temperature (T oven = 70 and 100°C) cross the phase separation region before reaching gelation. In these conditions the sample must phase separate. Figures 12 a and 12 b shows the SEM of the cryoscopic fracture of the copolymer with 10% of PU cured at 70°C at the center and the wall of the piece, respectively. Comparison of the spherical rubbery domains indicates that there is no important effect due to the different histories of temperature at the two positions analyzed. Although there is a difference in the temperature reached at the center and wall, microscopy did not show any noticeable difference of size and size distribution of the dispersed phase probably, because the conversions at which the separation took place is approximately the same at the two positions. Figures 13 a and 13 b show the SEM image in the wall of a plaque of copolymer cured at an oven temperature of 100°C with 10 and 20wt% PU respectively. Comparison of the size of the inclusions in Figure 12a and 13a (for 10wt% of PU) indicates that there is essentially no effect of the To in the temperature interval observed (70 – 100°C). Comparison between Figures 13a and 13b allow to confirm that the main variable that affect the size of the separated phase is the initial concentration of the urethane comonomer added to the system [19, 22, 49].

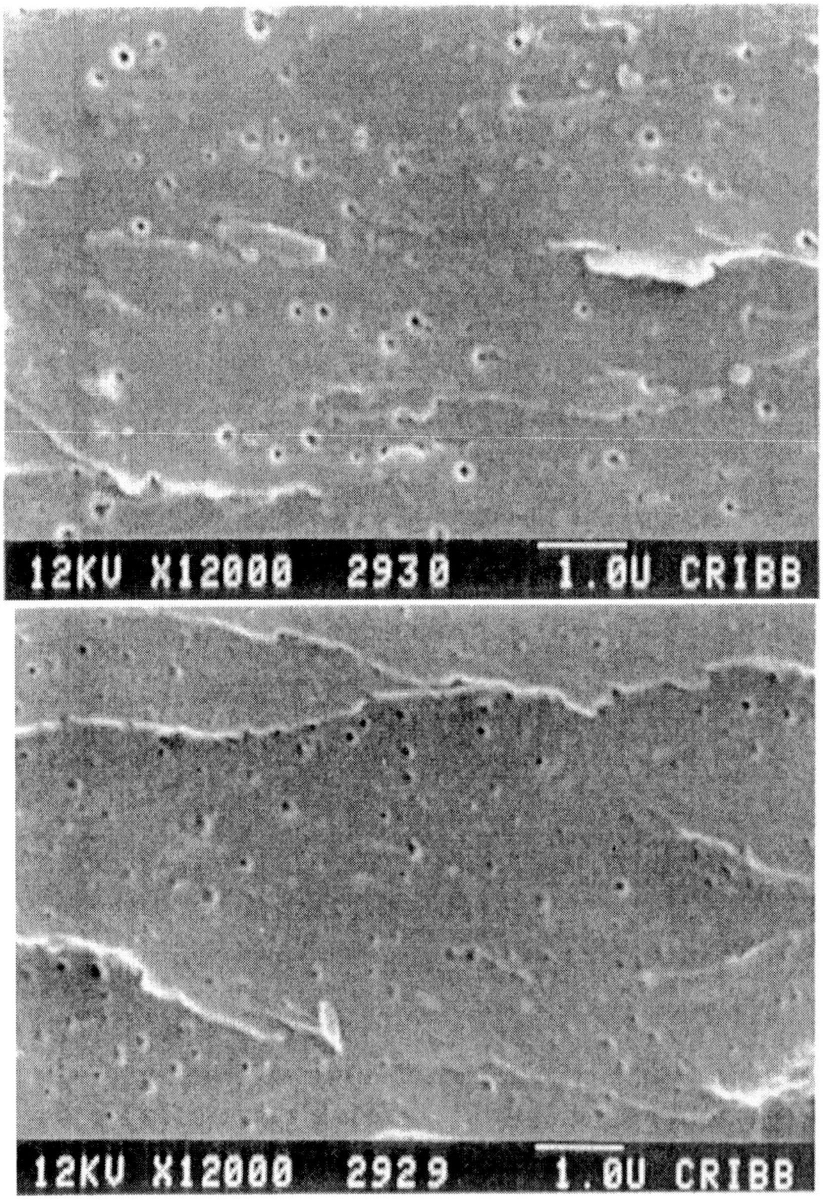

Figure 12: Morphology of the plaques modified with 10 wt % of PU and cured at oven temperature of 70°C (SEM): (a) center, (b) wall.

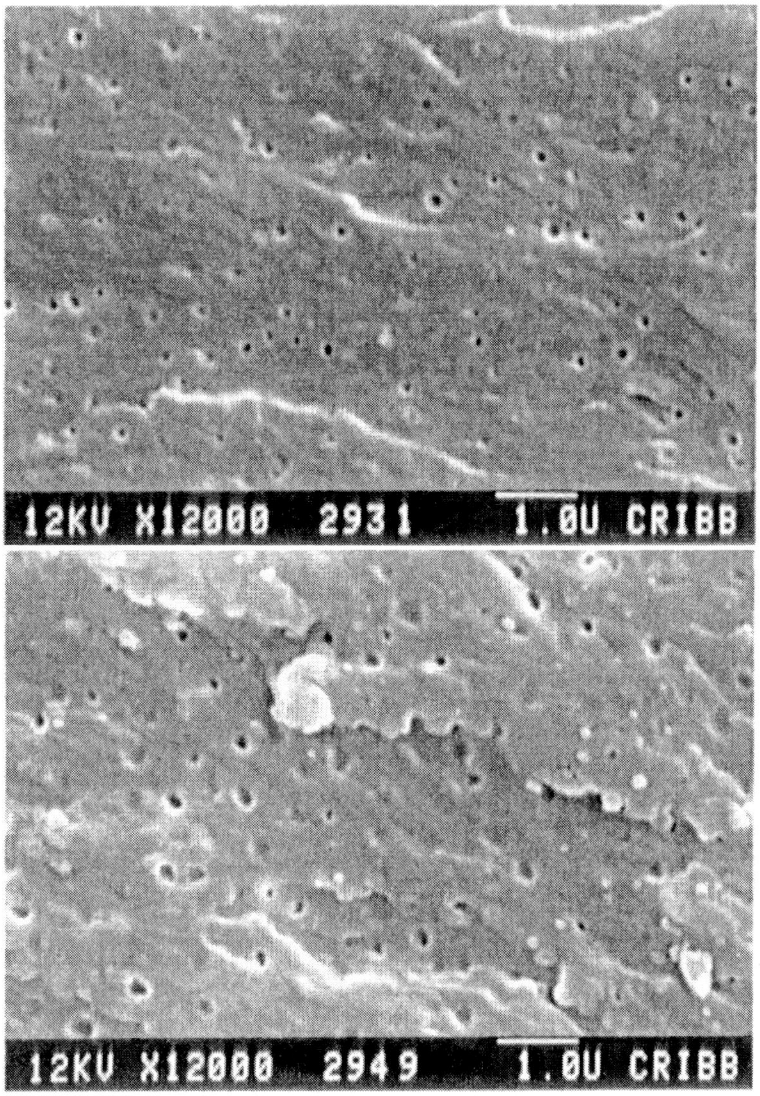

a)

b)

Figure 13: Morphology of the plaques modified with 10 wt % of PU and cured at oven temperature of 100°C, in the wall of plaque by SEM: (a) 10 wt % PU; (b) 20wt% PU.

3.5. Relation Morphology-Properties

3.5.1 Characterization of the Copolymers

The test specimens used in the mechanical characterization were prepared with 0, 10, and 20% by weight of PU in the epoxy resin. To avoid large temperature gradients inside the molds (discussed in the previous section), the following curing cycle was used: 1 hour at 40ºC, 1.5 hours at 100ºC. The samples were further postcured at 160ºC during 6 hours.

The characteristics of the generated morphology were determined as the average particle size (Dp) and volume fraction (VD) of PU dispersed phase. Both variables increased with the increment of the initial concentration of PU (Table 5). However the difference between initial volume fraction of PU and V_D indicates that a large amount of PU is co-reacted in the continued phase. The chains of PU have a high probability of co-reaction with the epoxy-amine system and therefore the thermoset is flexibilized, while its Tg is reduced.

3.5.2. Mechanical and Fracture Properties of Copolymers

The flexural modulus (E_F) and compression yield stress (σ_{YC}) of the copolymers are affected by the initial mass fraction of prepolymer, as shown in Table 5. In all cases E_F and σ_{YC} decrease with the content of prepolymer. There are two factors causing the drop of the modulus: the increase of the volume fraction of elastomeric dispersed phase (the rigid phase decreases) and the decrease of rigidity of the continuous phase due to the copolymerization with the prepolymer. Regarding the last effect, Wang and Chen [50] worked with a similar system and reported that the modulus of the network at room temperature decreased due to the effect of the soft segment structure of the co-reacted elastomer. The increase of the dispersed phase as well as the modification of continuous phase contribute to the modulus reduction. Thus, as the initial amount of elastomer increases, a different and more flexible continuous phase is generated.

Table 5: Morphology characterization and mechanical properties of copolymers

Sample	E_F (Gpa)	σ_{CY} (MPa)	G_{IC} (kJ/m^2)	$\phi_{PU}^{O\ a}$	Dp (μm)	$V_D^{\ b}$
EA	2.80±0.17	113±7	0.456±0.062	-	-	-
EA – 10% PU	2.60±0.1	105±3	0.646±0.032	0.085	0.10	0.029
EA – 20% PU	1.99±0.15	89±4	0.771±0.062	0.173	0.17	0.078

[a] Initial volume fraction of PU
[b] volume fraction of dispersed phase

Table 5 shows the values of G_{IC} for the copolymers. In all cases, G_{IC} increases as the initial concentration of prepolymer increases. It has been frequently reported in the literature, that the elastomer particles promote the multiple, but localized, shear-yielding in the matrix initiated by the stress concentrations associated with the presence of the rubbery particles. The relatively modest increment in G_{IC} is due to the high testing rate (pendulum sticker, impact test), which leads to reduced shear deformation [22, 51].

The ductility of the matrix has also an important effect on the fracture energy of the material [25]. The ductility of the network increases due to the copolymerization of the epoxy- amine with the flexible PUs chains and thus, the presence of the rubber particles is more effective in toughening the thermoset.

4. CONCLUSIONS

The use of a simple, but flexible, mathematical model that takes into account the chemical and diffusional controlled parts of the reaction allowed to obtain excellent predictions for the conversions and reaction rates of the urethane –epoxy amine copolymers. A single set of parameters is needed for each system independent of the conditions of cure, ie: isothermal (low or high temperatures) or dynamic conditions. The model predicts successfully the decrease of the reaction rate and the final conversion as the vitrification sets in. It can also predict the accelerating effect of the PU copolymerization on the chemical and diffusional controlled reactions.

The global kinetic expression was utilized in the prediction of temperature profiles inside a heated mold. Predicted curves were compared with experimental results obtained for different PU concentrations, showing an excellent agreement at different curing conditions and mold thicknesses. The determination of isothermal cloud point results and its incorporation to the conversion-temperature phase diagrams allowed to analyze the expected final morphologies of the molded plaques. Thus, homogeneous samples were predicted for curing at low oven temperatures (30'C) and phase separated systems for the other two higher curing temperatures (70 and 100 'C). These predictions were in complete agreement with the morphologies found experimentally and observed by SEM.

The mechanical and fracture characterization of the copolymers showed direct correlation with the final morphologies of the specimens. The presence of an elastomeric dispersed phase and the flexibilization of continuous phase, as a result of copolymerization epoxy-urethane, produce an improvement of toughness respect to the unmodified system. However, this improvement is accompanied by a slight decrease in the mechanical properties and glass transition temperature. The choice of the optimum amount of PU will depend on the final use of copolymer.

ACKNOWLEDGMENTS

The authors thank CONICET (National Research Council of Argentina) for the finantial support.

5. REFERENCES

[1] Verchère, D., Pascault, J.P., Sautereau, H., Moschiar, S.M., Riccardi, C.C. and R.J.J. Williams, R.J.J., *J. Appl. Polym. Sci*,, 43 293-304 (1991)

[2] Bussi, P. and Ishida, H., *J. Appl. Polym. Sci.,* 53 441-454 (1994)

[3] Huang, Y. and Kinloch, A.J., *Polymer,* 33:6 1330-1332 (1992)

[4] Huang, Y. and Kinloch, A.J., *J.Mater. Sci. Lett.*, 11 484-487 (1992)

[5] Huang, Y., Hunston, D.L., Kinloch, A.J., and Riew, C.K., *"Toghened Plastic 1"*, Ed. Riew, C.K. and Kinloch, A.J., American Chemical Society, Washington DC (1993) chapter 1.

[6] Bucknall, O.B. and Yoshit, T., *Brit. Polym.J.*, 10 53-59 (1978).

[7] Lanzetta,N., Laurienzo, P., Malinconico, M., Martuscelli, E., Rasgosta, G. and Volpe, M.G., *J. Mater. Scie.*, 27 786-792 (1992).

[8] Yee, A.F. and Pearson, R.A., *J. Mater. Sci.*, 21:7 2462-2474 (1986)

[9] Pearson, R.A. and Yee, A.F., *J. Mater. Sci.*, 21:7 2475-2488 (1986)

[10] Calabrese, L. and Valenza, A., *Eur, Polym. J.*, 39 1355-1363 (2003)

[11] Simon S.L. and Gillham J.K., *J. Appl. Polym. Sci.,* 46 1245-1270 (1992).

[12] Girard-Reydet E., Riccardi C.C., Sautereau H. and Pascault J.P., *Macromolecules,* 28:23, 7599-7607 (1995)

[13] Monserrat, S., Roman, F. Colomer, P., *Polymer,* 44 101-114 (2003)

[14] Monserrat, S. And Martín, J.G., *Thermochim. Acta*, 388 343-354 (2002)
[15] Van Assche, G., Swier, S. and Van Mele, B., *Thermochim. Acta.*, 388 327-341 (2002)
[16] Verchère, D., Pascault, J.P., Sautereau, H., Moschiar, S.M., Riccardi, C.C. and R.J.J. Williams, R.J.J., *J. Appl. Polym. Sci,*, 41 467-485 (1990)
[17] Ruseckaite, R.A., Hu, L., Riccardi, C.C. and Williams, R.J.J., *Polym. Int.*, 30:3 287-295 (1993).
[18] Grillet, A.C., Galy, J. and Pascault, J.P., *Polymer*, 33:1 34-43 (1992).
[19] S.M. Moschiar, C.C. Riccardi, R.J.J. Williams, D. Verchère, H. Sautereau and J.P. Pascault *J. Appl. Polym. Sci.*, 42 717-735 (1991)
[20] Bussi, P. and Ishida, H., *J. Polym. Sci.: Part B: Polymer Physics*, 32 647-657 (1994).
[21] D.P. Fang, P.M. Frontini, C.C. Riccardi and R.J.J. Williams, *Polym. Eng. Sci*, 35 1358-1363 (1995)
[22] Kinloch, A.J. and Hunston, D.L., *J. Mater. Sci. Lett.*, 6 131-139 (1987)
[23] Huang, Y., Kinloch, A.J., Bertsch, R.J. and Siebert, A.R., *"Toughened Plastic 1"*, Ed. Riew, C.K. and Kinloch, A.J., American Chemical Society, Washington DC (1993) Chap 8.
[24] Bagheri R. and Pearson R.A., *J. Appl. Polym. Sci.*, 58 427-437 (1995)
[25] Chen, T.K. and Jan, Y.H., *Polym. Eng. Sci.*, 35:9 778-785 (1995).
[26] R. Muelhaupt and V. Buchholz, *Polym. Mater. Sci. Eng*, 70 4 (1993)
[27] Williams, J.G., *Fracture Mechanical of Polymers*, Ellis Horwood, Chichester, 1984.
[28] Plati, E. and Williams, J.G., *Polym. Eng. Sci*, 15:6 470-477 (1975)
[29] Ahmed, S. and Jones, F.R., *J. Mat. Sci.*, 25:12 1933-4942 (1990)
[30] Verchère, D., Pascault, J.P., Sautereau, H., Moschiar, S.M., Riccardi, C.C. and Williams, R.J.J., *J. Appl. Polym. Sci*, 42 701-716 (1991)
[31] Stefani P. M., Moschiar S.M., Aranguren M. I., *J. Appl. Polym. Sci.*, 68 1781-1789 (1998)
[32] Stefani P. M., Moschiar S.M., Aranguren M. I., *J. Appl. Polym. Sci.*, 79 1771-1779 (2001)
[33] Kamal M.R. and Sourour S., *Polym. Eng. Sci.,* 13:2 59-64 (1973)
[34] Kamal M.R., *Polym. Eng. Sci.*, 14:3 231-239 (1974)
[35] Ryan M.E. and Dutta A., *Polymer*, 20 203-206 (1979)
[36] Han C.D. and Lem K.W., *J. Appl. Polym. Sci.,* 28:2 743-762 (1983)
[37] F. Rabinowitch, *Trans. Faraday Soc.,* 33 1225 (1937)
[38] G. Adam and J.H. Gibbs, *J. Chem. Phys.,* 43:1 139-150 (1965)
[39] Marquardt, W., *SIAM J.*, 11 431 (1963)
[40] Barton J.M. in "Epoxy Resins and Composites I", *Advances in Polymer Science* 72, Editor K. Duek, Springer-Verlag, Berlin, 1985.
[41] Nielsen, L.E., *J.Macromol. Sci, Revs. Macromol. Chem.*, C3, 69 (1969)
[42] Pascault, J.P. and Williams, R.J.J., *J. Polym. Sci.: Part B: Polym. Phys.*, 28 85-95 (1990)
[43] Pascault, J.P. and Williams, R.J.J., *Polym. Bull.*, 24 115-121 (1990)
[44] G.M. Maistros and C.B. Bucknall, *Polym. Eng. Sci.* 34: 20, 1517-1528 (1994)
[45] R.J.J. Williams, M.A. Benavente, R.A Ruseckaite, M.S. Churio and H.G. Hack, *Polym. Eng. Sci.*, 30:18, 1140-1145 (1990)
[46] Chater, M. and Vergnaud, J.M., *Eur. Polym. J.,* 24:3 245-250 (1988)
[47] Reboredo M.M. and Vazquez, A., *Polym. Eng. Sci.*, 35:19 1521-1526 (1995)

[48] Williams, R.J.J., *"Developments in Plastic Technology-2"*, Eds. A. Welar & J. Craft, Elsevier Applied Science, London, 1985, pag 339.
[49] Montarnal, S., Pascault, J.P. and Sautereau, H., in *Adv. Chem. Ser*, N° 222, American Chemical Society, Washington D.C. 1989, p 193.
[50] Wang, H., Chen, J.C., *Polym. Eng Sci*, 35:18 1468-1475 (1995)
[51] S. Bandyopadhyay, *"Toughened Plastic 1"*, Ed. C.K. Riew, and A.J. Kinloch, American Chemical Society, Washington DC (1993) Chap 9

In: Homolytic and Heterolytic Reactions: Problems and Solutions ISBN 1-59033-980-0
Editors: G.E. Zaikov, et al., pp. 261-266

Chapter 10

THE EXTRUTION OF POLYMERS IN THE ULTRASONIC ACTION

O. F. Kiselyova[1], A. A. Panov[1], K. S. Minsker[2] and A. K. Panov[1]
[1]Branch UGNTU, Sterlitamak
[2]Bashkirean State University, Ufa

The phenomenon of highly elastic restoration extruded through forming tool is well-known in the plastics processing practice. A number of works [1-4], in which models of various degree of complexity allowing to estimate this phenomenon quantitatively are discussed, are devoted to the description of this phenomenon. However, it is necessary to point out that the use of simplified models gives an approximate estimate and does not corresponds to the experimental data adequately enough. More complex models are big enough big it practical application [3], and, as a rule, are not effective enough. Moreover, none of the models consider one of the most important operational and technological operational and characteristics - the "swelling" of polymeric products of the complex profile received in conditions of ultrasonic fluctuations influence. Usually, as a rule description of the phenomenon of "swelling" is limited to extruders as twig of round cross section or a flat sheet [4].

In this connection, the mathematical dependence allowing to define quantitatively the effect of "swelling" at pressing the melts of polymers through channels of any complex section when using intensive ultrasonic vibrations, is of practical interest.

The size of "swelling" extrudates is influenced, first of all, with molecular characteristics and physical properties of material, technological conditions of processing (temperature, speed, pressure of shift), and also the geometrical sizes of forming channel.

Modeling the effect of "swelling" of the extrudate, we shall consider that when a polymer runs through the channel, its particles, undergoing shift deformation, become longer and, after going out from the channel due to relaxation, they are reduced, besides the stretching and reduction of particles has an elastic character.

Thus, in the equation, mathematically describing the coefficient of "swelling", in is necessary to take into account the length of the channel L and its area S. Besides these values it is necessary to take into account pressure p at the extrusion of polymeric composition, the effective viscosity η_{ef}, the gradient of speed of shift $\overline{\gamma}$ and a certain parameter Θ, taking into account highly elastic properties of environment:

$$K = A \cdot \overline{\gamma}^{n_1} \cdot \Theta^{n_2} \cdot P^{n_3} \cdot \eta_{ef}^{n_4} \cdot L^{n_5} \cdot S^{n_6} \tag{1}$$

Here A is the dimensionless coefficient taking into account the nature of material, n1 - n6 parameters of degrees.

Using the p - theorem and the theory of groups [3] the dependence for definition the coefficient of the "swelling" of polymeric material in the cylindrical channel is received:

$$K = A \cdot (\overline{\gamma} \cdot \Theta)^{n_1} \cdot \left(\frac{\eta_{эф}}{P \cdot \Theta}\right)^{n_2} \cdot \left(\frac{L}{S_K}\right)^{n_3} \tag{2}$$

Constant A and parameters of degrees n_1 - n_6 are defined experimental (table. 1).

To receive the necessary model of the calculation of factor K for channels of complex form, it is necessary (2) to introduce the coefficient of the form of the channel a and b, which are also determined experimentally according to the method membranes analogies [3] into the equation:

$$K = A \cdot a^{m_1} \cdot b^{m_2} \cdot (\overline{\gamma} \cdot \Theta)^{n_1} \cdot \left(\frac{\eta_{эф}}{P \cdot \Theta}\right)^{n_2} \cdot \left(\frac{L}{\sqrt{S_K}}\right)^{n_3} \tag{3}$$

where m_1, m_2 are parameters of degrees (table. 1).

When ultrasonic fluctuations are imposed on the melt stream, a significant decrease of the coefficient of "swelling" is observed. First of all it occurs due to decrease of effective viscosity of melt η_{ef} up to some value η_ω, determined from the equation [5].

$$\eta_\omega = \frac{\eta_{эф}}{1 + \omega^2 \cdot r^2}, \tag{4}$$

where ω is an angular frequency of ultrasonic fluctuations, η_{ef}; r is the time of relaxation describing the speed of decreasing pressure:

$$r = \frac{\eta_{эф}}{E}, \tag{5}$$

where E is the module of the elasticity of environment, Pa.

Table 1 - Values of physical quantities and constant coefficient

Material	Temp, K	$\overline{\gamma}$, 1/c	Θ, c	η_ω, Па·с	N_1	n_2	n_3	A	m_1	m_2
Polythene	338	3,546	0,1	4550	0,077	-0,015	-0,118	2,625	-0,021	-0,017
	403	3,548	0,1	3020	0,077	-0,015	-0,118	2,625	-0,021	-0,017
	418	3,548	0,1	1897	0,077	-0,015	-0,118	2,625	-0,021	-0,017
	433	3,548	0,1	1479	0,077	-0,015	-0,118	2,625	-0,021	-0,017
	488	3,548	0,1	1324	0,077	-0,015	-0,118	2,625	-0,021	-0,017
Polystyrene	438	3,548	0,1	4514	0,089	-0,088	-0,127	6,150	-0,016	-0,014
	448	3,548	0,1	3388	0,089	-0,088	-0,127	6,150	-0,016	-0,014
	458	3,548	0,1	2729	0,089	-0,088	-0,127	6,150	-0,016	-0,014
	468	3,548	0,1	2483	0,089	-0,088	-0,127	6,150	-0,016	-0,014
	478	3,548	0,1	2300	0,089	-0,088	-0,127	6,150	-0,016	-0,014
PVH-plastic compound	403	3,548	0,1	5889	0,065	-0,020	-0,107	2,147	-0,005	-0,004
	413	3,548	0,1	3981	0,065	-0,020	-0,107	2,147	-0,005	-0,004
	423	3,548	0,1	3715	0,065	-0,020	-0,107	2,147	-0,005	-0,004
	433	3,548	0,1	3506	0,065	-0,020	-0,107	2,147	-0,005	-0,004
	443	3,548	0,1	1514	0,065	-0,020	-0,107	2,147	-0,005	-0,004

Therefore it is expedient to introduce the parameter η_ω characterizing the influence ultrasound on a degree of "swelling" of extrudate of polymeric material equation (3)

$$K = A \cdot a^{m_1} \cdot b^{m_2} \cdot (\overline{\gamma} \cdot \Theta)^{n_1} \cdot \left(\frac{\eta_\omega}{P \cdot \Theta}\right)^{n_2} \cdot \left(\frac{L}{\sqrt{S_K}}\right)^{n_3} \tag{6}$$

The received equation (6) represents a mathematical model describing influence of imposing ultrasonic fluctuations on the "swelling" of the extrudate during the extruded polymeric material at ultrasonic influence.

To confirm the adequacy of the offered correlation (6) to the phenomenon observably practice, the experimental researches to estimate the coefficient of "swelling" depending on the geometry of the channel, parameters of process extruded, physical and some other properties of used polymer, and also from frequency of ultrasonic fluctuations carried out.

For an estimation of adequacy of mathematical dependences and opportunities of their application in concrete engineering calculations a number of experiments have been carried out. For which the industrial extruder ATL-45 was used, with the characteristics: the length of a worm is 0,8 m, diameter 4×10^{-2} m. The extrusion installation includes the forming knot consisting of forming heads, which is made square section 0,045×0,045 m. For creation of ultrasonic fluctuations on forming head two magnetostrictive converter were used, such as PMS-6-22, ultrasonic fluctuations UZG1-4 connected to the generator.

It is necessary to note positive influence of ultrasound on decrease of the coefficient "swelling". Pay attention, that the greatest factor of "swelling" in experiences without ultrasound (fig. 1) have extrude at use of the channel of the triangular form, then П - and Г - forms, and the least Ш-forms, thus greatest "swelling" extrude observes on the long party of a sample and near to a sharp corner of triangular section.

At use of ultrasound the observably picture appreciably changes. Distortion of samples is much less, thus decrease of factor of "swelling" K on the average on 10 - 12 % takes place, thus the greatest decrease K is observed for channel SH - forms, the least - for the triangular form. Numerical value of factor of "swelling" K is influenced also with a chemical nature of a used polymeric material.

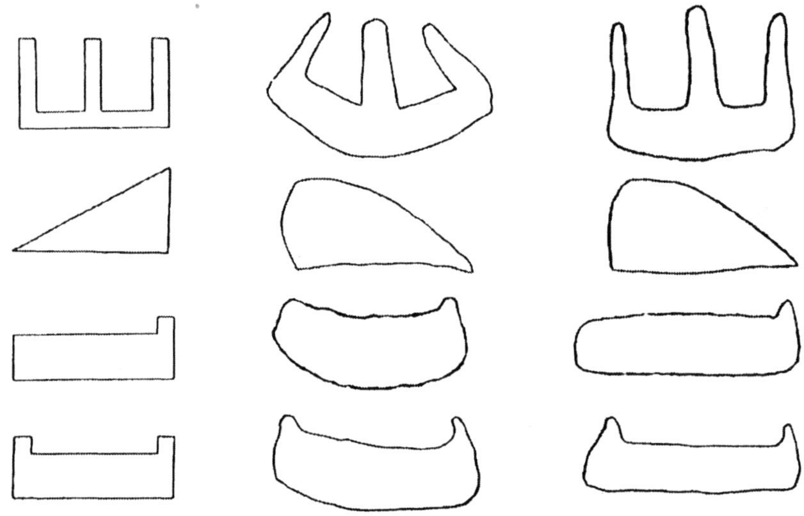

Figure 1. Characteristic contours extrude, received at extruded polyvinylchloride paste, polystyrene and polythene; a - section of a product; b - samples extrude, received without ultrasound; c - the samples received with ultrasound.

The greatest "swelling" of extrudate is typical of polystyrene, the least - for plastic compound on the basis of polyvinylchloride paste.

The decrease of the coefficient "swelling" is also observed when the length of the channel L increases in the extruder. It is true for all forms of the channel and for all the investigated polymers. The lower the temperature of formation, the less the coefficient of “swelling” K. Besides, the best results are received when the frequency of ultrasound is 21,6 kHz,

The comparison of the results of experiment with the calculated values of the coefficient of "swelling" K (fig.2) allowed to reveal the following pequliarities:

1) The decrease of the coefficient of "swelling" of polymeric materials under the influence of ultrasound is observed for all the forms of the investigated channels in an extruder. The divergence between the calculated and experimental data is about 15 %;

2) The frequency of ultrasonic fluctuations also influences the productivity of the extruder, the mass expenditure of polymeric products. Taking in into account the best results are received when the frequency of ultrasound is 21,6 kHz;
3) When comparing the influence of the form of section of channels in extruder, the greatest positive influence of ultrasound is marked for channels triangular and Ш - figurative forms. It is obviously due to the fact that though in these channels there are stagnant zones and sharp corners, because of the ultrasound influence;
4) In the process of pressure increase during the polymer extrusion the rate growth of the coefficient of "swelling" is reduced and when the pressure is more than 5,0 MPa its value is practically unchanged. The sharp increase of the coefficient of "swelling" when the pressure is not great is the characteristic feature for investigated polymers. It is also confirmed in works [3,4].
5) The reduction of the coefficient of “swelling” is typical to the polymers investigated in work (polythene, polypropylene, polyvinylchloride plastic compound) when the length of the channel increases. Besides, there is a critical value of length L =110 mm, above which the "swelling", remains practically unchanged. It is the essential factor in designing forming channel.
6) When the temperature of extrusion increase, the coefficient "swelling" also increases. Besides, the increase of K is more noticeable for polystyrene for other kinds of investigated polymers.

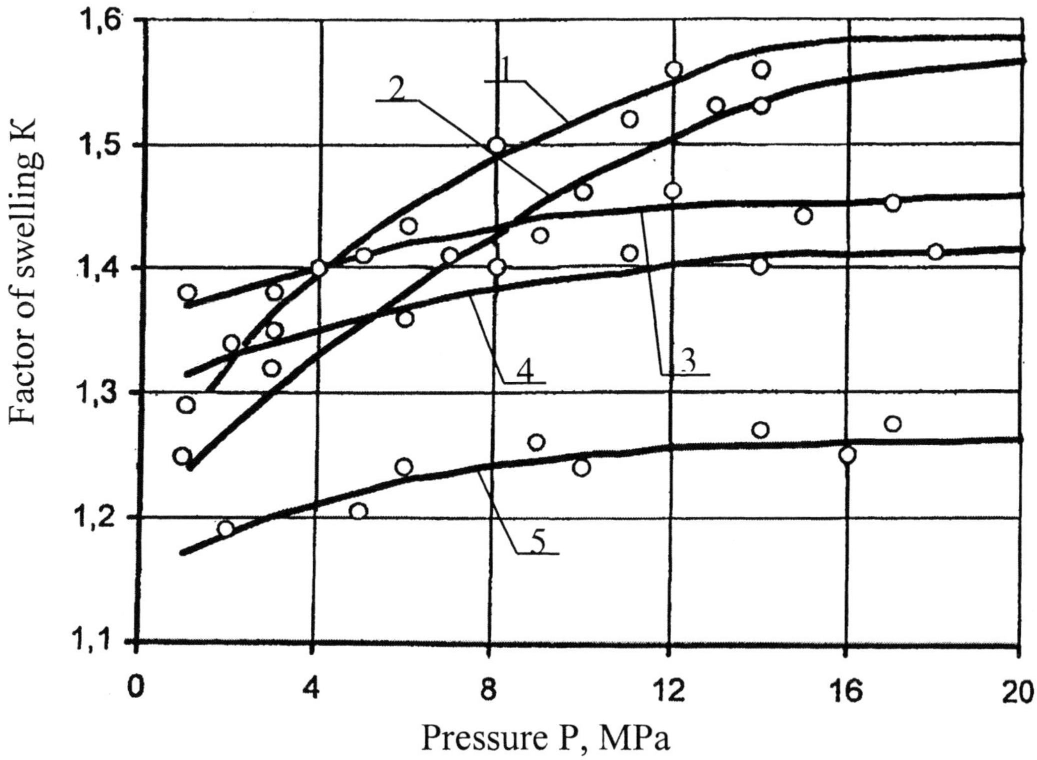

Figure 2. Dependence of factor of "swelling" on pressure, the channel triangular, 1 - polystyrene L = 70 mm at 453 K, 2 - polystyrene L = 70 mm at 438 K, 3 - polythene L = 110 mm at 430 K, 4 - polythene L = 110 mm at 418 K, 5 – polyvinylchloride paste L = 90 mm at 413 K; frequency of ultrasound 21,6 kHz

Thus, the received results for estimating the constant of "swelling" K, can be used for calculating the forming tool, both without, and under the influence of ultrasonic influences. Besides, the given results can be used in the processes of free extrusion, when the product which has left the forming head, does not adjoin with calibrated tool and does not undergo an extract and mechanic proceeding.

REFERENCES

[1] Gul V.E., Kuleznev V.N., *Structure and mechanical properties of polymers*. - M.: the higher School, 1972. - 320 with.

[2] Basov N.I.&, Broy V. *Technology of processing of plastic*. - M.: Chemistry, 1985. - 530 with.

[3] Panov A.K., Anasov A.R. *hydrodynamics of streams of abnormal - viscous polymeric systems in forming channels*. - Ufa: UGNTU, 1994. - 260 with.

[4] Khan C.D. *Reologija during processing polymers*. - M.: Chemistry, 1979. - 396 with.

[5] Mihajlov I.T., Solov'ev V.A., *JU.P.bas's Cheesecakes of molecular acoustics*. - M.: the Science, 1964. - 516 with.

In: Homolytic and Heterolytic Reactions: Problems and Solutions ISBN 1-59033-980-0
Editors: G.E. Zaikov, et al., pp. 267-272

Chapter 11

DESIGNS AND A METHOD OF CALCULATION ACOUSTIC EXTRUSION – THE HEAD FOR MANUFACTURING PROFILE-POGONAGE POLYMERIC PRODUCTS

O. F. Kiselyova*[1]*, A. A. Panov*[1]*, K. S. Minsker*[2]*,
A. K. Panov*[1] *and G. E. Zaikov*[3]*,
[1]Branch UGNTU, Sterlitamak
[2]Bashkirean state university, Ufa
[3]Institute of Biochemical Physics, Moscow

Nowadays there is the theoretical ground and the experimental researches [1-3] confirming that influencing the stream of melt periodic deformation, rotation and vibration the throughput of the channel is increased, the resistance in units of forming tool is reduced, there is an opportunity to conduct process of extruded at lower temperatures [2].

On the basis of these studies rotating heads and various elements of mechanical influence are designed [2,3]. However, the use of ultrasonic fluctuations, is more economic and there is an opportunity to simplify a design of the extrusion head and to reduce expenses of energy due to absence of moving elements. The application of ultrasound allows to reduce the temperature of formationto raise speed of extrusion, to reduce the post-extrusion swelling of products that results in the increase of process productivity.

At studying the process of melt polymers with the use of ultrasonic fluctuations basically have been used till now round and slot-hole channels, the application of which is limited unlike channels of a complex configuration the use off which allows to receive various kinds profile-pogonage products [2,3].

In this connection, the perfection of calculation methods and the creation of new designs of extrusion head for manufacture of products of a complex structure in the conditions of the use of ultrasound is an actual problem.

The analysis of designs and methods of calculation of thin-plane and trumpet acoustic heads [2-4] allows to draw the following conclusions: choosing the type of a radiator one should prefer magnetostrictive, instead of piezoceramic as the last are more effective. Among magnetostrictive radiators it is more expedient to use the designs which have been built - inside the head extruder. The installation of the vibrator on the forming tool reduces the efficiency of penetration of ultrasonic fluctuations in melt polymer mass as the wall of the case has significant thickness. Therefore the decrease of melt viscosity before wall layer occurs insignificantly and has little influences on the improvement of the quality product surface the system of cooling of an active element of a radiator of ultrasonic fluctuations as it is obligatory, as in works under conditions of the raised temperatures. The number of used industrial acoustic heads now is limited now in comparison with the forming tool working without ultrasonic influence, despite of their higher efficiency. Besides existing designs allow to make only film, sheets and pipes whereas the demand for high-quality products of a complex structure is great.

Working in the field of the development of extrusion head designs with elements of complex profile together with studying the rheological characteristics polymers melt in conditions of the use of ultrasound, the design multilane extrusion the head for manufacturing profile-pogonage polymeric products with the application of ultrasonic fluctuations (fig. 1) was offered, allowing to improve the quality extrusion profile-pogonage products and to raise the productivity of extrusion installations [4].

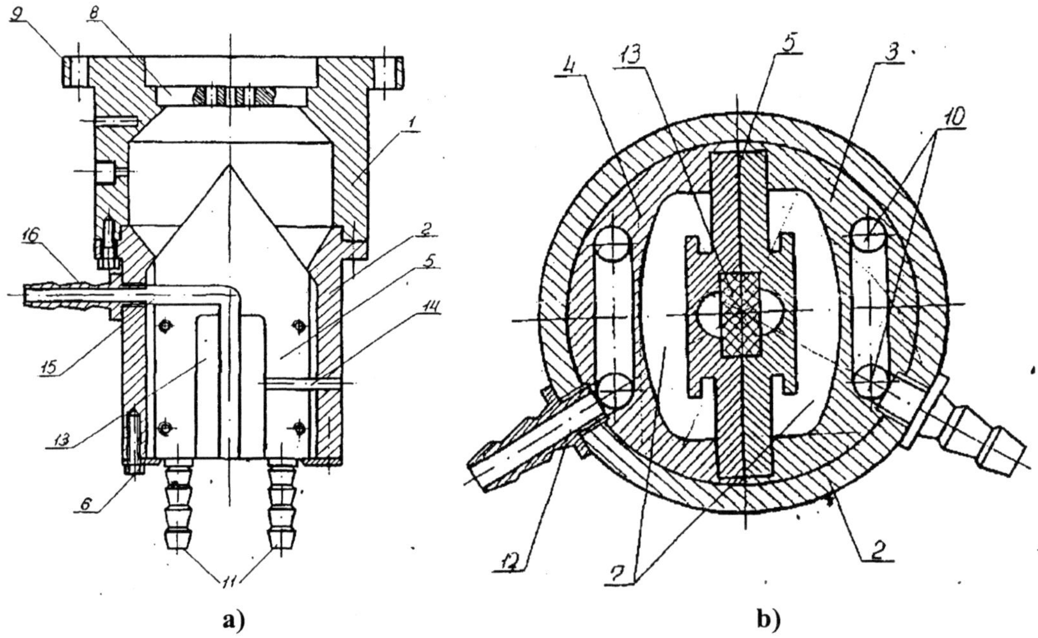

a) b)

Figure 1. Multilane extrusion head for manufacturing profile-pogonage polymeric products with application of ultrasound: 1 - the case; 2 - a holder; 3,4 - semicylindrical section; 5 - dorn; 6 - a washer; 7 - the profil channel; 8 - a lattice; 9,16 - a flange; 10,16 - channels for cooling; 11,12 - union; 13 –a magnetostrictive radiator; 14 - the channel for connection of a source of ultrasonic fluctuations; a) a longitudinal section, б) a transverse incision

Despite of the importance of the problem of the use of ultrasonic vibrations during processing polymers, it has been investigated insufficiently till now [3], and the majority of publications including last years, concerning the consideration of influence of ultrasound on polymers melts only in round and thin-plane channels.

On the basis of the equations describing pressure current of liquids thin-plane and cylindrical channels in conditions of influence of ultrasound [2] the dependence for definition the expenditure of liquid in profile channels of acoustic extrusion head is offered:

$$Q = -\frac{a\rho S}{\tau_0^{\text{в}}}\left\{\int_0^{\tau_1}\frac{k_1\tau^{\text{в}}\left(R_\Gamma - \delta\right)}{\eta_{\text{эф}}}d\tau + \int_{\tau_1}^{\tau_0}\frac{k_2\tau^{\text{в}}\delta}{\eta_\omega}d\tau\right\} \quad (1)$$

Here Q is the mass expenditure of polymers, kg/sec; a, b are factors of the form; ρ is melt density, kg/m^3; S is the area of cross section of the channel, m^2; τ_0 - an average pressure of shift at the wall of the channel, Pa; R_Γ is the hydraulic radius of the channel, m; δ - is the depth of ultrasound penetration, m; η_{ef} is the effective viscosity, Pa·sec^{-1}; η_ω, is the viscosity of polymer at the influence of ultrasound, Pa·sec^{-1}; k_1 and k_2 are correction coefficients.

For the estimation of the increase of the productivity of extruded process at acoustic forming tools it is possible to offer the dependence for definition the capacity of ultrasonic fluctuations:

$$N_\omega = 0{,}25 \cdot k_1 \cdot \Pi \cdot L \cdot \rho \cdot A^2 \cdot \omega^2 \cdot c \quad (2)$$

Here Π is the perimeter of the channel, m; L is the length of the channel, m; A is the amplitude of fluctuations, ω is the angular frequency of ultrasonic fluctuations, sec^{-1}; c is the speed of a sound in polymer mass, m/sec.

For an estimation of adequacy of mathematical dependences and opportunities of their application in concrete engineering calculations a number of experiments have been carried out. For which the industrial extruder ATL-45 was used, with the characteristics: the length of a worm is 0,8 m, diameter 4×10^{-2} m. The extrusion installation includes the forming knot consisting of forming heads, which is made square section 0,045×0,045 m. For creation of ultrasonic fluctuations on forming head two magnetostrictive converters were used, such as PMS-6-22, ultrasonic fluctuations UZG1-4 connected to the generator.

The channels of complex profile were defined. The rheological properties of polymer melts and the dependence of account testimonials from of temperature, pressure at extruded, frequencies of ultrasound, the design of the channel, and also capacity of ultrasonic fluctuations from type of used polymer, the geometry of the channel and parameters of ultrasound were used.

The equation (1) for an estimation of throughput of the channel at extruded includes the coefficients depending on the form of the channels section. Their calculation is connected with great difficulties as it is necessary to calculate initial sizes to know the true speed of melt in the channel, which is difficult to define, and also it is necessary to have dependence of change of fluidity of melt from the shift pressure. Therefore for the definition of the coefficients a and b more convenient method in the practical attitude membrane analogies [2] that has allowed to estimate factors of the form for four various kinds of researched sections of channels (table. 1) was used.

Table 1 - Values of coefficient of the form of researched sections.

Parameter	Section of a product			
	П – figurative	Г - figurative	Triangular	Ш – figurative
$R_Г \cdot 10^3$, m	1,81	1,88	1,52	0,96
A	1,348	1,645	2,208	1,209
B	1,989	1,996	2,573	1,985

Three kinds of polymers have been chosen: polyvinylchloride plastic compound (cable) (GOST 5960), polystyrene PS-S (GOST 20282) and polythene of a high pressure (GOST 150802).

The polymer melts, chosen for realization of experimental researches are typical representatives of viscoelastic liquids and their physical and chemical properties are investigated well enough and described in the literature [1-3,5].

For confirming the validity of the equation (1), experimental researches by the definition of the dependence of the mass expenditure polymer melt from the pressure gradient in the researched channel were carried out. The current of polymers in channels of a complex profile of different length for each section was studied. Thus, the experimental data have been obtained for 12 channels and three kinds of polymers (polythene, polystyrene and polyvinylchloride plastic compound) at interval of temperatures 403 - 453 K, pressure of extrusion up to 6 MPa and the frequencies of ultrasound - 18,5; 20,5; 21,6; 22,1; 23,5 kHz.

The analysis of the received results shows, that in all case using the ultrasonic fluctuations, the increase of the mass expenditure of polymers for all the forms of channels was observed. The greatest increase of the expenditure of polymer products was for was observed for polyvinylchloride paste (20 - 25 %), the least - for polystyrene (10 - 15 %).The greatest effect from ultrasonic influence was observed for the channel of the form of a triangle, the lowest - for channel Ш - forms. In process of increase of temperature in a zone of polymer at extruded the effect of the use of ultrasound was reduced. The frequency 21,6 kHz was optimal.

Alongside with studying of account characteristics, the study dependence of the capacity of ultrasonic fluctuations from polymer, geometry of the channel is of interest. With a view of realization in practice of dependence (2) the appropriate calculations which results of wish are given in table. 2, were carried out.

The analysis of experimental results shows that the greatest capacity of radiation absorbed by any polymer, is characteristic for polyvinylchloride paste. This polymer has higher density and lower viscosity in comparison with polystyrene and polythene. The speed of a sound for the chosen polymers is accordingly, 1650 m/s for polyvinylchloride paste, 1500 m/s for polystyrene and for polyethene of a high pressure - 1600 m/s. With the increase of temperature the capacity of ultrasonic fluctuations decreases, as the density of polymeric products decreases, thus the greatest capacity is characteristic for the triangular channel, the least - for Ш - forms of the channel. In the first case ultrasonic fluctuations operate with the greater efficiency through all perimeter of the channel in extruder whereas in the second case operate only on his part, due to the peculiarities of the design of the channel and dissipation energy.

Optimum frequencies of ultrasonic radiation 21,6 - 22,1 kHz - for polyvinylchloride paste, polystyrene and polythene are revealed. Thus the greatest amplitude makes 6 microns.

Thus, the calculations on the equation (2) will be coordinated to the experimental value on the parameter - the throughput of the channel extrusion at ultrasonic influence, i. e. on the productivity of extruder. The recommended modes of extrusion of the researched polymers are given in table. 3.

Table 2 - The results of the calculation of the capacity of ultrasonic fluctuations (W).

Frequency USF, kHz	The channel							
	Triangular		Г - figurative		П – figurative		Ш - figurative	
Polyvinylchloride paste (T = 413 K)								
18,5	438	435	400	402	419	421	364	367
20,5	846	840	772	770	809	806	699	703
21,6	1345	1346	1229	1232	1287	1282	1111	1115
22,1	1409	1403	1286	1290	1348	1349	1165	1161
23,5	1107	1105	1276	1277	1059	1056	914	918
Polystyrene (T = 438 K)								
18,5	282	285	258	260	270	267	233	235
20,5	543	539	497	495	520	521	449	447
21,6	865	866	790	794	827	829	715	718
22,1	711	710	574	571	602	606	520	523
23,5	455	458	416	417	436	432	376	377
Polyethene (T = 403 K)								
18,5	283	280	259	258	271	266	234	236
20,5	546	546	502	498	523	527	451	453
21,6	869	872	793	791	831	832	717	713
22,1	632	630	577	572	604	609	522	520
23,5	457	452	418	416	438	433	378	375

Table 3 – The recommended modes in an extruder at forming the profile- pogonage products

Researched polymer	Temperature extruded, To	Pressure extruded, MPa	Viscosity, 10-4 (Па·s)	Optimum frequency, kHz
Polyvinylchloride paste of GOST 5960	403-423	4,0-4,5	0,024-0,35	21,6
Polystyrene of GOST 20282	438-453	4,0-5,0	0,028 - 0,35	21,6
Polythene of a high pressure of GOST 150802	388-418	3,5-4,0	0,013-0,35	21,6

REFERENCES

[1] Basov N.I., Kazankov J.V., Lubartovich V.A. *Calculation and designing of the equipment for manufacture and processing of polymeric materials*. - M.: Chemistry, 1986. - 486 with.

[2] Panov A.K., Anasov A.R. *Hydrodynamics of streams of abnormal - viscous polymeric systems in forming channels*. - Ufa: UGNTU, 1994. - 260 with.

[3] Fridman M.L. *Technolog of processing crystal polyolephine*. - M.: Chemistry, 1977. - 398 with.

[4] Stalemate. 2147989 Russian Federations, МКИ^3 B29C47/12, 47/30 *Multilane extrusion the head for manufacturing profile-pogonage polymeric products with application of ultrasonic fluctuations* / A.K.Panov, O.F.Kiselyova, N.S.Shulaev; It is declared. 05.05.98; It is published. 27.04.2000; The bulletin. ¹ 21. A priority 05.05.98.

[5] Vinogradov G.V., Malkin A.J. *Reologija of polymers*. - M.: Chemistry, 1977. - 438 with.

In: Homolytic and Heterolytic Reactions: Problems and Solutions ISBN 1-59033-980-0
Editors: G.E. Zaikov, et al., pp. 273-282

Chapter 12

FEATURES OF DESIGNING OF ACOUSTIC EXTRUSION – THE HEAD FOR MANUFACTURING PROFILE-POGONAGE POLYMERIC PRODUCTS

O. F. Kiselyova[1], A. A. Panov[1], K. S. Minsker[2], A. K. Panov[1] and G. E. Zaikov[3],
[1]Branch UGNTU, Sterlitamak
[2]Bashkirean state university, Ufa
[3]Institute of Biochemical Physics, Moscow

Nowadays there is the theoretical ground and the experimental researches [1-3] confirming, that influencing the stream of melt periodic deformation, rotation and vibration the throughput of the channel is increased, the resistance in units of forming tool is reduced. Therefore, there is an opportunity to conduct process of extrusion at lower temperatures [2]. On the basis of these studies heads with rotating dorn and various elements of mechanical influence are designed [2,3].

However the use of ultrasonic fluctuations is more economic and there is an opportunity to simplify the design of the extrusion head and to reduce expenses of energy due to absence of moving elements. The application of ultrasound allows to reduce the temperature of formation to raise the speed of extrusion, to reduce the post-extrusion swelling of products that results in the increase of process productivity.

At studying the process of melt polymers with the use of ultrasonic fluctuations basically have been used till now round and slot-hole channels, the application of which is limited unlike channels of a complex configuration the use of which allows to receive various kinds of profile-pogonage products [2,3].

In this connection, the perfection of calculation methods and the creation of new designs of extrusion head for the manufacture of products of a complex structure in the conditions of the use of ultrasound is an actual problem. The analysis of designs and methods of calculation of thin-plane and trumpet acoustic heads [2-4] allows to draw the following conclusions: choosing the type of a radiator one should prefer magnetostrictive, instead of piezoceramic as the last are more effective. Among magnetostrictive radiators it is more expedient to use the designs which have been built inside the head extruder. The installation of the vibrator on the case of forming tool reduces the efficiency of penetration of ultrasonic fluctuations in melt polymer mass as the wall of the case has significant thickness. Therefore the decrease of melt viscosity the fore wall layer occurs insignificantly and has little influence on the improvement of the quality product surface. The system of cooling is an active element of a radiator of ultrasonic fluctuations as it obligatory, in works under conditions of the raised temperatures. The number of used industrial acoustic heads is limited now in comparison with the forming tool working without ultrasonic influence, despite of their higher efficiency. Besides existing designs allow to make only one film, sheets and pipes whereas the demand for high-quality products of a complex structure is great.

Working in the field of the development of extrusion head designs with elements of complex profile together with studying the rheological characteristics polymers melt in conditions of the use of ultrasound, the design multilane extrusion the head for manufacturing profile-pogonage polymeric products with the application of ultrasonic fluctuations (Fig. 1) was offered, allowing to improve the quality extrusion profile-pogonage products and to raise the productivity of extrusion installations [4].

Despite of the importance of the problem of the use of ultrasonic vibrations during processing polymers, it has been investigated insufficiently till now [3], and the majority of publications last years, concern the consideration of the influence of ultrasound on current of polymers melts only in round and thin-plane channels.

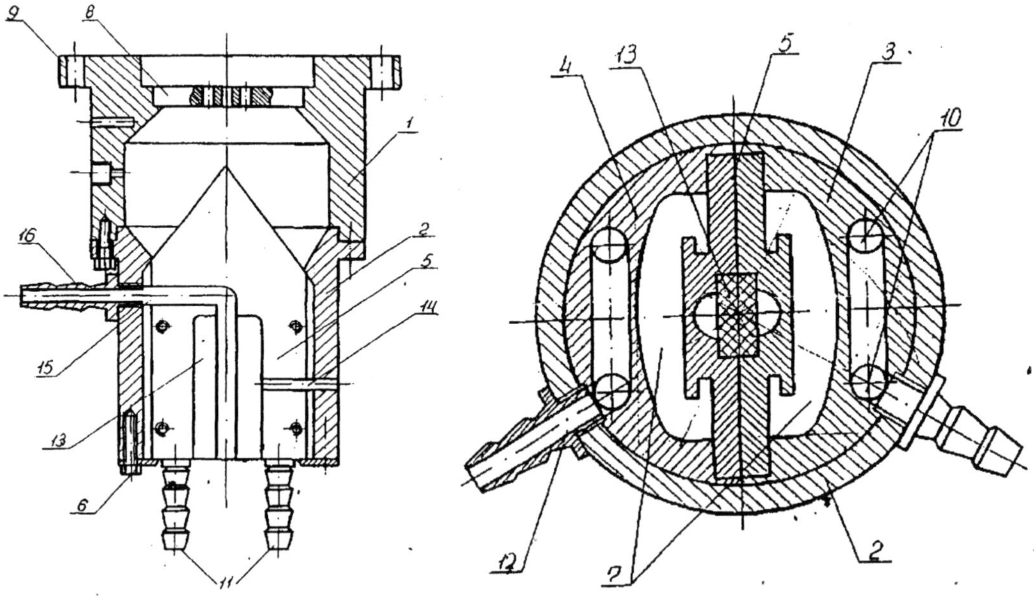

a) **b)**

Figure 1. Multilane extrusion head for manufacturing profile-pogonage polymeric products with application of ultrasound: 1 - the case; 2 - a holder; 3,4 - semicylindrical section; 5 - dorn; 6 - a washer; 7 - the profil channel; 8 - a lattice; 9,16 - a flange; 10,16 - channels for cooling; 11,12 union; 13 –a magnetostrictive radiator; 14 - the channel for connection of a source of ultrasonic fluctuations; a) a longitudinal section, б) a transverse incision

On the basis of the equations describing pressure current of liquids thin-plane and cylindrical channels in conditions of the influence of ultrasound [2], the dependence for definition the expenditure of liquid in profile channels of acoustic extrusion head is offered:

$$Q = -\frac{a\rho S}{\tau_0^{B}}\left\{\int_0^{\tau_1}\frac{k_1\tau^{B}(R_{\Gamma}-\delta)}{\eta_{\text{эф}}}d\tau + \int_{\tau_1}^{\tau_0}\frac{k_2\tau^{B}\delta}{\eta_\omega}d\tau\right\} \qquad (1)$$

Here Q is the mass expenditure of polymers, kg/sec; a, b are factors of the form; ρ is melt density, kg/m^3; S is the area of cross section of the channel, m^2; τ_0 - an average pressure of shift at the wall of the channel, Pa; R_Γ is the hydraulic radius of the channel, m; δ is the depth of ultrasound penetration, m; η_{ef} is the effective viscosity, $Pa\cdot sec^{-1}$; η_ω, is the viscosity of polymer at the influence of ultrasound, $Pa\cdot sec^{-1}$; k_1 and k_2 are correction coefficients.

For the estimation of the increase of the productivity of extruded process at the of acoustic forming tools it is possible to offer the dependence for definition the capacity of ultrasonic fluctuations:

$$N_\omega = 0{,}25\cdot k_1\cdot \Pi\cdot L\cdot\rho\cdot A^2\cdot\omega^2\cdot c \qquad (2)$$

Here Π is the perimeter of the channel, m; L is the length of the channel, m; A is the amplitude of fluctuations, ω is the angular frequency of ultrasonic fluctuations, sec^{-1}; c is the speed of a sound in polymer mass, m/sec.

For an estimation of the adequacy of mathematical dependences and opportunities of their application in concrete engineering, calculations of a number of experiments have been carried out. The industrial extruder ATL-45 was used, with the following characteristics: the length of a worm is 0,8 m, diameter 4×10^{-2} m. The extrusion installation includes the forming knot consisting of forming heads, which is made square section 0,045×0,045 m. For creation of ultrasonic fluctuations on forming head two magnetostrictive converter were used, such as PMS-6-22, ultrasonic fluctuations UZG1-4 connected to the generator.

The channels of complex profile were defined. The rheological properties of polymer melts and the dependence of account testimonials from temperature, pressure at extruded, frequencies of ultrasound, the design of the channel, and also capacity of ultrasonic fluctuations from type of used polymer, the geometry of the channel and parameters of ultrasound were used.

The equation (1) for the estimation of throughput of the channel at extruded includes the coefficients depending on the form of the channels section. Their calculation is usually connected with great difficulties as it is necessary as initial sizes to know the true speed of melt current in the channel which is difficult to define, and also it is necessary to have dependence of change of fluidity of melt from the shift pressure. Therefore for the definition of the coefficients a and b a more convenient method in the practical attitude membrane analogies [2] that has allowed to estimate factors of the form for four kinds of research sections of channels (table. 1) was used.

Table 1 - Values of coefficient of the form of researched sections.

Parameter	Section of a product			
	П - figurative	Г - figurative	Triangular	Ш – figurative
$R_Г \cdot 10^3$, m	1,81	1,88	1,52	0,96
A	1,348	1,645	2,208	1,209
B	1,989	1,996	2,573	1,985

Three kinds of polymers have been chosen: polyvinylchloride plastic compound (cable) (GOST 5960), polystyrene PS-S (GOST 20282) and polythene of high pressure (GOST 150802).

The polymers melts, chosen for the realization of experimental researches are typical representatives of viscoelastic liquids and their physical and chemical properties are investigated well and described in the literature [1-3,5].

For confirming the validity of the equation (1) experimental researches, by the definition of the dependence of the mass expenditure polymer melt from the pressure gradient in the researched channel were carried out. The current of polymers in channels of a complex profile of different length for each section was studied. Thus, the experimental data have been obtained for 12 channels and three kinds of polymers (polythene, polystyrene and polyvinylchloride plastic compound) at interval of temperatures 403 - 453 K, pressure of extrusion up to 6 MPa and the frequencies of ultrasound - 18,5; 20,5; 21,6; 22,1; 23,5 kHz.

The analysis of results shows that in all case using the ultrasonic fluctuations, the increase of the mass expenditure of polymers for all the forms of channels was observed. The greatest increase of the expenditure of polymer products was observed for polyvinylchloridplaste (20 - 25 %), the lowest for polystyrene (10 - 15 %).The greatest effect from ultrasonic influence was observed for the channel of the form of a triangle, the least for channel Ш forms. In the process of increase of temperature in a zone of polymer the effect of the use of ultrasound was reduced. The frequency 21,6 kHz was optimal.

Alongside with studying of account characteristics, the study dependence of the capacity of ultrasonic fluctuations from polymer geometry of the channel is interesting. With a view of realization in practice of dependence (2) the appropriate calculations, given in Table 2, were carried out.

The analysis of experimental results shows that the greatest capacity of the radiation absorbed by the polymer is characteristic for polyvinylchloridplaste. This polymer has a higher density and lower viscosity in comparison with polystyrene and polythene. The speed of a sound for the chosen polymers is accordingly,1650 m/s for polyvinylchloridplaste, 1500 m/s for polystyrene and for polythene of a high pressure 1600 m/s. With the increase of temperature, the capacity of ultrasonic fluctuations decreases, as the density of polymeric products, thus the greatest capacity is characteristic for the triangular channel, the lowest - for Ш - forms of the channel. In the first case, ultrasonic fluctuations operate with the greater efficiency through all perimeter of the channel in extruder whereas in the second case operates only on his part, due to the peculiarities of the design of the channel and dissipation energy.

Optimum frequencies of ultrasonic radiation 21,6 - 22,1 kHz - for polyvinylchloridplaste, polystyrene and polythene are revealed. Thus the greatest amplitude makes 6 microns. Thus, the calculations on the equation (2) will be coordinated to the experimental value on the parameter - the throughput of the channel extrusion at ultrasonic influence, i. e. on the productivity of the extruder.

The recommended modes or extrusion of researched polymers obtained experimentally are given in table. 3.

Table 2. Results of the calculation of the capacity of ultrasonic fluctuations (W).

Frequency USF, kHz	The channel							
	Triangular		Г - figurative		П – figurative		Ш - figurative	
Polyvinylchloridplaste (T = 413 K)								
18,5	438	435	400	402	419	421	364	367
20,5	846	840	772	770	809	806	699	703
21,6	1345	1346	1229	1232	1287	1282	1111	1115
22,1	1409	1403	1286	1290	1348	1349	1165	1161
23,5	1107	1105	1276	1277	1059	1056	914	918
Polystyrene (T = 438 K)								
18,5	282	285	258	260	270	267	233	235
20,5	543	539	497	495	520	521	449	447
21,6	865	866	790	794	827	829	715	718
22,1	711	710	574	571	602	606	520	523
23,5	455	458	416	417	436	432	376	377
ПЭВД (T = 403 K)								
18,5	283	280	259	258	271	266	234	236
20,5	546	546	502	498	523	527	451	453
21,6	869	872	793	791	831	832	717	713
22,1	632	630	577	572	604	609	522	520
23,5	457	452	418	416	438	433	378	375

Table 3 Recommended modes in an extruder at forming the profile- pogonage products

Researched polymer	Temperature extruded, To	Pressure extruded, MPa	Viscosity, 10-4 (Па·s)	Optimum frequency, kHz
Polyvinylchloridplaste of GOST 5960	403-423	4,0-4,5	0,024-0,35	21,6
Polystyrene of GOST 20282	438-453	4,0-5,0	0,028 - 0,35	21,6
Polythene of a high pressure of GOST 150802	388-418	3,5-4,0	0,013-0,35	21,6

The phenomenon of highly elastic restoration extruded through forming tool is well-known in the practice of plastics processing. A number of works [6-8], in which models of various degree of the complexities allowing to estimate this phenomenon quantitatively are discussed. However, it is necessary to point out that the use of simplified models gives an approximate estimate and does not corresponds to the experimental data. More complex models are high and with no practical application [2]. Moreover, none of the models consider one of the most important operational and technological operational and characteristics - the "swelling" of polymeric products of the complex profile received in conditions of ultrasonic fluctuations influence. Usually, as a rule description of the phenomenon of "swelling" is limited by extruders as twig of round cross section or a flat sheet [8].

In this connection, the mathematical dependence allowing to define quantitatively the effect of "swelling" at pressing the melts of polymers through channels of any complex section when using intensive ultrasonic vibrations, is of practical interest.

The size of "swelling" extrudates is influenced, first of all, with molecular characteristics and physical properties of the material, technological conditions of processing (temperature, speed, pressure of shift), and also the geometrical sizes of forming channel.

Modeling the effect of "swelling" of the extrudate, we shall consider that when a polymer runs through the channel, its particles, undergoing shift deformation, become longer and, after going out from the channel due to relaxation, they are reduced, besides the stretching and reduction of particles has an elastic character.

Thus, in the equation, mathematically describing the coefficient of "swelling", is necessary to take into account the length of the channel L and its area S. Besides these values it is necessary to take into account pressure p at the extrusion of polymeric composition, the effective viscosity η_{ef}, the gradient of speed of shift $\overline{\gamma}$ and a certain parameter Θ, taking into account highly elastic properties of environment:

$$K = A \cdot \overline{\gamma}^{n_1} \cdot \Theta^{n_2} \cdot P^{n_3} \cdot \eta_{ef}^{n_4} \cdot L^{n_5} \cdot S^{n_6} \quad (3)$$

Here A is the dimensionless coefficient taking into account the nature of material, n1 - n6 parameters of degrees.

Using the p - theorem and the theory of groups [2] the dependence for definition of the coefficient of the "swelling" of polymeric material in the cylindrical channel is received:

$$K = A \cdot (\overline{\gamma} \cdot \Theta)^{n_1} \cdot \left(\frac{\eta_{эф}}{P \cdot \Theta} \right)^{n_2} \cdot \left(\frac{L}{S_K} \right)^{n_3} \quad (4)$$

Constant A and parameters of degrees n_1 - n_6 are defined experimental (table. 4).

To receive the necessary model of the calculation of factor K for channels of complex form, it is necessary (4) to introduce the coefficient of the form of the channel a and b, which are also determined experimentally according to the method for membranes analogies [2] into the equation:

$$K = A \cdot a^{m_1} \cdot b^{m_2} \cdot (\overline{\gamma} \cdot \Theta)^{n_1} \cdot \left(\frac{\eta_{эф}}{P \cdot \Theta} \right)^{n_2} \cdot \left(\frac{L}{\sqrt{S_K}} \right)^{n_3} \quad (5)$$

where m_1, m_2 are parameters of degrees (table. 1).

When ultrasonic fluctuations are imposed on the melt stream, a significant decrease of the coefficient of "swelling" is observed. First of all it occurs due to the decrease of effective viscosity of melt η_{ef} up to some value η_{ω}, determined from the equation [9].

$$\eta_{\omega} = \frac{\eta_{эф}}{1 + \omega^2 \cdot r^2}, \tag{6}$$

where ω is an angular frequency of ultrasonic fluctuations, η_{ef}; r is the time of relaxation describing the speed of the decreasing pressure:

$$r = \frac{\eta_{эф}}{E} \tag{7}$$

where E is the module of the elasticity of environment, Pa.

Therefore it is expedient to introduce the parameter η_{ω} characterizing the influence of ultrasound on a degree of "swelling" of extrudate of polymeric material equation (5).

$$K = A \cdot a^{m_1} \cdot b^{m_2} \cdot (\bar{\gamma} \cdot \Theta)^{n_1} \cdot \left(\frac{\eta_{\omega}}{P \cdot \Theta}\right)^{n_2} \cdot \left(\frac{L}{\sqrt{S_K}}\right)^{n_3} \tag{8}$$

Table 4 - Values of physical quantities and constant coefficient

Material	Temp K	$\bar{\gamma}$, 1/c	Θ, c	η_{ω}, Па·с	N_1	n_2	n_3	A	m_1	m_2
Polythene	338	3,546	0,1	4550	0,077	-0,015	-0,118	2,625	-0,021	-0,017
	403	3,548	0,1	3020	0,077	-0,015	-0,118	2,625	-0,021	-0,017
	418	3,548	0,1	1897	0,077	-0,015	-0,118	2,625	-0,021	-0,017
	433	3,548	0,1	1479	0,077	-0,015	-0,118	2,625	-0,021	-0,017
	488	3,548	0,1	1324	0,077	-0,015	-0,118	2,625	-0,021	-0,017
Polystyrene	438	3,548	0,1	4514	0,089	-0,088	-0,127	6,150	-0,016	-0,014
	448	3,548	0,1	3388	0,089	-0,088	-0,127	6,150	-0,016	-0,014
	458	3,548	0,1	2729	0,089	-0,088	-0,127	6,150	-0,016	-0,014
	468	3,548	0,1	2483	0,089	-0,088	-0,127	6,150	-0,016	-0,014
	478	3,548	0,1	2300	0,089	-0,088	-0,127	6,150	-0,016	-0,014
PVH-plastic compound	403	3,548	0,1	5889	0,065	-0,020	-0,107	2,147	-0,005	-0,004
	413	3,548	0,1	3981	0,065	-0,020	-0,107	2,147	-0,005	-0,004
	423	3,548	0,1	3715	0,065	-0,020	-0,107	2,147	-0,005	-0,004
	433	3,548	0,1	3506	0,065	-0,020	-0,107	2,147	-0,005	-0,004
	443	3,548	0,1	1514	0,065	-0,020	-0,107	2,147	-0,005	-0,004

Equation (8) represents a mathematical model describing the influence of imposing ultrasonic fluctuations on the "swelling" of the extrudate during the extruded polymeric material at ultrasonic influence.

To confirm the adequacy of the offered correlation (8) to the phenomenon observably in practice, the experimental researches to estimate the coefficient of "swelling" depending on the geometry of the channel, parameters of process extruded, physical and some other properties of the used polymer, and also from frequency of ultrasonic fluctuations were carried out.

It is necessary to note the positive influence of ultrasounds on the decrease of the "swelling" coefficient. Paying attention to the greatest factor of "swelling" in experiences without ultrasound (fig. 2) have extruded at use of the channel of the triangular form, then П - and Г - forms and the least Ш-forms, thus greatest "swelling" extrude observes on the long party of a sample and near to a sharp corner of triangular section.

At use of ultrasounds the observably picture appreciably changes. Distortion of samples is much lower. Thus, the decrease of factor of "swelling" K on the average on 10 - 12 % takes place. The greatest decrease in K is observed for channel SH - forms, the least - for the triangular form. Numerical value of factor of "swelling" K is influenced also with a chemical nature of a used polymeric material.

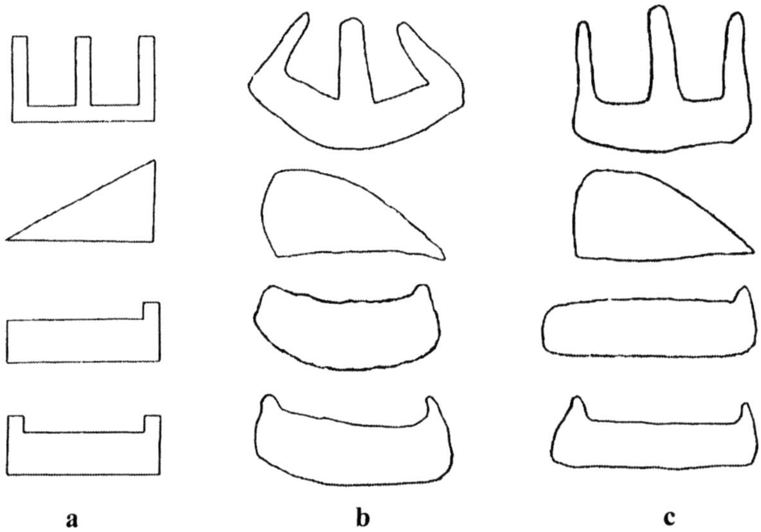

Figure 2. Characteristic contours at extruded polyvinylchloridplaste, polystyrene and polythene; a - section of a product; b - samples extruded without ultrasound; c - the samples with ultrasound.

The greatest "swelling" of a extrudate is typical of polystyrene, the least - for plastic compound on the basis of polyvinylchloridplaste. The decrease of the "swelling" coefficient is also observed when the length of the channel L increases in the extruder. It is true for all forms of the channel and for all the investigated polymers. The lower the temperature of formation, the lower the coefficient of "swelling" K. Besides, the best results are observed when the frequency of ultrasound is 21,6 kHz. The comparison of the results of the experimental with the calculated values of the coefficient of "swelling" K (fig.3) allowed to reveal the following peculiarities:

1) The decrease of the coefficient of "swelling" of polymeric materials under the influence of ultrasounds is observed for all the forms of the investigated channels in an extruder. The divergence between the calculated and experimental data is about 15 %;
2) The frequency of ultrasonic fluctuations also influences the productivity of the extruder, the mass expenditure of polymeric products. Taking into account the best results, the frequency of ultrasound is 21,6 kHz;
3) When comparing the influence of the form of section of channels in extruder, the greatest positive influence of ultrasound is marked for channels triangular and Ш - figurative forms. It is obviously due to the fact that though in these channels there are stagnant zones and sharp corners, because of the ultrasound influence;

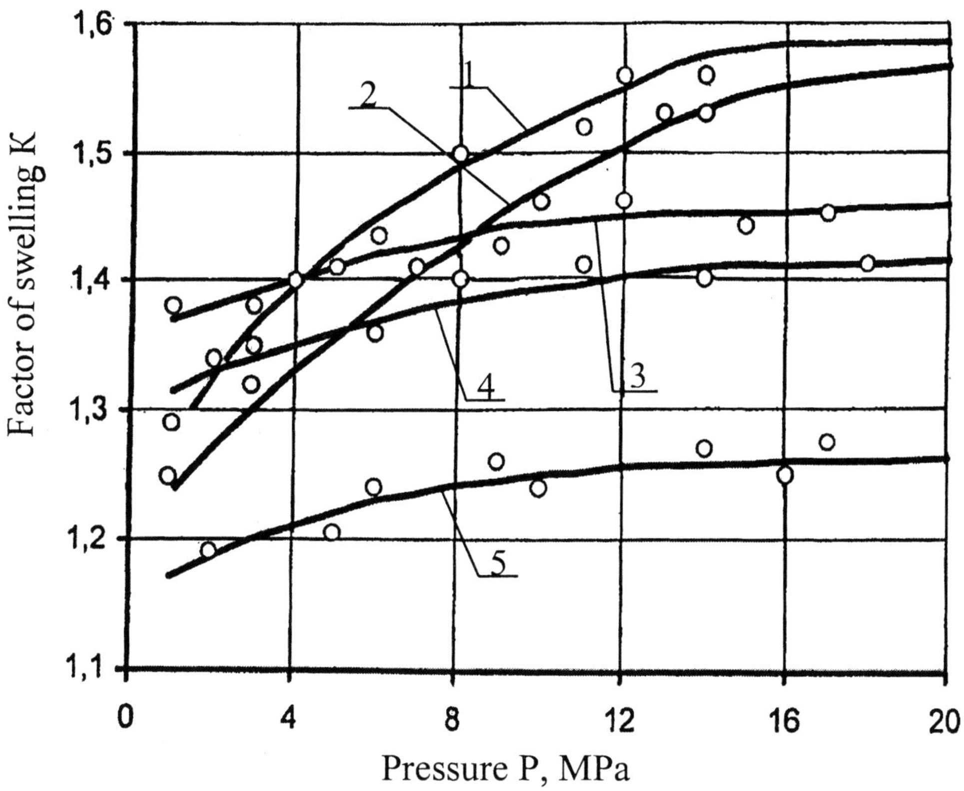

Figure 3. Dependence of factor of "swelling" on pressure, the channel triangular, 1 - polystyrene L = 70 mm at 453 K, 2 - polystyrene L = 70 mm at 438 K, 3 - polythene L = 110 mm at 430 K, 4 - polythene L = 110 mm at 418 K, 5 - polyvinylchloridplaste L = 90 mm at 413 K; frequency of ultrasound 21,6 kHz

4) In the process of pressure increase during the polymer extrusion the rate growth of the coefficient of "swelling" is reduced and when the pressure is more than 5,0 MPa, its value is practically unchanged. The sharp increase of the coefficient of "swelling" when the pressure is not great is the characteristic feature for investigated polymers [2,8].
5) The reduction in the coefficient of "swelling" is typical of the polymers investigated in work (polythene, polypropylene, polyvinylchloride plastic compound) when the

length of the channel increases. Besides, there is a critical value of length L =110 mm, above which the "swelling", remains practically unchanged. It is the essential factor in designing forming channel;

6) When the temperature of extrusion increase, the coefficient "swelling" also increases. Besides, the increase of K is more noticeable for polystyrene for other kinds of investigated polymers.

Thus, results for estimating the "swelling" K, can be used for calculating the forming tool, both without and under the influence of ultrasonic influences. Besides, the given results can be used in the processes of free extrusion, when the product which has left the forming head, does not adjoin with calibrated tool and does not undergo an extract and mechanic proceeding.

REFERENCES

[1] Basov N.I., Kazankov J.V., Lubartovich V.A. *Calculation and designing of the equipment for manufacture and processings of polymeric materials.* - M.: Chemistry, 1986. - 486 with.

[2] Panov A.K., Anasov A.R. *Hydrodynamics of streams of abnormal - viscous polymeric systems in forming channels.* - Ufa: UGNTU, 1994. - 260 with.

[3] Fridman M.L. *Technology of processing crystal polyolephine.* - M.: Chemistry, 1977. - 398 with.

[4] .Stalemate. 2147989 Russian Federations, МКИ^3 B29C47/12, 47/30 *Multilane extrusion the head for manufacturing profile-pogonage polymeric products with application of ultrasonic fluctuations* / A.K.Panov, O.F.Kiselyova, N.S.Shulaev; It is declared. 05.05.98; It is published. 27.04.2000; The bulletin. ¹ 21. A priority 05.05.98.

[5] Vinogradov G.V., Malkin A.J. *Reologija of polymers.* - M.: Chemistry, 1977. - 438 with.

[6] Gul V.E., Kuleznev V.N., *Structure and mechanical properties of polymers.* - M.: the higher School, 1972. - 320 with.

[7] Basov N.I.&, Broy V. *Technology of processing of plastic.* - M.: Chemistry, 1985. - 530 with.

[8] Khan C.D. *Reologija during processing polymers.* - M.: Chemistry, 1979. - 396 with.

[9] Mihajlov I.T., Solov'ev V.A., *JU.P.bas's Cheesecakes of molecular acoustics.* - M.: the Science, 1964. - 516 with.

In: Homolytic and Heterolytic Reactions: Problems and Solutions ISBN 1-59033-980-0
Editors: G.E. Zaikov, et al., pp. 283-305

Chapter 13

The Transport of Water and its Effects on Properties of Cold-Curing Epoxy Adhesives

Mariaenrica Frigione
Department of Innovation Engineering
University of Lecce. Lecce, Italy
mariaenrica.frigione@unile.it

Abstract

This review assesses the hygrothermal effects in epoxy adhesives, illustrates the different types of interactions between molecules of water and the polymer network and evidences what are the parameters that influence the absorption process. Although the study would be addressed to cold-curing epoxy adhesive, most of the available literature refers to heat-curing epoxies. Great attention is also devoted to the test procedures used to measure the diffusion parameters of water absorption, evidenced how these procedures can affect the properties of the samples before the immersion. Finally, a brief outlook is given to the accelerated tests regarding the effects of water on properties of epoxy resins, underlining the effectiveness and limits of the mentioned tests.

Keywords: Adhesives, Cold-curing epoxies, Water absorption, Durability.

Introduction

Thermosetting adhesives, in particular epoxy based, have been used from long time in the construction and building industries, in many different applications. Their use continues to increase in this area because they offer improved quality as well as economic advantages. During their service life, these adhesives may be exposed to various substances and conditions: water and moisture; high and low temperatures (including freezing of absorbed moisture); solvents, that may be present in stains and paint; cleaning agents and chemicals; insects, bacteria, mold and other biological agents. All the mentioned agents are able to affect in different extents the final properties and the performances of the adhesives. Moreover, the deterioration of these products associated with aging over several decades must be also taken into account in evaluating their durability.

The epoxy adhesives suitable for applications in civil engineering repairing and in cultural heritage restoration are "cold-curing" resins, i.e. they are based on bisphenolic epoxy resins and are cured with the addition of aliphatic amines at ambient temperatures. Two are the main consequences of the curing process carried out at relatively low temperatures: long curing times (in the order of weeks) are necessary to achieve sufficient mechanical properties of the adhesives, and a moderate Tg (50-60°C) attainable by these systems [1].

The effects produced by environmental agents on cold-curing adhesives have received minor attention in the literature. The previous experience in other fields, on the other hand, proved that the good properties of epoxy resins undergo a considerable decay after a long period of immersion in water [2]. The possible effects of this agent on the properties of cold-curing epoxy based adhesives require, therefore, a deep analysis.

The presence of humidity or liquid water is probably the most harmful environment that can commonly be encountered by epoxies used as adhesives for civil engineering applications. All polymeric resins are susceptible, to some degree, to the effects of exposure to water or water vapor. The effect of exposure to moisture is to alter the physical, mechanical and chemical characteristics of the polymers. Water may enter a resin either by diffusion or by capillary action through cracks and crazes. Once inside, the water may alter the properties of the polymer either in a reversible manner, for example by plasticization, or in an irreversible manner, for example by hydrolysis, cracking or crazing.

Epoxy adhesives are prone to water absorption because they possess polar sites that attract water molecules. These water molecules are able to bind with resin through hydrogen bonding. In this way, water is able to disrupt the interchain Van der Waals forces inside the network producing an increase of segmental mobility [3]. As a consequence, the absorption of limited amounts of water can be regarded as beneficial in terms of improved toughness, static fatigue resistance and plastic deformation of the cured resin. On the other hand, an excessive presence of water is generally considered harmful, leading to a reduction in modulus and strength with a consequent marked unsuitable decrease of load-bearing capacity though plasticization effects [4]. Finally, it would not be easy to remove the sorbed water completely.

The water acting as a plasticizer causes reductions also in Tg values [5]. As a general rule for most thermosetting resin systems, the Tg is reduced by 10-20°C for every 1% of absorbed water or moisture [6-10]. Water absorption, therefore, will generally produce a deterioration in the already poor high temperature load-bearing capacity of epoxy adhesives cured at room temperature. Hence, it is critical that the resin should have a Tg a minimum of 30 degrees above the maximum service temperature to allow for this potential depression.

The interface adherent/adhesive also plays an important role in moisture effects. Wicking is a well-known moisture effect; in some cases, water actually tends to displace the adhesive.

All the effects taking place in a cured resin as consequence of exposure to water (plasticization, swelling, etc.) influence its behavior as an adhesive. Unfortunately, the description of these mechanisms occurring in cold-curing epoxies still remains a qualitative matter, and it is strongly associated with the chemical nature of the components of resin and on the curing conditions.

MECHANISM OF WATER ABSORPTION

The mechanism of water absorption in different types of epoxy has been widely investigated, but it is still not fully understood. Moreover, to the best of author's knowledge, not any of these studies was specifically devoted to cold-curing epoxies. On the other hand, if not differently specified, the main conclusions found for heat-cured epoxies can be extended to cold-curing systems.

One important issue is the state of aggregation of the water molecules within the bulk of the material. The penetrant population can be divided into molecules forming an ordinary polymer-diluent solution and those absorbed onto hydrophilic sites or trapped into the "excess" free volume frozen in the glass structure, often referred as "holes or microvoids". There is, however, no direct evidence for the presence of these microvoids and whether they are, indeed, formed as a result of the penetration of water into the network [11]. The multiplicity of states of the penetrant molecules within the matrix generates different effects on the properties of the cured epoxy resin. Therefore, the overall penetrant up-take cannot be considered, for example, as a reliable measure of the degree of plasticization [12, 13].

Another relevant and controversial issue concerns the kind of molecular interactions between the water molecules and the epoxy network. Several spectroscopic studies, solid-state NMR [14-16] and FTIR in the mid infrared range spectroscopy [17, 18] have been employed but no definitive conclusions have been reached so far: the exact sorption sites to which water may be bonded are still uncertain.

In the past decades, two mechanistic approaches emerged that generally characterize the nature of water in epoxy. One is the free volume approach which presumes that water diffuses into epoxy resin and resides in the free volume of the material. For this approach, bonding between water molecule and epoxy resin network is deemed insignificant [19-20]. The other approach is the interaction concept that suggests water molecules couple strongly with certain hydrophilic functional groups such as hydroxyl or amine in epoxy resins [21]. The enthalpy of hydrogen bond formation is in the range of 14.2 to 27.6 kJ/mol (3.4 to 6.6 kcal/mol) (22). The relatively high water absorption capacity of epoxy resins derives from the presence in the epoxy chains of –OH groups attracting the polar water molecules. Thus, strong localized interactions could develop between water molecule and polar groups in epoxies.

Several researchers [15, 23-25] proposed that water may exist as either small clusters in voids or in a molecularly dispersed state within the resin matrix. The water molecules in voids were designated as "free" water molecules. Water, which is dispersed in the matrix and is usually strongly bonded through hydrogen bonding to specific functional groups, was designed as "bound" water. Characterization of water in polymers in terms of bound water vs. unbound clusters is important since bound water in the polymer matrix rather than the total amount of water uptake is expected to lower the Tg of the polymer [24]. Antoon et al. [18] affirmed that the absorption of water dispersed in the epoxy matrix and bonded to hydroxyl groups is completely reversible.

Another similar theory proposed that some water molecules interact by forming hydrogen bonds with hydrophilic groups in epoxy resins while other water molecules are retained in free volume of the material [26]. The same theory stated that the unbound molecules of water contained in the free volume are relatively free to travel through the holes and do not cause swelling, while the bound water molecules are immobilized and are responsible for the dimensional increase of the polymer. Whereas the availability of a larger free volume within the polymer results in increasing the amount of water molecules in the first state, a higher resin polarity accounts for more water molecules in the second state. Grave et al. were even able to calculate the relative amounts of bound water and free water through dielectric measurements [27].

Another theory [28, 29] suggested three water absorption modes in glassy epoxy resin: i) bulk dissolution of water in polymer network; ii) water absorption onto the surface of vacuoles which define the excess free volume of the glassy structure; and iii) hydrogen bonding between polymer hydrophilic groups and water.

From spectroscopic studies carried out by other researchers, three different species of molecules of water were identified in epoxy networks, i.e. S_0, S_1 and S_2, where the subscripts denote the number of hydrogen atoms of the H_2O molecule involved in hydrogen bonding [11, 30]. Therefore, the first, S_0, is the "non-associated water", i.e. the water that has not been linked through hydrogen bonds. The other two types are characterized by hydrogen bonds, weaker (S_1) or stronger (S_2). The species of water with lowest interactions with epoxy (S_0 and S_1), restricted in the free volume of the resin, are characterized by a high mobility along the network and a reduced plasticizating effect. On the other hand, S_2 molecules are tightly bound to the specific sites along the network, exhibiting a limited mobility and a higher plasticizating effect [30].

Competing effects of the sorption of water in the free volume and of strong interactions between water molecules and polar groups of the epoxy network were used to explain the diffusional behavior also in another study [31]. Changes in a tetraglycidyl diaminodiphenylmethane (TGDDM) and novolac glycidyl ether resin microstructure as a result of the different curing treatments were found to influence the water diffusion in epoxy, as it will be reported later. The different behavior for the material with cures at different temperatures could not be explained just with free-volume considerations, which predict a higher water up-take in the materials with less cross-link density, independently of the immersion temperature. It was found, in fact, that the water uptake at low immersion temperatures was higher in the cure characterized by a higher conversion degree compared to cure that produced a lower degree of conversion, i.e. a lower cross-linking density. The diffusional behavior observed was explained by a combination of two factors: one of them, the unoccupied molecular volume of the epoxy resin; the second one, the polymer water affinity due to hydrophilic centers of the network.

The increment in the cross-linking density would produce lower water-absorption levels. In addition, regions of high density might severely hinder water diffusion, due, at least in part, to the inaccessibility of hydrogen-bonding sites [15, 32, 33]. Therefore, to explain the unexpected behavior observed in samples with higher cross-linking density, the authors took into account the epoxy-water affinity of the particular epoxy-rich formulation. A kinetics study showed that for the material being vitrified the epoxide-amine reaction was virtually complete, regardless of temperature, but the epoxide-hydroxyl reaction was only partially complete and depended on the curing temperature. A higher curing temperature promoted etherification reactions, providing an additional source for the consumption of epoxide groups and thus modifying the distribution of various functional groups inside the epoxy network; in particular, a higher presence of unreacted amine groups, with a highly polar nature. An increased water sorption in epoxy-amine systems is reported with higher unreacted secondary amine group content [34]. Therefore, the strong water affinity of cured epoxies, due to the polar hydroxyl groups created by the epoxy-amine reactions, might be intensified by unreacted amine groups and hydroxyl-ether units as a consequence of etherification reactions. The superior water-uptake levels in a more densely cross-linked structure at low temperatures would be related to its highly polar structure. To confirm this hypothesis, the authors reported the following consideration. The formation of the bond between –OH groups and water requires breaking of the intramolecular hydrogen bonds between the polar groups of the resin, but this hydrophilic procedure can take place only al low temperatures, when the hydrogen-bond formation is thermodynamically preferable [35]. Thus, at higher immersion temperatures, the epoxy-water molecule interactions would be reduced, as confirmed by the experimental data.

In a recently published paper based on NIR (near-infrared) studies [11], approximately 30% of water was found to be hydrogen bonded to a diamine (4,4'-diaminodiphenyl sulfone, DDS) curing agent of a TGDDM resin even during early stages of water uptake. It reaches up to 40% at equilibrium uptake, apparently without disturbing the hydrogen-bonded epoxy network. Since only bound water is expected to affect the longer relaxations associated with the glass transition of the cross-linked resin, the use of NIR spectroscopy makes it possible to determine the extent of plasticization due to absorbed water, with undoubted advantages over thermal technique. On the basis of these careful NIR studies, moreover, the authors proposed that water can form hydrogen bonds with either the tertiary amino group or the SO_2 group of the curing agent DDS. Similar results were obtained by other researchers that used UV reflection spectroscopy to determine the fraction of DDS hydrogen-bonded with water in a diglycidyl ether of butanediol (DGEB) epoxy (36). The results showed that, when the epoxy is saturated with water, at 9% wt, 32% of absorbed water is hydrogen bonded to the SO_2 group of DDS.

Another recent study affirmed that water molecules bind with epoxy resins only through hydrogen bonding, but suggesting that two different types of bound can tie water with epoxy resin [3]. The binding types are classified as Type I or Type II bonding, depending on difference in the bond complex and activation energy (the activation energy of Type I is slightly lower than that of Type II). Type I bonding corresponds to a water molecule which forms a single hydrogen bond with the epoxy resin network. This water molecule possesses lower activation energy and is easier to remove from the resin. Type II bonding is as a result of a water molecule forming multiple hydrogen bonds with the resin network. This water molecule, therefore, possesses higher activation energy and is correspondingly harder to remove.

Referring to the effects of the two kinds of absorbed water, Type I bound water, which is the dominant form of the total amount sorbed water, diffuses into the epoxy network and breaks the initial inter-chain Van der Waals force resulting in the increase of chain segment mobility and swelling. As a consequence, Type I bound water readily plasticizes the epoxy resins decreasing their Tg's. However, Type I bound water is more easily desorbed from the resin.

Water molecules which form multi-site interconnective bond complexes, i.e. Type II, do not contribute significantly to plasticization of the resin. Moreover, these bond complexes create bridging between chain segments resulting in (pseudo cross-linking) secondary cross-linking. Therefore, Type II bound water contributes to an increase in Tg in water saturated epoxy resins. The experimental Tg values encompass the combined effect of the two water-resin interaction mechanisms. It has been found that higher values of Tg resulted for longer immersion time, higher than the temperature at which the second stage of water absorption process begins, and higher exposure temperature [37].

The formation of Type I bonded water occurs readily in the moisture sorption process; particular at low temperature hygrothermal exposure, however, the impetus to form Type II bonding is substantially less. The amount of Type II bound water strongly depends, in fact, on the exposure temperature and time: higher immersion temperature and longer exposure time result in a greater amount of Type II bound water.

The same study found for a given material that the saturation water content is virtually the same irrespective of the immersion temperature. This behavior indicates that water diffusion in these materials is Fickian in nature [3].

This last hypothesis is in contrast with another study performed on glass reinforced epoxy resin [38]. In this research, in fact, higher immersion temperatures were found to increase the moisture diffusivity. The underlying hypothesis was that the same degradation mechanism takes place both at room and at elevated temperatures. Nevertheless, the "wet-aging" at high temperature must give an over-degradation of thermal and mechanical properties.

The conclusion of the mentioned studies on the mechanism of absorption of water in epoxy resins is the unavailability of a single model, supported by sufficient experimental evidences, to explain all diffusion phenomena.

Factors Affecting Water Absorption of Epoxy Resins

As already mentioned, the first factor affecting diffusion processes is essentially a geometrical one, i.e. the amount of liquid that can diffuse into a polymer sample depending on the size of the diffusing molecule relative to the free volume available within the polymer. The second factor concerns the chemical nature of the penetrant versus that of the polymer. This factor determines the affinity of the diffusing molecule to the specific functional groups present in the polymer [39]. Epoxy adhesives are prone to water absorption, because they possess polar sites that attract water molecules that are, on the other hand, relatively small. As already pointed out, water molecules are most likely bonded to hydrophilic groups of the cured resin, mainly hydroxyl and amine groups [5]. Both the amount of absorbed water and the rate of absorption depend on formulation variables, such as the epoxy resin and curing agent types employed, together with environmental variables, such as temperature and relative humidity, as well as curing conditions. A wide range of equilibrium water concentration values and diffusion coefficients have been quoted in literature for an equally wide range of formulations and absorption conditions [13, 40-42]. In particular, equilibrium concentrations from 0.25% to 10% by weight have been quoted, depending also on the stoichiometry of the formulation, on the presence of fillers (with a hydrophobic nature, for example) and on curing conditions.

The value of maximum moisture content at infinite time, i.e. M_∞, is strongly dependent on the polarity of the cured resin structure. Generally, the more polar, the higher the equilibrium moisture concentration. As a result, hardeners which yield "polyester" or "polyether" molecular structures rather than hydroxyl amines are preferred for matrices of composites [43].

Heat-cured epoxies are often based on aromatic amines, which are less reactive than aliphatic amines, but which are much more rigid molecules. This rigidity reduces their level of molecular motion and hinders water diffusion. With either type of curing agent, complete cure will lead to more cross-linking and reduced water transport [4].

As a confirmation, polyaminophenolic oligomers were found to be effective as curing agents giving a good cross-linking density to DGEBA epoxy resins, even if the curing reaction takes place at low temperatures (i.e. 20°C) [44]. Water absorption tests indicated a clear superiority of these hardeners in comparison with other not aromatic amino-hardeners, probably due to the presence of hydrophobic aromatic rings, which perhaps are able to screen the polar amino groups, mainly responsible of a superior water absorption. As a consequence, the composite manufactured with polyaminophenolic curing agents showed an enhanced environmental resistance, retaining their good mechanical properties also after extended immersion in water.

Referring to the holes of molecular size present in the polymer network, the presence of these holes is determined by the polymer structure and morphology, reflected in its cross-linking density and in the molecular chain stiffness and ability to closely pack in the amorphous state. The formation of an appropriate hole also depends on the cohesive energy density of the polymer.

By increasing the molecular weight between cross-link points, M_c, the density of the resin decreases, indicating the presence of more free volume. This should produce an increased water absorption. However, a systematical decrease of diffusion parameters (i.e., rate of moisture take-up, equilibrium weight gain and coefficient of diffusion) was observed by Diamant et al. with increasing M_c, in contradiction to the expected increase as a consequence of the larger free volume available for moisture penetration [39]. This indicates that other effects which compete with that of M_c would dominate the moisture absorption process and they must be taken into account. These effects were analyzed by the authors and are as follows: changes in the morphology and the microstructure of the cured resin, with the formation, for example of a two-phase morphology; development of microdamage under severe humidity conditions. The authors concluded that it is difficult to predict which of all the mentioned factors, or a combination of them, dominates the moisture diffusion process into a given epoxy resin. The hygrothermal conditioning strongly affects the water absorption mechanism in epoxy resins.

The physical modification occurring in epoxies exposed to liquid and vapor phase water has been associated with micro-mechanical cavitation (crazing) occurring in a region of different cross-linking densities [45-47]. From liquid water sorption tests, performed on amino (TETA) hardened bisphenolic epoxy heat-cured films (Tg = 142°C) at 20° and 70°C, the equilibrium water uptake at 70°C was found moderately higher than that measured at 20°C, i.e. 4.00% and 2.96%, respectively [48]. Moreover, when the sample conditioned at 70°C was brought down at 20°C, additional water was absorbed and finally reached the value of 4.60%. The excess of water present in the sample previously conditioned at high temperature, i.e. 1.64%, was recognized as trapped in craze microcavities formed during the thermal aging in presence of sorbed water. However, tensile tests performed on wet samples showed that the higher degree of plasticization was reached by the epoxy conditioned at lower temperature. The elastic moduli and the stresses at break, compared for the dry and water saturated epoxy, in fact, are progressively lowered by the lower temperature conditioning, irrespective of the corresponding higher water uptake. The same epoxy system, finally, have been found to be differently deteriorated also when equilibrated in environments of different relative humidities. In particular, a progressive damage in the resin emerges when the sample are conditioned at higher levels of relative humidity.

In a more recent study [3], the maximum water content measured for three heat-cured epoxy systems, i.e. a DGEBA/mDPA, a TGDDM/DDS and a TGDDM/DDS with small amounts of additives, has been found essentially independent on the immersion temperatures (ranging from 45° to 90°C). On the other hand, the results of desorption tests showed that more residual water retention occurs at higher exposure temperature. Similar results were found by other researchers on a DGEBA/monofunctional epoxy phenyl glycidyl ether heat-cured by a DDM [49]. Immersion of thick samples (d = 2 mm) was performed at temperatures ranging between 30° and 70°C. It was observed that, as the temperature increases, the diffusion coefficient increased whereas the equilibrium weight up-takes remained constant (2-2.5%). A similar study was conducted on moisture absorption (98% R.H.) at different temperatures, i.e. 25°, 40°, 55° and 70°C of bisphenolic epoxy resin, cured by different amounts of aromatic amine/aniline [39]. The equilibrium moisture content was found not depending on the exposure temperature but only on the composition of the epoxy system. In conclusion, different studies ascertained that the amount of residual water in epoxy systems varies with hygrothermal exposure history. The amount of residual water depends strongly on the exposure time and temperature, i.e. both higher immersion temperatures and longer immersion times enhance the amount of residual water in the resin.

The maximum volume increase, corresponding to the slow swelling controlled process, was found to increase with immersion temperature [50]. This effect was explained by the temperature increase that produces an increase in the probability of a water molecule being bound by a functional group in the resin. Moreover, at higher temperatures a thermal agitation effect is attained and, as a consequence, more water should have the possibility to interact with the functional groups in the polymer as time goes by.

The effects of thermal excursions on the kinetic of diffusion of water in epoxy resins are also relevant. Enhanced moisture absorption as a result of a thermal spike has been reported (43). During the thermal spike, in fact, moisture is lost but on re-immersion in the humid environment, the moisture climbs to a higher value. The exact mechanism of this phenomenon is not fully clear but may involve the re-equilibration of the network molecular structure, since the critical thermal spike temperature above which this phenomenon is observed appears to be related to the glass transition of the wet resin.

The amount of water absorbed at room temperature in cured TGDDM/DDS epoxy resins as function of curing time or temperature was analyzed by curing the system for 1 to 5 hours at temperatures ranging from 150 to 207°C [51]. The equilibrium moisture absorption of the resin showed a much stronger dependence on curing temperature at a constant curing time than curing time at a constant temperature (i.e. 177°C). The amount of water absorbed increases approximately linearly over the temperature range of 152-177°C, but increases significantly at 207°C. Since the higher the curing temperature of an epoxy resin system, the higher the extent of reaction that is achieved, the higher content of water at greater extent of reaction was explained by the higher number of generated hydroxyl groups at highest curing temperature employed. The hydroxyl groups, in fact, are more electronegative than the remaining unreacted hydrogen-bonding groups and the number of the hydroxyl groups was thought to dominate the absorptivity.

The effect of the curing conditions on the transport of water in amine-cured epoxy system based on TGDDM/novolac glycidyl ether resin was also analyzed more recently at different immersion temperatures by Nogueira et al. [31]. The diffusivity of the system, which is directly related to the rate of water diffusion in the network structure, was found to increase with immersion temperature for both the cures conducted at 120°C and 160°C. At high temperatures, the rate of diffusion for samples cured at 160°C was significantly increased, while, at low temperatures the differences in diffusivity between the cures did not appear to be significant. On the other hand, as already mentioned, the saturation levels for samples cured at 160°C were generally high (about 5%) but they did not show significant changes with temperature. The saturation levels appreciably increased with temperature for cure at 120°C, reaching comparable or slightly superior levels than those registered for cure at 160°C.

The different behavior of the different cure employed at low immersion temperatures, previously illustrated, was explained through an excess of unreacted amine-groups. The effects influencing the behavior at high immersion temperatures were, on the other hand, mainly justified by the different cross-linking densities. The cure at 120°C was found to lead to a heterogeneous structure, with a phase of unreacted and/or partially reacted material together with a minor phase of highly cross-linked material (conversion = 0.70, Tg = 172°C). Cure at 160°C, on the other hand, revealed a more homogeneous network of a highly cross-linked phase (conversion = 0.92, Tg = 251°C). The authors stated that temperature would affect the mobility in the low-density regions more than in the highly cross-linked regions. The progressive increments of water up-take levels with temperature in cure at 120°C seem to be related to lower cross-link density of this the material. A higher value of the activation energy was calculated for cure at 160°C and it was again ascribed to the different network structures, caused by the different cures. The superior activation energy for cure at 160°C was attributed, in fact, to the higher cross-link density of the network, which diminished the availability of molecular-sized holes in the polymer structure.

The rate of diffusion and solubility of water in an adhesive is important also because water can displace the adhesive from its substrate. Thus, adhesive formulations which are essentially hydrophobic are desirable. This may be achieved by the use of highly cross-linked polymers, polymers containing plate-like fillers, the incorporation of hydrophobic additives and polymers possessing only enough polar groups for adhesion [4].

Mastronardi et al. showed how the presence of hydrophobic coal-tar blended with epoxy polymer matrix of coatings strongly reduced the affinity with water, minimizing water transport and maximizing durability [52]. Several thermosetting and thermoplastic modifiers can also be employed to reduce moisture sensitivity of epoxy resins, such as polyethersulfone (PES), polyimide (PI), cyanates, bismaleimide (BMI), polyetheretherketone (PEEK) [53].

EFFECTS OF ABSORPTION OF WATER ON PROPERTIES OF EPOXY RESINS

Water ingress into a polymer matrix leads to a range of effects; plasticization through interaction of the water molecules with polar groups in the matrix, creation of micro crazes through environmental stress cracking, leaching of unreacted monomer and in certain cases degradation of the resin [54]. In particular, the kind and extent of different effects on physical properties are expected to be associated mainly to the different types of interaction of water molecules with the epoxy network.

Relatively short time of exposure leads to more or less reversible plasticization, producing a lowering of the Tg [55]. The depression of Tg as consequence of immersion in water is a physical change that can partially be reversed upon drying. The glass transition temperature is a very important parameter of epoxy resin and epoxy matrix composites because the Tg establishes the service environment for the material's usage. Usually, when the material is exposed in a hygrothermal environment the Tg decreases and, as a consequence, the service temperature of the material changes. This modification in Tg reflects the degree of resin plasticization and water/resin interactions occurring in the material. It has been reported that heat-cured composites based on epoxies exposed at different temperatures ranging between 45° and 90°C show a large Tg variation (>35°C) when fully saturated in water [56]. As already pointed out, this effect is particularly worrying for cold-curing epoxies whose typical glass transitions, when dry, is not much higher than the possible service temperatures. Hence, the need arises to select adhesives whose Tg's do not drop substantially with water sorption or to assure controlled ambient conditions, when possible.

The effect of the chemical nature of the epoxy resin and the hardener on the depression of Tg associated to the water induced plasticization is also worthy of attention. One representative study of relatively low Tg materials was published by Apicella et al. [57], who experimentally determined the extent of the depression of the glass transition point (ΔTg) for different epoxy/hardener systems. For example, a TGDDM/DDS (tetraglycidyl-diaminodiphenil methane/diaminodiphenil sulfone) epoxy showed ΔTg values of 50-80°C, while DGEBA (diglycidil ether of bisphenol A) cured with more reactive linear amines had ΔTg values of 20-40°C at equivalent levels of absorbed water. Other epoxy resin films, based on a diglycidyl ether of resorcinol (DGER) and meta-phenylene diamine), showed an equilibrium moisture absorption at 20°C of 4-5% with ΔTg values in the range 50-80°C [58].

Long term exposure to water can also lead to loss of material by degradation due to hydrolysis, oxidation, or dehydration reactions involving loss of hydroxyl groups [59]. Comyn [60] has observed that when epoxy resins are left in water for an extended period a small residue remains after evaporation of the water, the origin of which is not clear. The value of Tg can be affected also by the hydrolysis of the cross-linked polymer leading to a decrease in the cross-link density and development of two-phase structure [2, 54].

Moisture can, therefore, induce chemical changes in the resin [61]. If the resin is not fully cured, the lowering in Tg can promote further curing. Additional cross-linking took place, in fact, because the epoxy samples are not fully cured at room temperature and immersion in water causes plasticization of the resin with a consequent reduction in Tg of the cured wet resin [62]. The lowering in Tg upon moisture ingress allows the polymer chains to become mobile; this promotes cross-linking and allows the curing reaction to tent to completion. On the other hand, if the resin is fully cured, water can cause hydrolysis. Whether one can observe cross-linking or hydrolysis it depends on the process conditions. The result can be a permanent change in the molecular weight between cross-links with a consequent change in both stiffness and strength of the polymer. Another possible effect of water ingress is the increase in volume or swelling of the sample, and this can induce stresses similar to thermal responses that could cause microcracks.

Swelling is a specific response accompanying moisture diffusion in epoxy resins. It is very important in composites as well in adhesive joint based on epoxy because it can significantly influence mechanical behavior through the build-up of residual stresses at and near interfaces [50]. Swelling phenomena were observed by different authors and it was found generally that the volume of the resin-containing water is less than that of the volume of the water absorbed plus the volume of the dry resin [6, 26, 40].

Referring to the effect of an immersion in water for a prolonged time on the mechanical properties of epoxy adhesives, it has been reported that the ultimate tensile strength of a bisphenolic epoxy, cured for 3 days at ambient temperature and subsequently post cured at 60°C for 3 hours, first increased with aging time up to 21% after a 3 months immersion. For longer permanence in distilled water (i.e. 5 months), on the other hand, the maximum tensile stress decreased to a value similar to that of the unaged polymer [61]. The initial increase in the ultimate tensile strength was explained in terms of an increase in cross-link density due to the completion of curing, as already described [63]. Later reductions in strength, finally, were the result of degradation due to the presence of water. This can be caused either by water-induced hydrolysis or by swelling-induced micro-cracking or both [64]. Based on measurements of the elastic modulus of aged epoxy in the rubbery region, De'Neve and Shanahan [62] suggested the strong possibility of chain scission along the macromolecular chain, leading to lower mechanical properties of aged samples.

For heat-cured epoxy adhesives, it has been reported that the alterations occurring in mechanical strength after prolonged exposure to water and humid atmosphere are not related with the amount of absorbed water, but they mainly depend on the temperature and on the time of exposure to water, when saturation has been reached [65]. In most cases, the mechanism of water absorption has been found to be reversible, suggesting that it takes place as a simple volumetric diffusion inside the resin, not able to alter the properties of the resin. On the other hand, when higher temperatures or longer immersion times are employed, other phenomena have been observed, such as the swelling of the resin and its plasticization, with a consequent decrease in its glass transition temperature. These mechanisms, moreover, seem to be thermo-activated, being more manifest in severe ambient, as boiling water, and appearing slow or not present at ambient temperatures and low humidity levels [65]. The same authors have identified a limit concentration value of water, corresponding to humidity levels equal to 60-70% R.H.: only for concentrations higher than this limit value, irrespective of the temperature, alterations in mechanical properties of the resin have been observed. In liquid water ambient, the limit concentration is always exceeded and the alterations are thermo-activated and proceed as function of exposure time.

An overall reduction in the mechanical properties of a tetraglycidyl diaminodiphenylmethane (TGDDM) and novolac glycidyl ether heat-cured resin was ascertained at different immersion temperatures, increasing the fragility of the material with the water content [31]. The plasticizating effect of water was recognized in the decrease in the hardness and elastic modulus of the system. On the other hand, a relative increase in tensile modulus was observed at moderate content of water up-take (1.9%) and explained, also in this case, with a reactivation of curing reactions with the water temperature of 100°C, after a 24 hours immersion. For longer immersion times, the modulus decreased up to lower values with respect to the initial one. For the same system, the larger variations occurred at saturation in the properties at break, the toughness becoming 40% with respect the dry material, the stress at break and tensile strength being about 65% of their initial values. A significant decrease of these properties was observed during the initial stages of the diffusion process, at longer times the properties seemed to stabilize.

From another study [61], the Young's modulus of the aged epoxy resulted marginally lower than that of the control samples, increasing the reduction in modulus by increasing the immersion time (after a 5 months immersion the reduction approached the 18%). The elongation at break, moreover, tended to increase initially (up to 76% after a 3 months immersion), but, at later times, the material became brittle (with an increase by about 30% with respect to unaged samples after a 5 months immersion). It has been reported that a reduction in the failure strain can be regarded as a clear and sensitive indicator of polymer degradation [66].

Similar results were found also for different adhesively bonded joints exposed to wet environment, i.e. an initial slight increase in joint strength in time [67-69], attributed to the relief of shrinkage stresses in the adhesive due to the presence of water or moisture [70]. However, compared to control specimens, samples exposed to 95% R.H. at 80°C did not exhibit an increase in shear strength after 24 hours of exposure, i.e. the shear strength decreased as the exposure time was increased [69]. This was explained to with an accelerated plasticization of the adhesive at 80°C that negated the advantage due to the relief of shrinkage stresses in the adhesive. At longer exposure time, the average shear strength was found to decrease in time at all the tested temperatures (ranging from 40° to 80°C), up to 40% for samples exposed to 95% R.H. at 80°C for 7 days.

The fracture toughness of epoxy adhesives generally increases with absorbed water, because of greater plastic deformation and enhanced crack-tip blunting mechanisms within a plasticized matrix [71, 72]. Cohesive strength may, however, sooner or later be reduced sufficiently to offset the increased toughness. The general implication is that the toughness benefit is negated through a loss of cohesive strength [4].

TEST PROCEDURES

Sample Preparation and Conditioning

The rate of water absorption in any solid system mainly depends by the ratio between the surface through which the water diffuses and the volume of the whole specimen. As a consequence, the comparison between different systems is feasible when equal surface/volume ratio's are employed. Commonly, the thickness of the water absorption test samples is chosen very small compared to its width and length. In such a way, the ratio of the edge surface area to the total surface area is only few percent, and as a result, edge effects could be ignored and simple one-dimensional diffusion model analysis can be applied without incurring significant error.

Following the standard for water absorption tests ASTM D 570-81 [73], before the immersion in distilled water, any sample must be subjected to a conditioning procedure as follows: the sample is dried in vacuum oven for 24 hours at 50°C and then cooled in a desiccator. The conditioning procedure assures the complete dryness to samples before the immersion in water. Initial dry weights of specimens are measured and recorded. Then, the specimens are placed into distilled water chambers maintained at constant temperature of 23°C (±0.2°C). The specimens are periodically removed from water and weighed using a digital balance to determine the percent weight change, and, thus, the water uptake. To ensure the removal of excessive surface (superficial) water, specimens must be gently wiped dry using clean, lint-free tissue paper and allowed to stand free at ambient laboratory environment for 2 minutes before the weight measurement. The procedure is repeated until the samples reach a saturation level.

The described conditioning procedure performed on samples before the immersion in water, can be regarded as a thermal treatment that can influence the properties of the adhesives. The effects of a thermal treatment on epoxy resins depend on initial structure and thermal properties of the resins. In particular, the heating of a cross-linked epoxy for prolonged time at a temperature close or higher than the Tg of the resin can cause one or both: the erasing of physical aging and the post-curing of the resin (in addition to the removal of the water eventually contained in the samples). All these effects have important influence on the properties of the cured products that must be taken into account. Therefore, different tests (thermal, mechanical, spectroscopic) should be performed on samples before and after the conditioning procedure in order to evaluate the effects of this treatment on the properties of the different adhesives.

Physical Aging

Physical aging is a universal phenomenon that occurs in all the amorphous polymers below the glass transition temperature (Tg) [74]. In a polymer below its Tg all large-scale molecular motion stops. Polymer glasses, however, are not at thermodynamic equilibrium and continue to proceed toward equilibrium through small-scale conformational changes. This leads to a reduction in the polymer's free volume over time, i.e. in a "densification". The reduction in free volume reduces the polymer mobility and increases the relaxation times.

Structural relaxation in the glassy state is a very slow process. Relaxation time, in fact, is estimated about 10^{+10} minutes at 30°C below the glass transition temperature, while the relaxation time is about 1 minute around the glass transition temperature and about 10^{-10} minutes at 30°C above the Tg [75, 76].

The slow approach to equilibrium occurring during the physical aging affects all the temperature-dependent properties that, therefore, change with time. The effects of physical aging are generally manifest in a reduction of creep compliance, in an embrittlement of the aged polymer (stiffening due to aging), in a reduction of ultimate elongation, in an increase in yield strength and in an increase of the enthalpy of relaxation [75, 77-81]. However, physical aging is a thermoreversible phenomenon that can be erased by heating the polymer above its glass transition temperature [74, 75, 82, 83], i.e. a subsequent quench from above Tg would render a "rejuvenated" epoxy.

The epoxy resins employed in civil engineering applications, being cured at ambient temperature using aliphatic amine as hardeners, possesses a glass transition temperature around 45-65°C [1]. A conditioning temperature of 50°C, therefore, will result very close or even higher than the Tg of the adhesive resins. As a consequence, the heating of the aged adhesives at temperatures higher than their Tg will cause their de-aging and the reestablishment of their initial properties.

Post-Curing

The erasing of physical aging does not affect the Tg of a cured epoxy resin. Eventual variations in Tg, that can be observed on conditioned samples must be attributed to a post-curing process taken place on the not-fully cured samples.

It has been observed that the thermal treatment at 50°C produces an increase in Tg, higher by increasing the time of heating [84]. Although after curing times (4 months) well higher than those suggested by suppliers, i.e. 15 days, the Tg of the resin reaches a constant value, the resin system may not be fully cross-linked. The curing (ambient) temperature, i.e. around 23°C, is about 30°C lower than the final Tg of system and any further cross-linking reaction may be slowed by kinetic restraints [85]. Hence, if the resin is heated at a temperature higher than the ambient temperature, i.e. 50°C, but still lower than its Tg, a post-curing process takes place. In this condition the cross-linking reactions start anew and the Tg increases by increasing the post-curing time. The entity of post-curing depends on the initial Tg of the system when compared with the conditioning temperature.

It must be emphasized, finally, that incomplete curing in epoxy resin is not desirable for the study of hygrothermal effects, since secondary curing during hygrothermal exposure may render experimental observations ambiguous and promote misinterpretation of results.

Effects on Mechanical Properties

The thermal treatments used to conditioning the adhesive samples before the immersion in water can produce different effects on mechanical properties in relation to the different extents of proceeding of de-aging and/or post-curing processes.

When analyzing a completely cross-linked adhesive, possessing a Tg lower than the conditioning temperature, the thermal treatment performed on this adhesive will determine the erasing of the physical aging, while it does not produce any post-cure. Since the major effects of physical aging on mechanical properties of a thermosetting resin are the increase in modulus of the glassy material, the reduction of ultimate elongation and the increase in yield strength, the erase of physical aging should produce reductions in modulus and maximum strength and an increased ultimate strain.

When the adhesive sample possesses a higher Tg than the conditioning temperature but it is not fully cured, the de-aging procedure does not take place but the thermal treatment, on the other hand, is able to post-cure the adhesive. As a consequence, the maximum strength should increase after the thermal treatment and the strain at break should decrease. However, a decrease in flexural modulus could also be observed as a consequence of the conditioning procedure, being this effect due to post-curing, as reported by other researchers [85].

When the conditioning procedure produces a partly removal of physical aging of an adhesive and it is also able to post-cure this system to a certain extent, the effects of thermal treatment on mechanical characteristics of the adhesive would be: an increase in strength, due to the increased cross-linking; a decrease in flexural modulus, as a consequence of post-curing process and of the erase of physical aging; and an increase in ultimate strain, as consequence of the de-aging process.

In conclusion, the major effect of post-curing results an increase in maximum strength and ultimate strain, being possible also a decrease in flexural modulus. The increase in ultimate strain is more marked when a de-aging process takes place together with the post-curing. These aspects must be taken into account by measuring the properties of the adhesives after the conditioning and using these values for subsequent comparisons of properties after immersion process.

KINETICS OF WATER ABSORPTION

The rate of water diffusion in a polymer is typically "non-Fickian" such that the diffusion coefficient (*D*) is not a constant, but it may depend strongly on the concentration and also the sample thickness [86]. The overall rate of water penetration can increase because of a number of factors, such as increase in temperature, presence of internal and external stresses, and swelling stresses. For the purpose of estimating sorption kinetics in epoxy adhesives, however, it is frequently used a Fickian diffusion model.

The water gain percentage, M%, can be expressed by the equation:

$$M\% = \frac{(W - W_d)}{W_d} \times 100\% \tag{1}$$

where: W is the weight of the water-sorbed epoxy specimen and W_d is the initial weight of the dry specimen.

The aforementioned absorption procedure yielded a series of water gain versus time curves. In particular, sorption data are usually reported as Fickian diffusion plots, that is as M_t/M_∞ vs $(\text{time})^{0.5}/L^{-1}$, where M_t and M_∞ represent the mass of penetrant absorbed at time *t* and at equilibrium (i.e. the water content at infinite time), respectively, and L is the sample thickness. Usually, the absorption isotherm displays a pronounced linear region extending up to about 60-80% of the total absorption range, until an equilibrium water concentration is achieved [13, 53].

For a plane polymer sheet exposed to a diffusing fluid, the change of the concentration of the diffusant, *C*, at distance *x* from the contacting surface as a function of time, *t*, is expressed by Fick's second law [12, 86-88]:

$$\frac{\partial C}{\partial t} = D\frac{\partial^2 C}{\partial x^2} \tag{2}$$

where: *D* represents the diffusion coefficient, independent of moisture concentration and of its through thickness location. If the initial concentration, C_0, of the diffusant is constant at the surface and reaches a value C_{max} at equilibrium, then the solution of Eq. (2) gives (12, 86-88):

$$\frac{C - C_0}{C_{\max} - C_0} = 1 - \frac{4}{\pi}\sum_{n=0}^{\infty}\frac{(-1)^n}{2n+1}\exp\left[\frac{-D(2n+1)^2\pi^2 t}{L^2}\right]\cos\frac{(2n+1)\pi x}{L} \tag{3}$$

where: *n* is an integer. The mass of diffusant taken up by the polymer as a function of time, *M*, is obtained by integrating Eq. (3) over the entire thickness, *L*, i.e.:

$$\frac{M_t}{M_\infty} = 1 - \frac{8}{\pi^2}\sum_{n=0}^{\infty}\frac{1}{(2n+1)^2}\exp\left[\frac{-D(2n+1)^2\pi^2 t}{L^2}\right] \qquad (4)$$

For M_t/M_∞ ratios less than 0.6, Eq. [4] may be approximated by the expression:

$$\frac{M_t}{M_\infty} = \frac{4}{L}\left(\frac{Dt}{\pi}\right)^{\frac{1}{2}} \qquad (5)$$

which provides a simple method for the determination of the diffusion coefficient, D, by measuring the initial slope of the plot M_t/M_∞ vs $(\text{time})^{0.5}/L$:

$$D = \frac{\pi}{16}\left(\frac{L}{M_\infty}\right)^2\left(\frac{M_{t2} - M_{t1}}{\sqrt{t_2} - \sqrt{t_1}}\right)^2 \qquad (6)$$

The temperature dependence of the diffusion coefficients can be expressed by an Arrhenius-type relationship [3, 12, 86, 88]:

$$D = D_0 \exp\left(-\frac{E_a}{RT}\right) \qquad (7)$$

where: the pre-exponential factor D_0 represents permeability index [6, 39], E_a is the activation energy of the diffusion process and R is the gas constant. The plot of lnD versus 1/T is often linear. Therefore, the values of activation energy and permeability index can be calculated from the slope and the intercept, respectively, of the mentioned straight line.

In Table 1, the diffusion parameters of liquid water in epoxy resins at ambient (20-23°C) temperature found in different studies, are reported, with the indication of the kind of epoxy resin/hardener mixture and the curing cycles employed.

It is confirmed that only few studies on water diffusion in cold-curing epoxies are present in literature.

Several discrepancies are observed for the values of D_0 found in different studies; for example for a similar epoxy/hardener system D_0 measured by McKague et al. [6] was 35 times lower than the value obtained by Musto et al. [13]. These differences were ascribed partly to the inherent inaccuracy in the calculation of D_0, which involves extrapolation over a wide abscissa range, and also to differences in the molecular structure and/or stoichiometry of the reactants in the two formulations in questions. The results of Majerus et al. [93] on Fiberite 934 compare even more favorably with those reported by Musto et al. [13]. The above comparison indicates that the type of resin (bifunctional, tetrafunctional, or a mixture of the two) has a limited influence on the diffusion parameters. It is reasonable to conclude that the dominant factor is represented by the functionality and molecular structure of the hardener, which is the same (DDS) for all the cases compared above.

Table 1: Coefficient of diffusion of water in different epoxy resins.

Epoxy	Hardener	Curing cycle	D (cm^2/s)	E_a (kcal/mol)	D_0 (cm^2/s)	Ref.
Not specified	Not specified	Heat-curing	$\approx 10^{-9}$			89
Not specified	Not specified	Heat-curing	2-8 x 10^{-9}			90
DGEBA	mPDA	2h at 75°C + 2h at 125°C + 8 h at 180°C	0.794 x 10^{-9}	12.2	0.81	3
DGEBA	mPDA	24h at 23°C + 1h at 80°C + 1h at 175°C	1.08 x 10^{-9}			39
DGEBA	DDA	1h at 140°C	0.215 x 10^{-9}	16.8	771	50
DGEBA	Benzyl alcohol + meta-xylene diamine	24h at 22°C + 24h at 60°C	$\approx$ 2 x 10^{-8}			91
DGEBA	Acid anhydride	9h at 102°C	$\approx$ 1.8 x 10^{-8}			91
Tetrafunctional epoxy	aromatic diamine	Heat-curing	0.575 x 10^{-9}	8.06	5.14 x 10^{-4}	6
TGDDM	DDS	Heat-curing	10^{-9}			92
TGDDM	DDS	1h at 80°C + 2h at 100°C + 4h at 150°C + 7 h at 200°C	0.83 x 10^{-9}	11.1	0.13	3
TGDDM	DDS	16h at 140°C + 4h at 200°C	1.10 x 10^{-9}	9.5	1.8 x 10^{-2}	13
TGDDM + bisphenol A	DDS	2h at 135°C + 4h at 177°C + 6h at 190°C	0.63 x 10^{-9}	10.4	3.0 x 10^{-2}	3
TGDDM + bisphenol A	DDS	Heat-curing	0.495 x 10^{-9}	8.8	1.56 x 10^{-3}	93
TGDDM + novolac glycidyl ether	DDS	2h at 120°C + 2h 30min at 170°C	1.50 x 10^{-9}	6.8	1.65 x 10^{-4}	31
TGDDM + novolac glycidyl ether	DDS	2h at 160°C + 2h at 220°C	1.20 x 10^{-9}	11.4	0.38	31
TGAP (triglycidyl-aminophenol)	DDS	30min at 140°C + 2h at 180°C	0.446 x 10^{-9}			94

KINETICS OF MOISTURE ABSORPTION

A wet environment may be either liquid water or a vapor of varying relative humidity, i.e. R.H. In the moisture diffusion, the R.H. determines the equilibrium moisture concentration. At 100% R.H., the chemical potential of the vapor is the same as that of the liquid; therefore, sorption, diffusion, and equilibrium moisture uptake will be the same as in a liquid water environment. At partial pressures of less than 100% R.H., however, the equilibrium moisture uptake will be substantially lower than that in liquid water. Therefore, the maximum moisture level is determined solely by relative humidity [37], higher relative humidity creates conditions for more water uptake in the resin and this, in turn, increases Tg depression. Also, if diffusivity is concentration dependent such that the diffusion coefficient increases with concentration, a lower R.H. environment may slow the sorption kinetics as well [95]. Equilibrium moisture uptake is reduced by the increase in degree of cross-linking in the epoxy. Finally, higher temperatures will accelerate the moisture sorption process [53]. Since the rate of moisture diffusion is low, in fact, it is usually necessary to use elevated temperatures to accelerate test programs intended to characterize the phenomenon.

Also in vapor ambient, the Fick's law of diffusion adequately describes the water absorption kinetics in most epoxy systems in current use, over much of their service temperatures and times [53, 65].

If the moisture absorption is independent of concentration, the one-dimensional Fickian diffusion law, already reported in Eq. (2) for diffusion of liquid water into cured epoxy resin, describes the transport of moisture through the thickness of the resin, assuming that the moisture flux is proportional to the concentration gradient. *D* can be again determined from the moisture absorption kinetics experimentally measured [43].

The deviation from a non-Fickian water diffusion phenomenon, in particular, occurs when the diffusion rate is close to the rate of structural relaxation of the matrix under the influence of moisture. As already stated, during the long-term exposure to water or moisture, physical and chemical transformations take place in epoxy resins. The hydrolysis of the resin is an example of chemical transformations. Chemical reactions are always accompanied by considerable structural relaxation phenomena, which exert a significant influence on the moisture transport process [96].

A combined "Fickian absorption + relaxation + convection + chemical reaction" model was recently proposed [96]. It was used for modeling the moisture transport process and was able to describe the singularities of non-Fickian moisture penetration into the materials. The experiments, carried out on different epoxy based composites, showed that, in a first stage, these materials possess highly pronounced non-Fickian properties, since they are susceptible to relaxation process when humidified. As a result, the moisture desorption of the samples was described by the second Fick's law with constant boundary conditions. The diffusion parameters obtained were used as a priori information for describing the absorption process, with a good approximation for the time dependence of the absorbed moisture for composite samples of varied geometry and size, at different degrees of plasticization, free volume contents and types of chemical modification.

In Table 2 the diffusion parameters of moisture in different epoxy resins at ambient (20-23°C) temperature, are reported.

Table 2: Coefficient of diffusion of moisture in different epoxy resins.

Epoxy	Hardener	Curing cycle	R.H. (%)	D (cm^2/s)	E_a (kcal/mol)	D_0 (cm^2/s)	Ref.
DGEBA	mPDA	24h at 23°C+ 1h at 80°C + 1h at 175°C	98	0.83×10^{-9}	11.60	0.24	39
Not specified	Not specified	Heat-curing	96	2.8×10^{-9}			53

Accelerating Tests

Several standards relative to accelerated weathering tests are available and give general conditions which should be set for typical accelerated weathering apparatus [97-103]. None of these standards, however, imposes rigid condition on how an accelerated test should be performed, which is left to the examiners, although there are some suggestions regarding important test parameters. For example, dry/wet cycle time is usually 51/9 or 102/18 minutes, but 1/1 and 18/6 hours are also suggested [104]. This freedom of choice does not seem to be dictated by some logical relation between conditions of material performance and material ability to withstand environmental conditions. It is rather the reflection of the opinion of a particular standard committee on what is possible to achieve and test in existing equipment. As an example, the mentioned dry/wet cycle 102/18 minutes was chosen, not because it is the most typical in nature (Central European conditions have 10-16% of rain), but because of the constrains of the instruments used in the past. It is possible that some of these constrains are long removed but the parameters of the tests are still in use and they are even employed in other equipments which never had these constraints. Finally, in some cases the conditions used in the standard tests are very far to be encountered in a real external exposure.

These practices do not provide satisfactory artificial weathering conditions and a precise correlation between the data obtained from accelerated tests and the performances of the materials exposed for long time to environment is not achievable. Therefore, serious efforts are required to improve the existing situation. In particular, it is strongly suggested that any artificial condition must be maximized only to a level which does not alter the typical degradation mechanisms of the particular material. The correspondence between artificial and natural weathering remains a thorny topic.

In conclusion, the accelerated weathering conditions should be selected to give the highest possible accelerating factor, but the conditions selected must produce degradation mechanisms which are similar as possible to the way in which the specific material would degrade in natural conditions. Finally, for each material, a correlation between the results obtained under natural and artificial weathering conditions must be precisely developed.

References

[1] Frigione, M., Naddeo, C. and Acierno, D., *J. Materials Engineering*, 11, 59-80 (2000).

[2] Antoon, M.K. and Koenig, J.L., *J. Polym. Sci., Polym. Phys. Ed.*, 19, 197 (1981).

[3] Zhou, J. and Lucas, J.P., *Polymer*, 40, 5505-5512 (1999).

[4] Mays, G.C. and Hutchinson, A.R., "*Adhesives in Civil Engineering*". Ch.2, Cambridge University Press, Cambridge (U.K.) (1992).

[5] Shaw, S.J., "Chemistry and Technology of Epoxy Resins". Ch. 7, *Epoxy Resin Adhesives,* Ed. Bryan Ellis, Blackie Academic & Professional, London (U.K.) (1994).

[6] McKague, E.L., Reynolds, J.D. and Halkias, J.E., *J. Appl. Polym. Sci.*, 22, 1643 (1978).

[7] Wright, W.W., *Composites*, 12, 201 (1981).

[8] Mijovic, J. and Lin, K.J., *Appl. Polym. Sci.*, 30, 2527-2549 (1985).

[9] Wypych, G., "*Handbook of Material Weathering*", Ch. 14, ChemTec Publishing, Toronto (Canada). (1995).

[10] Pritchard, G., "*Reinforced Plastics Durability*", Ch. 1, Ed. Geoffrey Pritchard, CRC Press & Woodhead Publishing Limited, Boca Raton (U.S.A.) & Cambridge (U.K.) (2000).
[11] Musto, P., Ragosta, G. and Mascia, L., *Chem. Mater.*, 12, 1331-1341 (2000).
[12] Vieth, W.R., "*Diffusion in and through Polymers*", Hansen, Munich (1991).
[13] Musto, P., Mascia, L., Ragosta, G., Scarinzi, G. and Villano, P., *Polymer*, 41, 565-574 (2000).
[14] Banks, L. and Ellis, B., *Polym. Bull.*, 1, 377 (1979).
[15] Moy, P. and Karasz, F.E., *Polym. Eng. Sci.*, 20, 315 (1980).
[16] Jelinski, L.W., Dumais, J.J., Chiolli, A.L., Ellis, T.S. and Karasz, F.E., *Macromolecules*, 18, 1091 (1985).
[17] Levy, R.L., Fanter, D.L. and Summers, C.J., *J. Appl. Polym. Sci.*, 24, 1643 (1979).
[18] Antoon, M.K., Koenig, J.L. and Serafini, T.J., *Polym. Sci., Polym. Phys. Ed.*, 19, 1567 (1981).
[19] Gupta, V.B. and Drzal, L.T., *J. Appl. Polym. Sci.*, 30, 4467 (1985).
[20] Woo, M. and Piggott, M. J., *Composite Technology Research*, 9, 101 (1987).
[21] Bellenger, V., Verdu, J. and Morel, E., *J. Mater. Sci.*, 24, 63 (1989).
[22] Gordon, M., Hope, C.S., Loan, D.L. and Roe, R.-J., *Proc. R. Soc.*, A258, 215 (1960).
[23] Mikols, W.J., Seferis J.C., Apicella, A. and Nicolais, L., *Polym. Compos.*, 3, 118 (1982).
[24] Maxwell, D. and Pethrick, R.A., *J. Appl. Polym. Sci.*, 28, 2363 (1983).
[25] Pethrick, R.A., Hollins, E.A., Mc Ewan, I., Pollock, E.A. and Hayward, D., *Polym. Int.*, 39, 275 (1996).
[26] Adamson, M.J., *J. Mater. Sci.*, 15, 1736. (1980).
[27] Grave, C., Mc Evan, I. and Pethrick, R.A., *J. Appl. Polym. Sci.*, 69, 2369 (1998).
[28] Apicella, A., Nicolais, L. and de Cataldis, C., *J. of Membrane Sci.*, 18, 211 (1985).
[29] Apicella, A., Nicolais, L. and de Cataldis, C., *Adv. Polym. Sci.*, 66, 189 (1985).
[30] Cotugno, S., Larobina, D., Mensitieri, G., Musto, P. and Ragosta, G., *Polymer*, 42, 6431-6438 (2001).
[31] Nogueira, P., Ramírez, C., Torres, A., Abad, M.J., Cano, J., López, J., López-Bueno, I. and Barral, L., *J. Appl. Polym. Sci.*, 80, 71-80 (2001).
[32] Barton, S.J. and Prichard, G., *Polym. Adv. Technol.*, 5, 245 (1994).
[33] Vanlandingham, M.R., Eduljee, R.F. and Gillespie, J.W. Jr., *J. Appl. Polym. Sci.*, 71, 787 (1999).
[34] Apicella, A., Nicolais, L., Mikols, W.J. and Seferis, J.C., in "*Interrelations between Processing Structure and Properties of Polymeric Materials*", Seferis J.C. and Theocaris P.S. Eds., Elsevier, Amsterdam, 629 (1984).
[35] Maggana, C. and Pissis, P., *J. Polym. Sci., B Polym. Phys.*, 37, 1165 (1999).
[36] Weir, M.D., Bastide, C. and Sung, C.S.P., *Macromolecules*, 34, 4923-4926 (2001).
[37] Zhou, J., and Lucas, J.P., *Polymer*, 40, 5513-5522 (1999).
[38] Zaffaroni, G., Cappelletti, C., Mariani, U. and Rigamonti, M., *Proceedings of the ECCM – 8 European Conference on Composite Materials*, 3-6 June, Naples, Italy, 183-190 (1998).
[39] Diamant, Y., Marom, G. and Broutman, L.J., *J. Appl. Polym. Sci.*, 26, 3015-3025 (1981).
[40] Wright, W.W. and Adamson, M.J., *J. Mater. Sci. Composites*, 12, 201 (1981).

[41] Carfagna, C., Apicella, A. and Nicolais, L., *J. Appl. Polym. Sci.*, 27, 105-112 (1982).
[42] Ellis, B. and Rashid, H.U., *J. Appl. Polym. Sci.*, 29, 2021-2038 (1984).
[43] Jones, F.R. "Chemistry and Technology of Epoxy Resins". Ch. 8, *Epoxy Resin Adhesives*, Ed. Bryan Ellis, Blackie Academic & Professional, London (U.K.) (1994).
[44] Rinaldi, G. and Maura, G., *Polym. Int.*, 31, 339-345 (1993).
[45] McKague, E.L., Halkias, J.E. and Reynolds, J.D., *J. Compos. Mater.*, 9, 2 (1975).
[46] Browning, C.E., *Polym. Eng. Sci.*, 18, 16 (1978).
[47] Apicella, A., Nicolais, L., Astarita, G. and Drioli, E., *Polym. Eng. Sci.*, 21, 18 (1981).
[48] Apicella, A., Nicolais, L. and Carfagna, C., "*The Role of Polymeric Matrix in the Processing and Structural Properties of Composites Materials*", Ed. J.C. Seferis and L. Nicolais, Plenum Publishing Co., New York, 215-229 (1983).
[49] Damian, C., Espuche, E. and Escoubes, M., *Polym. Degrad. Stab.*, 72, 447-458 (2001).
[50] Xiao, G.Z. and Shanahan, M.E.R., *Polymer*, 39, 3253-3260 (1998).
[51] Yang, F., Gilbert, R.D., Fornes, R.E. and Memory, J.D., *J. Polym. Sci., A Polym. Chem.*, 24, 2609-2618 (1986).
[52] Mastronardi, P., Carfagna, C. and Nicolais, L., *J. Mat. Sci.*, 18, 1977 (1983).
[53] Jones, F.R., "*Reinforced Plastics Durability*", Ch. 3, Ed. Geoffrey Pritchard, CRC Press & Woodhead Publishing Limited, Boca Raton (U.S.A.) & Cambridge (U.K.) (2000).
[54] Ivanova, K.I., Pethrick, R.A. and Affrossman, S., *Polymer*, 41, 6787-6796 (2000).
[55] Li, C., Dickie, R.A. and Morman, K.N., *Polym. Eng. Sci.*, 30, 249 (1990).
[56] Zhou, J. and Lucas, J.P., *Proceedings of the 9th Conference of the ASC*, p.1213, Technomic Publishing. (1994).
[57] Apicella, A., Nicolais, L., Mensitieri, G. and del Nobile, M., *Proceedings International Conference Advanced Materials, Symposium A4: Composite Materials*, May, Strasbourg, North-Holland, 11-21 (1992).
[58] Nechvolodnova, E.M., Prut, E.V., Belgovskiy, I.M., Ponomarenko, A.T. and Shevchenko V.G., *Acta Polymerica*, 43: 3, 191-192 (1992).
[59] Luoma, G.A. and Rowland R.D., *J. Appl. Polym. Sci.*, 32, 5777 (1986).
[60] Comyn, J., *J. Polym. Marine Environ.*, 153 (1989).
[61] Kajorncheappunngam, S., Gupta, R.K. and GangaRao, H.V.S., *J. of Composites for Construction*, 6, 61-69 (2002).
[62] De'Neve, B. and Shanahan, M.E.R., *Polymer*, 34, 5099-5105 (1993).
[63] Gupta, V.B., Drzal, L.T., Lee, C.Y.-C. and Rich, M.J., *Polym. Eng. and Sci.*, 25, 812-823 (1985).
[64] Lee, C.L. and Peppas, N.A., *Prog. in Polym. Sci.*, 18, 947-961 (1993).
[65] Bonniau, P. and Bunsell, A.R., *Poliplasti*, no. 300, 22-28 (1982).
[66] White, J.R. and Turnbull, A., *J. Mater. Sci.*, 29, 584-613 (1994).
[67] Cotter, J.L., in "*Developments in Adhesives*", W.C. Wake Ed., Elsevier Applied Science, London, pg.1 (1977).
[68] Minford, J.D., in "*Durability of Structural Adhesives*", A.J. Kinloch Ed., Applied Science, London, 135-214 (1983).
[69] Tiwari R.K., Balan, M., Stumpff, P., Soni, S.R., Mijovic, J. and Miura, N., *Proceedings of the SAMPE 2001* (Society for the Advancement of Materials and Process Engineering), 6-10 May, Long Beach, California, U.S.A. (2001).
[70] Bowditch, M.R., *Int. J. Adhesion and Adhesives*, 16, 73 (1996).

[71] Kinloch, A.J. and Shaw S.J., "*Developments in Adhesives – 2*". Kinloch, A.J. Ed., Applied Science Publishers, London, 81 (1981).
[72] Kinloch, A.J., *J. Mat. Sci.*, 17, 617 (1982).
[73] ASTM D 570-81 "*Standard Test Method for Water Absorption of Plastics*" (Re-approved 1988).
[74] Struik, L.C.E., "*Physical Aging in Amorphous Polymers and Other Materials*". Elsevier, New York (1978).
[75] Nichols, M.E., Wang, S.S. and Geil, P.H., *J. Macomol. Sci. – Phys.*, B29: 4, 303-336 (1990).
[76] Clough, R.L. and Gillen, K.T., "*Irradiation Effects on Polymers*", D.W. Clegg & A.A. Colleyer (eds) (1991).
[77] Morgan, R.J., *J. Appl. Polym. Sci.*, 23, 2711 (1979).
[78] Kong, E.S.-W., *J. Appl. Phys.*, 52, 5921 (1981).
[79] Berens, A.R. and Hodge, I.M., *Macromolecules*, 15, 756 (1982).
[80] Hodge, I.M., *Macromolecules*, 16, 898 (1983).
[81] Cook, W.D., Mehrabi, M. and Edward, G.H., *Polymer*, 40, 1209-1218 (1999).
[82] Kong, E.S.-W.,"*Advances in Polymer Science 80*", Springer-Verlag Berlin Heidelberg (Ed.), 125-171 (1986).
[83] Montserrat, S., *J. Appl. Polym. Sci.*, 44, 545-554 (1992).
[84] Frigione, M., Lettieri, M., Mecchi, A.M. and Santamaria, U., *Proceedings of ICOM-CC 13th Triennial meeting*, 22-27 September, Rio de Janeiro, Brazil, Preprints: ICOM Committee for Conservation, London, James & James, 888-893 (2002).
[85] Ellis, B., "*Chemistry and Technology of Epoxy Resins*", Chap. 3, Ellis, B. Ed., Blackie Academic & Professional, London (1993).
[86] Crank, J. and Park, G.S., "*Diffusion of Polymers*", Academic Press, New York (1968).
[87] Crank, J., "*The Mathematics of Diffusion*", 2, Oxford University Press, Oxford (1975).
[88] Comyn, J., "*Polymer Permeability*", Chap. 2, Elsevier, London, pp. 20-27 (1985).
[89] Mays, G.C. and Hutchinson, A.R., "*Adhesives in Civil Engineering*". Ch.4, Cambridge University Press, Cambridge (U.K.) (1992).
[90] Kinloch, A.J., *J. Adhes.*, 10, 193 (1979).
[91] González-Benito, J., Bravo, J., Mikes, F. and Baselga, J., *Polymer*, 44, 653-659 (2003).
[92] Morgan, R.J., O'Neal, J.E. and Fanter, D.L., *J. Mater. Sci.*, 15, 751 (1980).
[93] Majerus, M.S., Soong, D.S. and Prausnitz, J.M., *J. Appl. Polym. Sci.*, 29, 2453 (1984).
[94] Pethrick, R.A., Hollins, E.A., Mc Ewan, I., Mac Kinnon, A.J., Hayward, D., Cannon, L., Jenkins, S.D. and Mc Grail, P.T., *Macromolecules*, 29, 5208-5214 (1996).
[95] Sung, N.-H., in "Adhesives and Sealants", Section 7: *Environmental Effects, Engineered Materials Handbook*, Vol. 3, ASM International (U.S.A.) (1990).
[96] Startsev, O.V., Krotov, A.S., Kuznetsov A.A., Anihovskaya L.I. and Senatorova O.G., *Twelfth International Conference on Mechanics of Composite Materials*, 9-13 June, Riga, Latvia, 192-193 (2002).
[97] ASTM D1435, "*Outdoor weathering of plastics*".
[98] ASTM D1499, "*Operating light and water exposure apparatus (carbon arc type) for exposure of plastics*".
[99] ASTM D2565, "*Operating xenon arc type (water cooled) light exposure apparatus with or without water for exposure of plastics*".

[100] ASTM D4329, "*Operating light and water exposure apparatus (fluorescence UV condensation type) for exposure of plastics*".
[101] DIN 53386 06, "*Exposure to natural weathering*".
[102] DIN 53387 06, "*Weathering in laboratory apparatus, exposure to filtered xenon arc radiation and periodic wetting*".
[103] ISO 4607, "*Plastics – methods of exposure to natural weathering*".
[104] Wypych, G., "*Handbook of Material Weathering*", Ch. 9, ChemTec Publishing, Toronto (Canada) (1995)

In: Homolytic and Heterolytic Reactions: Problems and Solutions ISBN 1-59033-980-0
Editors: G.E. Zaikov, et al., pp. 307-312

Chapter 14

MODELING OF DIFFUSION PROCESSES, ACCOMPANYING THE CONTACT OF RUBBERS WITH MULTI-COMPONENT HYDROCARBON MEDIA

N. N. Petrova*, A. F. Fyodorova*, O. V. Startsev** and A. S. Krotov **

* Institute of nonmetallic materials SB RAS, 20 Avtodorognaya St., Yakutsk, Russia, 677002

** Altai State University, 66 Dimitrov St., Barnaul, Russia, 656099

ABSTRACT

The paper deals with the investigation of influence of hydrocarbon medium on the properties of rubbers of sealing application under the conditions of cold climate. The mathematic modeling of processes accompanying rubber contact with oil at room temperature was carried out.

Key words: Rubber, climatic stability, plasticizer, frost resistance, diffusion processes.

Nature and mechanism of effect of low-molecular weight substances on polymers are the main problematic questions of diverse investigations. These problems are less of all studied for multi-component mixtures including oil and mineral oils. Difference in bellicosity of the components, presence of the process of extraction of important and performance determining ingredients from rubbers and masticating action of swelling on rubber are referred to the main peculiarities of the medium impact on a polymer.

Injection of plasticizers, which raise kinetic flexibility of rubber chains and decreasing vitrifying temperature of the system is the most prevalent method to raise the rubber frost resistance. B-14 rubber based on butadiene-nitrile caoutchouc SKN-18 containing a small amount of acrylonotrile, whose recipe includes 30 wt. parts of dibutylphtalate (DBP) plasticizer is a good example of rubbers, which is widely used for producing seals for arctic application. However, as it was shown by investigations of climatic stability of rubbers under the conditions of cold sharply continental climate (Yakutsk, Russia), contact with oils, operation liquids (often representing organic substances of oil derivation) causes intense plasticizer wash-out. Fluctuation of frost resistance coefficient at elongation (All-Union Standard 408-78) for rubber B-14 after 2-year exposition under the conditions of in-cite experiment in Talakan deposit oil is submitted in Fig. 1. Rubber samples were exposed in oil at ambient temperatures without displacement of the operation medium.

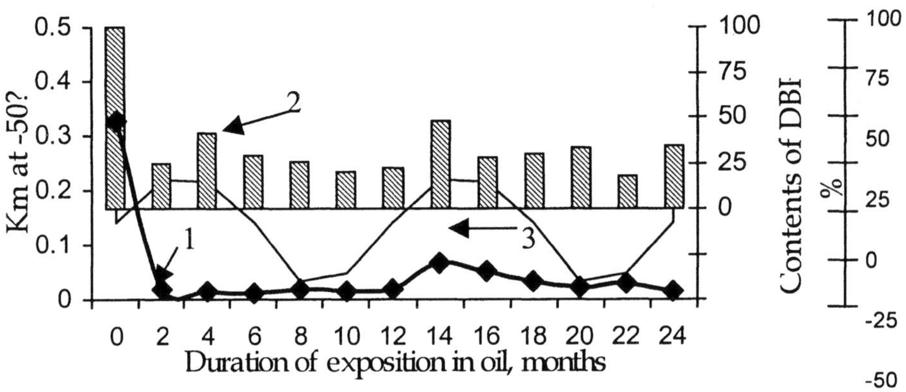

Figure 1. Dependence of frost resistance coefficient at -50°C (1), plasticizer contents (2) in B-14 rubber and ambient temperature (3) on duration of detention in oil under the conditions of in-cite exposition.

The first months of exposition of B-14 rubber in oil revealed sharp cutback of its frost resistance, which can be explained by dibutylphtalate (DBP) plasticizer extraction into the oil medium. This was confirmed by the results of experiments aimed at determining DBP contents in rubbers using IR-spectroscopy (Fig. 1, bar chart 2). IR-Fourier spectrometer "Paragnon 1000"allowed studying chloroform extractions of rubber crumb produced of the samples exposed under combined impact of low temperatures and hydrocarbon medium. Here fixed was the decrease of intensity of characteristic stripes (1725 cm^{-1}, 1280 cm^{-1}, 1120 cm^{-1}) [1], which was due to DBP devourment depending on oil exposition period.

Thus, investigations devoted to B-14 rubber behavior in Talakan oil under the conditions of in-cite exposition after relatively long periods of time (2 years) showed that the rubber, which underwent the impact of hydrocarbon medium was characterized by high instability of low-temperature properties: at low temperatures (lower than -50°C) it completely looses its frost resistance, though, according to specification, it had to preserve high operability up to -55°C, and at higher temperatures it performed significant oscillations in this coefficient due to diverse diffusion processes within the system "rubber-oil medium".

Interaction of rubbers and oil causes a number of diffusion processes, such as penetration of the first molecules of hydrocarbons in oil initiates plasticizer wash out, later the elastomers start diffusing other hydrocarbons, as oil is a complicated multi-component system. As a rule, rubber unit producers do not take all these processes into account and after short-term influence of the operation hydrocarbon medium (normally lubricants, fuel, hydraulic liquids) on the rubber sealing device, one can observe sharp aggravation of low-temperature properties of the material declared as a frost resistant one. As diffusion processes progress and the sealing material aging cause changes in its chemical composition and structure, shrinkage stresses appearing due to significant differences in the coefficients of linear expansion of rubbers and metals within the area close to that of vitrifying of rubber causes decrease of contact pressure values to the minimum and depressurization of the sealing junction.

The importance of evaluation of the processes taking place while the rubber is contacting oil media, development of rubber units and study of their operability under real exploitation conditions doomed the following sense of investigations: detailed exploration and modeling of rubber swelling processes in oil at room temperature. The rubber samples based on B-14 were placed into Talakan oil at room temperature and their swelling kinetics was studied during 4 months (before achieving the equilibrium state), in addition the sample thickness was monitored together with the swelling degree. To determine the influence of the plasticizer on velocity, peculiarities of diffusion processes performance and low-temperature properties of rubbers we have prepared compositions containing different amounts of dibutylphtalate: 0.5, 5, 10, 20 and 30 wt. parts (B-14-1, B-14-2, B-14-3, B-14-4, B-14-5, respectively). Mathematic modeling of the degree of swelling of rubbers from time was carried out using FITTER software.

Fig. 2 shows experimental dependencies of swelling degree for D-14 rubber containing different amounts of a plasticizer on time of exposition in Talakan oil at room temperature in normalized form. Obtained data showed that while the rubber units and oil are contacting, there are two diffusion processes related to penetration of oil into the material. Within the first day light hydrocarbons diffuses into the rubber and initiates extraction of the plasticizer from the material. After 6 days of exposition the diffusion process dealing in penetration of heavier hydrocarbons starts to dominate.

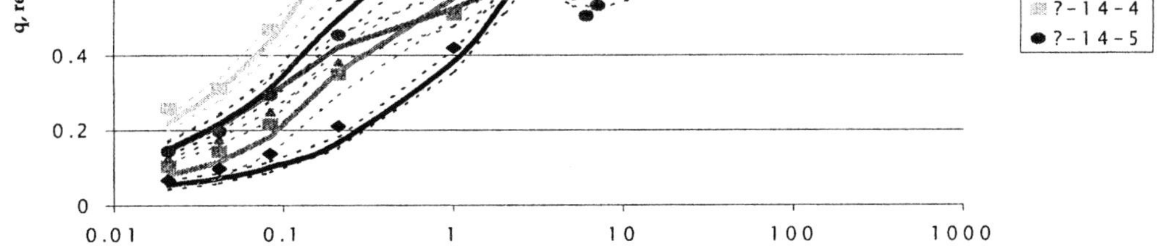

*- $q=Q/Q_{\infty}$

Figure 2. Kinetics of swelling for B-14 rubber containing different amounts of plasticizer: points – experiment; lines – model; dotted lines – confidence interval.

The system of equations (2), (4) with initial and boundary conditions (3), (5) in the univariate area (1) determines the kinetics of distribution of light and heavy oil fractions in the B-14 rubber on the assumption of Fick law for the stated system

$$\Omega = \{x | 0 < x < h\} \tag{1}$$

$$\frac{\partial c_1}{\partial t} = D_1 \frac{\partial^2 c_1}{\partial x^2}; \quad x \in \Omega, \ t > 0 \tag{2}$$

$$\begin{gathered} c_1(x,0) = 0; \ x \in \Omega \\ c_1(0,t) = c_1(h,t) = c_{1\infty}; \quad t > 0 \end{gathered} \tag{3}$$

$$\frac{\partial c_2}{\partial t} = D_2 \frac{\partial^2 c_2}{\partial x^2} - kc_2; \quad x \in \Omega, \ t > 0 \tag{4}$$

$$\begin{gathered} c_2(x,0) = 0; \ x \in \Omega \\ c_2(0,t) = c_2(h,t) = c_{2\infty}; \quad t > 0 \end{gathered} \tag{5}$$

where $c_1(x, t)$ – concentration of heavy oil fractions in the rubber sample; $c_2(x, t)$ – concentration of light oil fractions; k – extraction constant; D_1, D_2 – coefficients of diffusion of heavy and light fractions, respectively (cm^2/sec.), h – sample thickness (cm).

The system (6)-(8) determines the correspondence of the system parameters of differential equations (1)-(5) with approximation equation (9)

$$Q(t) = \frac{1}{h} \int_0^h \left(c_1(x,t) + c_2(x,t) \right) dx \tag{6}$$

$$Q_\infty = c_{1\infty}, \ K = \frac{c_{2\infty}}{c_{1\infty}} \tag{7}$$

$$D_a = D_1; \ D_b = D_2; \ D_c = k \tag{8}$$

To find the parameters of equation

$$Q = Q_\infty \times ((1 - S_a) + K \times (1 - S_b) \exp(-D_c \times t)) \tag{9}$$

where Q_∞ is a boundary swelling degree, $(1\text{-}S_a)$ – the general part of diffusion due to penetration of heavy hydrocarbons into the rubber, K – parameter depending on a plasticizer part, $(1\text{-}S_b)$ – the part describing accumulation of light oil hydrocarbons during the first day of exposition, $exp(-D_c t)$ – a multiplier describing extraction of a plasticizer from the rubber matrix

$$S_a = \sum_{n=1}^{4} A_n \times \exp(-\alpha_n^2 F_a)\text{, where } \alpha_n = \frac{\pi}{2}(2n-1);\ A_n = \frac{2}{\alpha_n^2};\ F_a = \frac{D_a \times t}{h^2}.$$

$$S_b = \sum_{n=1}^{4} B_n \times \exp(-\beta_n^2 F_b)\text{, where } \beta_n = \frac{\pi}{2}(2n-1);\ B_n = \frac{2}{\beta_n^2};\ F_b = \frac{D_b \times t}{h^2}$$

one can find the functional minimum

$$\delta \equiv \sum_{i=1}^{n} \left(Q(t) - Q_{\exp}(t)\right)^2 \xrightarrow{Q_\infty, K, D_a, D_b, D_c} \min \tag{10}$$

where $Q_{exp}(t)$ represent experimental points; $Q(t)$ – the model (9).

Values of the diffusion coefficient and extraction constants, which characterize the processes occurring in the described system have extreme performance and can be stated as follows:

$$D_i = D_{i,o} + D_{i,k}\left(1 - \exp\left(-D_{i,1}x\right)\right)\exp\left(-D_{i,2}x\right) \tag{11}$$

where i changes the values a, b, c; x – a plasticizer part.

The parameter K, which depends on a portion of extracted plasticizer can be described by a polynomial of the third degree:

$$K = K_0 + K_1 x + K_2 x^2 + K_3 x^3 \tag{12}$$

As a result of description of all variables one can have a general model, which reflects the processes occurring in the system B-14 rubber – plasticizer dibutylphtalate – Talakan deposit oil (Fig. 2). The model parameters are listed in Table 1.

Thereby, it was investigated the influence of diffusion processes, which occur while rubbers based on butadiene-nitrile caoutchouc contact with oil from Talakan deposit both at room temperature and in the conditions of in-cite exposition, on their low-temperature properties and swelling degree. Using FITTER software we have carried out modeling of swelling process for the rubbers containing different amounts of plasticizers, determined the mechanism of interaction of the rubbers and oil (three basic stages) and substantiated their longevity, developed the method of such investigations, which allowed further regulation of velocity and degree of swelling of rubbers in the hydrocarbon media to decrease their negative impact on basic operational properties of the material.

Table 1. Values of parameters from the equation (9) describing the process of swelling of B-14 rubber containing different amounts of plasticizer

Parameter value	
K_0	0.295
K_a	0.0798
$K_в$	-0.00702
K_c	0.000155
D_{a0}, mm²/24hrs	0.373
D_{aa}, mm²/24hrs	47.9
D_{a1}	0.0750
D_{a2}	0.0814
$D_{в0}$, mm²/24hrs	0.00352
$D_{вa}$, mm²/24hrs	77.2
$D_{в1}$	0.180
$D_{в2}$	0.173
D_{c0}, 1/24hrs	0.0202
D_{ca}, 1/24hrs	7.99
D_{c1}	0.0113
D_{c2}	0.202

REFERENCES

[1] Tarutina L.I., Pozdnyakova A.O. *Spectrum Analysis of Polymers*. – L. "Chemistry", 1986. – 234 p.

In: Homolytic and Heterolytic Reactions: Problems and Solutions ISBN 1-59033-980-0
Editors: G.E. Zaikov, et al., pp. 313-319

Chapter 15

GENERAL TECHNIQUE FOR INVESTIGATION OF BIODEGRADATION OF MATERIALS BY MICROORGANISMS

S. A. Semenov, K. Z. Gumargalieva and G. E. Zaikov*

N.N.Semenov Institute of Chemical Physics, Russian Academy of Sciences. 4 Kosygin st., Moscow, 119991, Russia

*N.M.Emanuel Institute of Biochemical Physics, Russian Academy of Sciences. 4 Kosygin st., Moscow, 119991, Russia

ABSTRACT

This review included information about materials used in tests, microorganisms – material destructors used in tests, facilities and conditions of tests on microorganism propagation on materials and controlable indices of material properties and methods of their determination.

Key words: Microorganisms, degradation, materials, properties, techniques, tests, control, methods, facilities, conditions.

Adhesion and growth of microorganisms and variations of the material properties were studied on the basis of experimental determination of characteristics which allow ascertaining the fact of proceeding and estimate quantitatively intensity of the processes mentioned. The characteristics were determined with the help of microbiological, biochemical and physicochemical methods of analysis of properties, composition and structure of materials and microorganisms, as well as the products of their interaction. The following methods were used: light and luminescent microscopy, sowing to nutritive media, centrifugal detachment, radiometry, ultraviolet, infrared, luminescent spectral and photometry, electrochemical analysis, thin-layer (surface) chromatography, mechanical, electrical and other tests of the material properties. Characteristics and methods used are discussed in [1].

Processes of microbiological damaging of operated technical facilities (materials, parts, aggregates, systems of articles) were revealed with the help of a technique achieved by the authors [1]. It provides for analysis of sediments (pollutants), detected on these objects, as well as damage products and damaged objects themselves. Hence, a complex of characteristics for interactions between microorganisms and materials is determined.

This method helps in estimation of microbiological ability to damage of the most various technical articles: aircrafts and helicopters, motor vehicles, etc. The results obtained allowed substantiation of the choice of materials and microorganisms for future investigations, interactions between which induce microbiological damage of technical parts and aggregates to the utmost telling upon its workability and technical conditions. These materials and microorganisms are shown in Tables 1 and 2.

Table 1. Materials used in tests

Material, trademark, notation	GOST, TU[1]	Characteristics of material samples
Low density polyethylene, trademark 10812-20, (PE)	GOST 16337-70	Film 0.1 mm thick
Poly(methyl methacrylate), organic glass SO-95, (PMMA)	GOST 10667-74	Film 0.1 mm thick
Polyvinylchloride plasticate, I-40-13, (PVC)	GOST 5960-72	Plate 0.6 mm thick, BPVL wire cover
Varnished fabric, (VF)	Cotton base, varnish ET-959, TU-6-10-691-74	Plate 0.8 mm thick, BPVL wire cover
Cellulose triacetate, (CTA)	GOST 7730-74	Film 0.1 mm thick
Polysulfide sealer U-30MES-5	TU-38-10-5462-80	Film 0.3 mm thick
Epoxy resin, (ER)	GOST 21505-73	Plate 0.3 mm thick
Poly(ethylene terephthalate), (PET)	TU 605-1454-71	Film 0.15 mm thick
Glass fiber laminate STK/EP, (GFL)	TU 16.503.055-75	Plate 3 mm thick
Cellulose film, (CF)	GOST 7730-74	Film 0.05 mm thick
Cotton thread of tarpaulin fabric, marking 11205	GOST 15530-76	Threads 0.5 mm in diameter (density 1.2×10^{-3} g/cm^3)
Oil distillate fuel, TS-1	GOST 10227-86	1st category fuel
Pressure oil, MN-7,5U	TU 38101722-78	1st category oil
Aluminum alloy, D-16	GOST 4784-65	Plate 2 mm thick
Steel, St.3	OST 23.4.122-77	Plate 3 mm thick

All studied materials are industrially produced. PMMA film 0.1 mm thick was produced by casting from solution of organic glass SO-95 in an organic solvent according to the method, described in ref. [2]. Varnished fabric plates were made by applying varnish ET-959

[1] Soviet and Russian state standards.

on a cotton support [3]. The samples were used, the shape, size and the method of preparation (from the initial material) of which were stipulated by the method of determining the characteristics of studied process, controlled in the experiment.

Strains of microorganisms preserved in a specialized collection were used. Spore radii (shown in Table 2) were accepted equal the mean equivalent sphere radius, equal by the surface square to a geometrical body (cylinder, ellipsoid, sphere, etc.), to which each spore of the current species of the microorganism is the most similar by shape and size. Values of such equivalent radii were calculated based on direct determination (taking a microscope image) of the linear size and shape of 100 – 120 spores and the normal law of distribution of its (equivalent radius) value, established during these preliminary investigations for every species of microorganisms.

Quantitative regularities of the microbiological damaging of technical facilities were investigated in laboratory experiments rendering (modeling) actual processes of adhesion, growth of microbial cells and variations of the material properties. Such experiments included execution of the following operations: preparing samples of materials and microorganism cultures, inspiration of the samples with microbial cells, and incubation of inspired samples (cultivation of microorganisms on the materials) under definite conditions (temperature, humidity, etc.). The above-mentioned operations were executed with the help of the known modes and methods regulated by the state standards to laboratory tests of resistance of appropriate materials to the action of microorganisms [4 – 7].

Table 2. Microorganisms – material destructors used in tests

Species of microorganism	Damaged material	Radius of spores, μm	Density of spores, g/cm³
Aspergillus niger v. Tieghem	Polymeric materials, metals, oils and lubricants	4.2 ± 1.8	1.12 ± 0.05
Paecilomyces varioti Baimer	Polymeric materials, oils and lubricants	3.6 ± 1.3	1.08 ± 0.08
Penicillium chrysogenum Thom	Polymeric materials, fuel, metals	2.6 ± 1.5	1.13 ± 0.03
Aspergillus flavus Link	Polymeric materials	2.3 ± 1.6	1.14 ± 0.07
Penicillium cyclopium Westling	Polymeric materials	1.6 ± 0.8	1.17 ± 0.05
Aspergillus terreus var aureus Thom and Raper	Polymeric materials	1.2 ± 0.6	1.12 ± 0.09
Cladosporium resinae Lindau de Vries f. Avellaneum	Fuels	2.8 ± 1.3	1.05 ± 0.04
Pseudomonas aerugenosa Schroeter	Fuels	Non-spore-forming	
Bacillus subtilis Ehrenberg	Oils and lubricants, metals	0.7 ± 0.3	1.01 ± 0.07

After a definite time of incubation, a part of samples were removed from tests and one quantitative characteristic or another of the studied process was determined using an appropriate method of analysis. Characteristics were determined regularly during the tests.

Such kinetic approach allowed quantitative description of the process at any particular moment, determination of its rate and features of the process proceeding.

The technique for adhesive interaction study [8] provided for sedimentation of fungal spores in calm air to the surface of material samples, incubation of inspired samples and determination of quantitative characteristics of the process – the adhesion number. This number represents the ratio between the quantity of spores remained on the surface after a force field action to that, initially present on the surface. At the initial stage of experiment, directly during precipitation of spores, the effect of force field of various intensities was provided by tilting the sample surface relative to the direction of the spore motion. Then after some time of contact (~ 1 hour) between adhering objects, the detachment force was created by the centrifugation method.

Experimental application of the simplest transportation mode (sedimentation from calm air) of microbial cells towards the material surface allowed neglecting the influence of such factors as speed and type of air flow, and the features of flowing over the sample on adhesion. Moreover, the sedimentation mechanism of transportation fully reflects the actual interaction of microorganisms with the surfaces of internal volumes of articles, materials and parts, present in storages and, frequently, in the open air (if the lamellar air layer at the earth surface is significant).

Spores were precipitated to samples with the help of special chamber, made from steel, equipped with clips moving up and down for placing samples at the current angle to the direction of falling spares, as well as with two removable cassettes at the lower panel. Petri dishes filled with water, designed for determination of the quantity of precipitating spores, are located in the cassettes. For spore dispersion, rubber membranes are placed in the upper part of the chamber. The membranes are connected with one another and with the air input bulb by thin glass tubes. At pulse air input, the membrane oscillates and disperses spores present on it, which then precipitate on the material samples and Petri dishes filled with water.

Specific expense of spores (the quantity of spores crossing the specific square of horizontal cross-section of the chamber) and the adhesion number at various sample tilts were calculated on the basis of spore quantities precipitated on Petri dishes and the samples. Time for spores to reach the sample surface and time for completing precipitation were measured simultaneously. After that the samples with precipitated spores were centrifuged in air.

It has been determined in preliminary investigations that if the force field intensity is changed to values providing detachment of not more than 15 – 18% of spores, the adhesion number varies within the range of experimental error. A significant experimental error is also observed in the range of the force field intensity causing detachment of, at least, 85% of cells. Consequently, true determination of adhesion numbers by the centrifugation method is possible in the range of 0.2 – 0.85. The authors have limited their experimental studies by this range.

The technique for microbiological propagation study [5, 8] has provided for cultivation of microorganisms on materials with regular determination of quantitative characteristics of the growth – dry specific biomass representing the quantity of microorganisms' dry mass on the specific square (or in the specific volume) of the material surface (or volume), inspired by the microbial cells. This characteristic was determined by gravimetric, chemoluminescent and radiometric methods [1]. Main indices for the test conditions are shown in Table 3.

Table 3. Facilities and conditions of tests on microorganism propagation on materials

Material, microorganism, GOST of the method for testing resistance to microorganism action	Solution for inspiration, method, and concentration of microbial cells on the sample	Conditions of microorganism cultivation on the material, method of specific dry biomass determination
Polyethylene, poly(methyl methacrylate), Polyvinylchloride cellulose triacetate, varnished fabric. *Aspergillus niger*, *Penicillium chrysogenum*, *Penicillium cyclopium*, *Paecilomyces varioti* GOST 9.049-91	Chapek-Dox medium without saccharose. Uniform application of fixed amount of spore suspension in aqueous-mineral solution by a micropipette, 10^6 spores per cm^2 of the sample surface	Surface cultivation in the quiescent state. Radiometric (for PE, PMMA, CTA), chemoluminescent (PVC), gravimetric (VF)
Fuel TS-1. *Cladosporium resinae*, *Pseudomonas aerugenosa*, GOST 9.023-74	Aqueous-mineral solution. Contact with aqueous-mineral solution containing 10^6 spores per cm^2 of the fuel – aqueous-mineral phase boundary	Deep cultivations under immovable conditions (Cladosporium) and at continuous mixing (Pseudomonas). Gravimetric
Oil MN-75U. *Bacillus subtilis*, GOST 9.082-77	Tap water. Contact with tap water containing 10^6 bacterial cells per cm^2 of the oil-water phase boundary	Deep cultivations at continuous mixing. Chemoluminescent

Note: The Chapek-Dox medium represents water solution of the following composition (mass parts): KH_2PO_4 – 0.1%; $MgSO_4$ – 0.05%; $NaNO_3$ – 0.2%; KCl – 0.05%; $FeSO_4$ – 0.001%; saccharose – 3%; aqueous-mineral solution is of the following composition (mass parts): KNO_3 – 0.2%; $MgSO_4$ – 0.04%; KH_2PO_4 – 0.03%; $NaNO_3$ – 0.07%.

Fungi and bacteria were cultivated on materials in the presence of a series of mineral components necessary for microorganism growth, specially injected with microbial cells or contained in tap water (in tests on oil MN-7,5U). Such test mode simulates the presence of mineral pollutions that reflects most properly the actual conditions of machinery operation.

Basing on preliminary investigations, primary sample selection for biomass determination was executed after 10-12 hours of microscopic fungi cultivation on them, and after 3 – 8 hours of bacteria cultivation. As a rule, the time period between samplings did not exceed 3 – 4 hours for bacteria and 1 – 3 days for fungi.

The technique for experimental studies of variations in the properties of materials affected by microorganisms [8] provided for cultivation of microorganisms on samples with regular determination of the property index under control. In some cases, material structure and composition were also determined. The main studied material-microorganism couples, indices of material properties controlled during experiments and methods of determination are shown in Table 4.

Indices of the properties were determined according to three main modes: 1 – not removing biomass, which occurred on the samples during cultivation of microorganisms; 2 – after biomass removal; 3 – after biomass removal and sample conditioning under standard (normal) conditions. Such modes most fully reflect the features of the microorganisms' effect on parts and articles during operation of machinery. Experimental data were analyzed using mathematical statistics methods and mathematical modeling of studied processes.

Table 4. Controllable indices of material properties and methods of their determination

Material-microorganism interacting couple	Controlled index of material properties	Method of controlled index determination
Poly(methyl methacrylate), *Aspergillus niger*	Induced elasticity limit, σ. Durability, τ_d	Elongation at constant rate of 0.5 – 5 mm/min. Elongation under constant stress of 3 – 35 MPa
Polyvinylchloride plasticate, *Aspergillus niger*	Electrical insulation resistance, *R*	Application of 1,000 V direct electric voltage
Varnished fabric, *Aspergillus niger*	Electrical insulation resistance, *R*	Application of 1,000 V direct electric voltage
Cotton thread, *Aspergillus niger*	Stress at break, σ	Elongation at constant rate of 5 mm/min
Polysulfide hermetic sealer, *Cladosporium resinae*	Induced elasticity limit, σ	Elongation at constant rate of 0.5 mm/min
Fuels, *Cladosporium resinae*	Quantity of mechanical admixtures	Weighing of dried insoluble admixtures
Oils, *Bacillus subtilis*	Quantity of mechanical admixtures	Weighing of dried insoluble admixtures
Aluminum alloy, *Aspergillus niger*	Corrosion depth, *h*	Microscope study of microsections
Steel alloy, *Bacillus subtilis*	Corrosion depth, *h*	Microscope study of microsections

Research which was done in Institute of Chemical Physics and Institute of Biochemical Physics showed that this technique is very important and fruitful for investigation in kinetic and mechanism of biodegradation of different materials (polymers, metals, composites etc.) by microorganisms [9].

REFERENCES

[1] Gumargalieva K.Z., Zaikov G.E., *Biodegradation and biodeterioration of polymers*, Nova Science Publishers, New York, 2000, 388 pp.

[2] Semenov S.A., Ozhegin F.F., Ryizhkov A.A., and Ivanov S.S., The effect of organic acids on mechanical properties of poly(methyl methacrylate), *Fiz.-Khim. Mekhanika Materialov*, 1986, No. 5, pp. 120 – 122. (Rus)

[3] Semenov S.A., Gerasimenko A.A., Zhdanova O.A., and Ryizhkov A.A., Forecasting of microbiological degradability of BPVL type wires, In: *Weapon Protection from Corrosion, Aging and Biodeterioration. KNS MO Materials*, Vedomstvennoe Izdatelstvo, Moscow, 1988, pp. 165 – 178. (Rus)

[4] *GOST 9.048-89. Uniform System of Corrosion and Aging Protection. Technical Articles. Laboratory Test Methods for Resistance to Mould Fungus Impact.* Moscow, Izd. Standartov, 1989. (Rus)

[5] *GOST 9.049-91. Uniform System of Corrosion and Aging Protection. Polymeric Materials. Laboratory Test Methods for Resistance to Mould Fungus Impact*, Moscow, Izd. Standartov, 1991. (Rus)

[6] *GOST 9.082-77. Uniform System of Corrosion and Aging Protection. Oils and Lubricants. Laboratory Test Methods for Resistance to Bacterium Impact*, Moscow, Izd. Standartov, 1977. (Rus)

[7] *GOST 9.023-74. Uniform System of Corrosion and Aging Protection. Laboratory Test Methods for Biological Resistance of Fuels Protected by Anti-bacterial Additives*, Moscow, Izd. Standartov, 1974. (Rus)

[8] Semenov S.A., Gorshkov V.A., and Gumargalieva K.Z., *Quantitative Estimation of Biosoiling of Polymeric Materials and Components of Weapons by Technophilic Microorganisms. Methodological Guidelines*, vol. **6221**, Vedomstvennoe Izdatelstvo, Moscow, 1990, 76 p. (Rus)

[9] Zaikov G.E., *Chemical and biochemical physics, problems and solutions*, Nova Science Publishers, New York, 2003, 168 pp.

In: Homolytic and Heterolytic Reactions: Problems and Solutions ISBN 1-59033-980-0
Editors: G.E. Zaikov, et al., pp. 321-331

Chapter 16

COMPLEX VANADIUM–TITANIUM CATALYSTS CONTAINING ORGANOALUMINUM AND ORGANOMAGNESIUM COCATALYSTS FOR BUTADIENE POLYMERIZATION

I. R. Mullagaliev, E. Yu. Kharitonova, O. I. Borisova and Yu. B. Monakov
Institute of Organic Chemistry Ufa Scientific Center,Russian Academy of Sciences.
71, Prospekt Oktyabrya, Ufa, 450054, Russia

ABSTRACT

Butadiene polymerization in toluene at 25°C in the presence of catalytic system on the base of $VOCl_3$ and $TiCl_4$ mixture in combination with $Al(i\text{-}C_4H_9)_3$ and $Mg(n\text{-}C_4H_9)(i\text{-}C_8H_{17})$ was investigated. It was established that addition of $TiCl_4$ into vanadium system and application of portion introduction of organometallic compound in combination with thermal treatment of primary catalyst suspension lead to the change of catalytic system activity and stereospecificity of action. Kinetic parameters of the process were determined. It was shown that concentration and reaction ability of active sites containing both transition metals depend on the nature of non-transition metal organic compound that was used as at the first, so at the second stage of catalytic systems preparation.

Key-words: Ziegler-Natta catalytic systems, stereospecific polymerization, polybutadiene, organomagnesium compounds.

INTRODUCTION

It is shown in works investigating 1,4-*trans*-polymerization of conjugated dienes that Ziegler-Natta catalytic systems (CS) containing two definite transition metals simulteniusly have another working parameters than catalysts on the base of the same metals separetly [1-

4]. Moreover, in some cases the additional complication of catalyst preparation method is necessary for achiving the maximum effect on its activity and stereospecificity of action. For example, the heating of $VOCl_3$ and $TiCl_4$ mixture with the part of organoaluminum compound (OAC) is used when preparing high-active catalytic complex for isoprene and pyperilene polymerization [5, 6]. By this, a very interesting fact was observed: there were two maximums of catalyst activity in dependence on concentration of the first portion of OAC. Authors in [7, 8] suggested that such occurrence exists only for this set of elements (V, Ti, Al) or, rather, for chlorides of their trivalent ions, that is the role of organometallic compound (OMC) is also very important. We studied the particularities of butadiene polymerization in the presence of [$VOCl_3$–$TiCl_4$–OMC]–(heating)–OMC catalytic system, where OMC – triisobutylaluminum (TIBA) or/and Mg(*н*-C_4H_9)(*i*-C_8H_{17}) (MgRR′), as a continuation of described investigations. The aim of the work was to determine how the working parameters of indicated catalyst should change if we substituted OAC by organomagnesium compound at the one or both stages of CS formation. Organomagnesium compound was chosen as a subject of inquiry because vanadium and titanium magnesium-containing catalysts revealed high activity under olefins polymerization [9, 10].

Experimental Part

Mixed catalytic complexes were prepared as in [6]: to the mixture of $VOCl_3$ and $TiCl_4$ (Ti/V=0.5) the first portion of chosen organometallic compound (OMC_1) was added, then reaction mass was treated at 130°C for 1 hour. After cooling down to room temperature the second portion of chosen cocatalyst (OMC_2) was added. Introduction of various OMC before and after the thermal treatment was carried out in following combinations: MgRR′–TIBA, TIBA–MgRR′, MgRR′–MgRR′ (systems I, II and III accordingly). The ready-made catalytic complex was introduced into toluene solution of butadiene. The polymerization of butadiene was carried out in toluene at 25±0.1°C under conditions excluding the penetration of air and moisture. The microstructure and molecular masses (MM) of polybutadiene (PB) were determined using IR-spectroscopy and gel-permeation chromatography methods [11]. Kinetic parameters of polymerization (k_P and number of active sites – C_a) were determined out of dependences of number-average MM of polymers on duration of process [12, 13].

Results and their Discussion

The influence of preparation conditions of catalyst [$VOCl_3$–$TiCl_4$–MgRR']–(heating) –TIBA (system I) on its activity and stereospecificity of action under butadiene polymerization was considered. The dependence of PB yield and microstructure on the MgRR' -to-$VOCl_3$ ratio at fixed ratios Ti/V=0.5 and Al_2/V=2.0 is presented in Fig. 1a. There is only one maximum of system I activity at Mg_1/V=1.0, in contrast to [$VOCl_3$–$TiCl_4$–TIBA]–(heating) –TIBA (system IV) [7]. Introduction of MgRR' at the first stage of catalyst preparation leads to the decrease of its activity and *trans*-stereospecificity of action: in polybutadiene 1,4-*cis*- and 1,2-structures were fixed (Fig.1a). Probably not only α-$TiCl_3$ but also β-$TiCl_3$ forming active sites (AS) of *cis*-polymerization of dienes are presented in studied system.

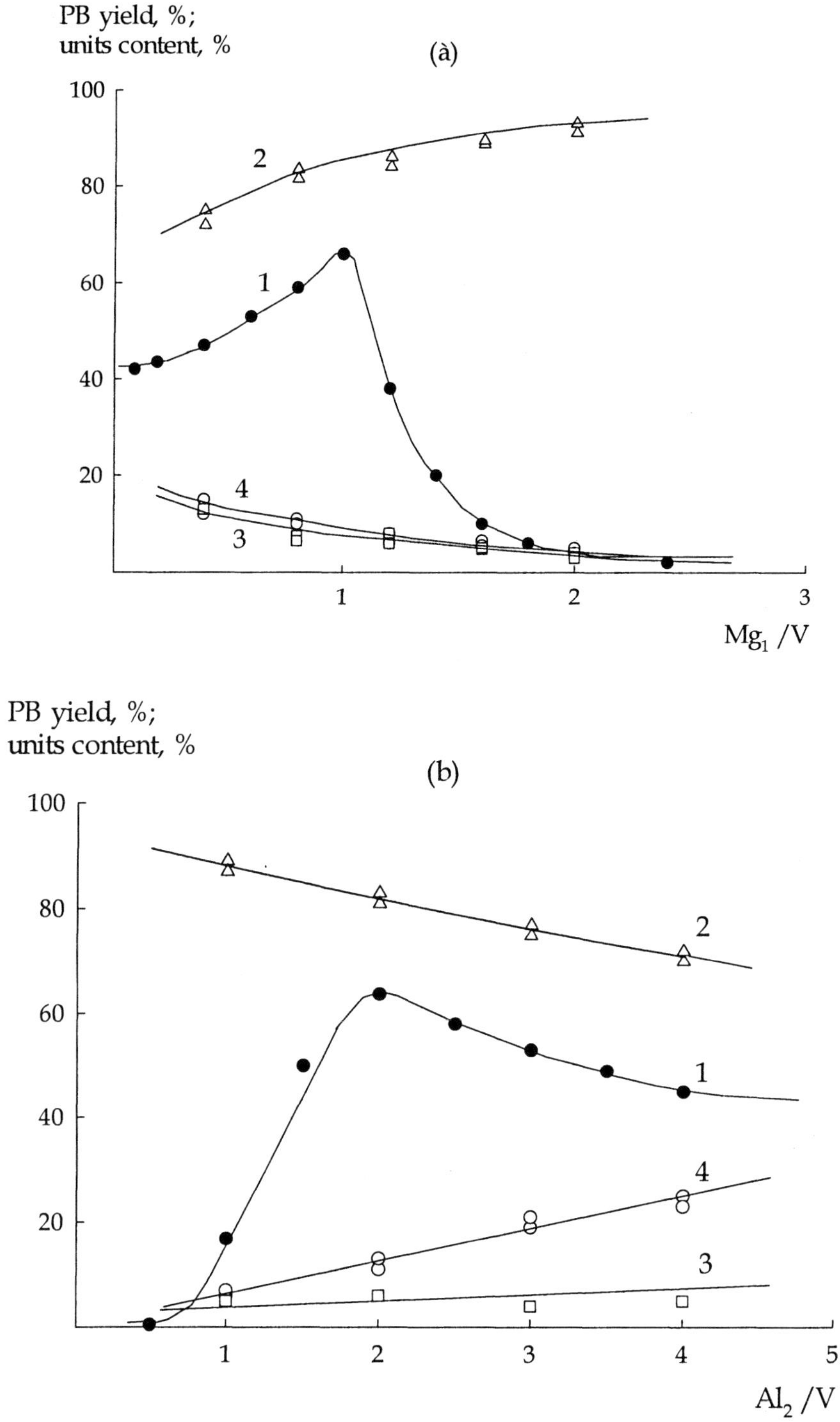

Figure 1. Variation in the (1) PB yield and (2-4) microstructure of polymer with the molar ratios Mg_1/V (a) and Al_2/V (b) in system [$VOCl_3$–$TiCl_4$–MgRR′]–(heating)–TIBA (2 – 1,4-*trans*-, 3 – 1,2-, 4 – 1,4-*cis*-units). Conditions: toluene, 25°C, 1 hour, Ti/V=0.5, C_V=0.01, C_M=2.0 mole/l; $TIBA_2/V$=2.0 (a), MgRR′/V=1.0 (b); thermal treatment: 130°C, 1 h.

Additional experiments showed that when in system I there is only one derivative of transition metal (either $VOCl_3$, or $TiCl_4$) the polybutadiene yield is dozens of time smaller than that one obtained on vanadium-titanium complex. In other words, we may assume that under studied conditions the synergism of titanium compound additives action is also conditioned by formation of double chlorides of metals with variable valence. Necessary conditions (such as thermal treatment and the presence of reducing agent) for this process are fulfilled. However, they are not optimal as the comparison of working characteristics of systems I and IV indicates. One of the reasons of this may be the highest reduction ability of dyalkylmagnesium as compared with OAC that consequently must affect the total quantity of V^{3+} and Ti^{3+} and the ratio between the last ones.

So, the maximum of catalyst I activity in dependence on the second portion of OMC (i.e. OAC) is observed at $Al_2/V=2$ (Fig. 1b), half as mach as in the case of system IV [7].

The same decrease of optimal quantity of alkylating agent was observed under butadiene polymerization initiated by [$VOCl_3$–$TiCl_4$–$Al(i\text{-}C_4H_9)_2H$]–(heating)–TIBA, although to a lesser degree [8]. Polybutadiene *trans*-stereoregularity is reduced a little at the expense of 1,4-*cis*-structures quantity increase when Al_2/V ratio is varied from 0.5 to 4.0; concentration of 1,2-units is remained at 6-8%. On the contrary, in the case of system IV increase of the second portion of OAC leads to the rise of 1,4-*trans*-units content [7]. Such distinction between comparing systems is probably conditioned by various sets of active sites' types differ in reaction ability, stereospecificity of action and stability.

We propose that absence of two maximums of activity of system I is explained by the fact that structural characteristics of magnesium chloride don't coincide with those ones of transition metals chlorides resulted from reduction of vanadium and titanium compounds. That is why it is possible that $MgCl_2$ (in contrast to $AlCl_3$) doesn't participate in the formation of combined lattice with VCl_3 and $TiCl_3$. The biggest quantity of double chlorides (judging by catalyst activity level) is produced at Ti/V=0.5, independently on used reducing agent – TIBA [7] or dialkylmagnesium. When we varyed Ti/V ratio the amount of 1,4-*trans*-units was significantly decreased, first of all at the expense of 1,4-*cis*-structures. This fact is probably caused by increase of β-$TiCl_3$ concentration. The content of 1,2-units remains constant and equal 5-8% (Fig. 2).

Then, proposing that it will be logically enough we expect that the use of OAC at the reduction stage should promote the display of bimodal dependence of activity of catalytic complex [$VOCl_3$–$TiCl_4$–TIBA]–(heating)– MgRR′ (system II) on the quantity of the first portion of introduced into system OMC. But as before there is only one activity maximum at $Al_1/V=2.0$ and polybutadiene of mixed microstructure is produced (Fig. 3a).

Probably, the final development of the base for *trans*-regulating AS, in other words formation of corresponding modifications of vanadium and titanium chlorides occurs at the second stage of catalyst preparation. The last fact can be determined by the rate and completeness of removing of non-transition metals derivatives out off catalytic residue.

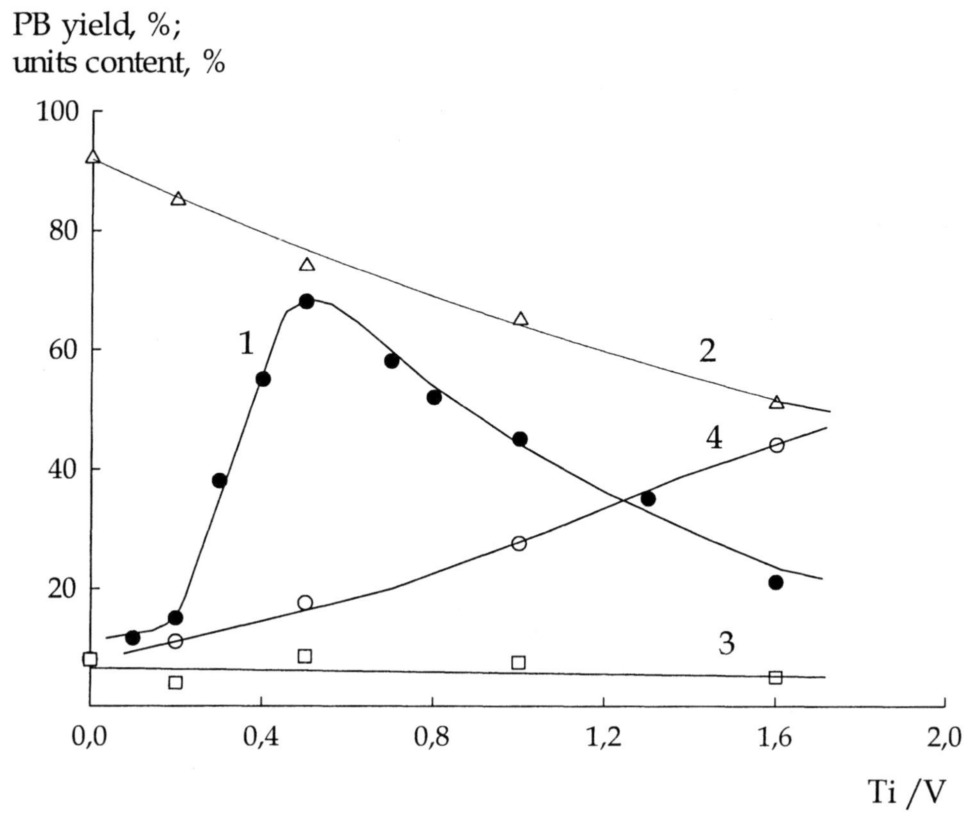

Figure 2. Variation in the (1) PB yield and (2-4) microstructure of polymer with the molar ratio Ti/V in [$VOCl_3$–$TiCl_4$– MgRR']–(heating) – TIBA (2 – 1,4-*trans*-, 3 – 1,2-, 4 – 1,4-*cis*-units). Conditions: Mg_1/V=1.0, Al_2/V=2.0, the rest as in Fig.1.

We can not except that titanium containing systems with valence of transition metal less than +3 may be responsible for *cis*-stereoregulating. The fact that at the second stage of preparation of system II significantly smaller amount of dialkylmagnesium is necessary: Mg_2/V=1 in comparison with Al_2/V=3.0÷4.0 [7], points to higher reduction ability of MgRR' than OAC. Moreover, the rise of content of MgRR' in reaction medium leads to the increase of 1,2- and 1,4-*cis*-units content in polybutadiene (Fig. 3b).

Substitution of TIBA at the both stages of vanadium-titanium catalyst preparation ([$VOCl_3$–$TiCl_4$–MgRR′]–(heating)–MgRR′ – system III) leads to decrease of PB yield down to level of two-component $VOCl_3$–MgRR′ catalyst [14]. As we expected, the only one activity maximum was observed at Mg_1/V=1.0 (Fig.4a). Resulting polymer contains 80% of 1,4-*trans*-, 10% of 1,4-*cis*- and 10% of 1,2-units in the whole diapason of Mg_1/V=0.1÷2.4. It is not quite clear yet why the highest polybutadiene yield produced on system III was obtained at Mg_2/V=2.0 (Fig. 4b). *Trans*-stereoregularity of polymer is reduced at the expense of 1,4-*cis*-structures, although to a less degree and 1,2-units content remains constant when Mg_2/V ratio was varied from 0.5 to 4.0.

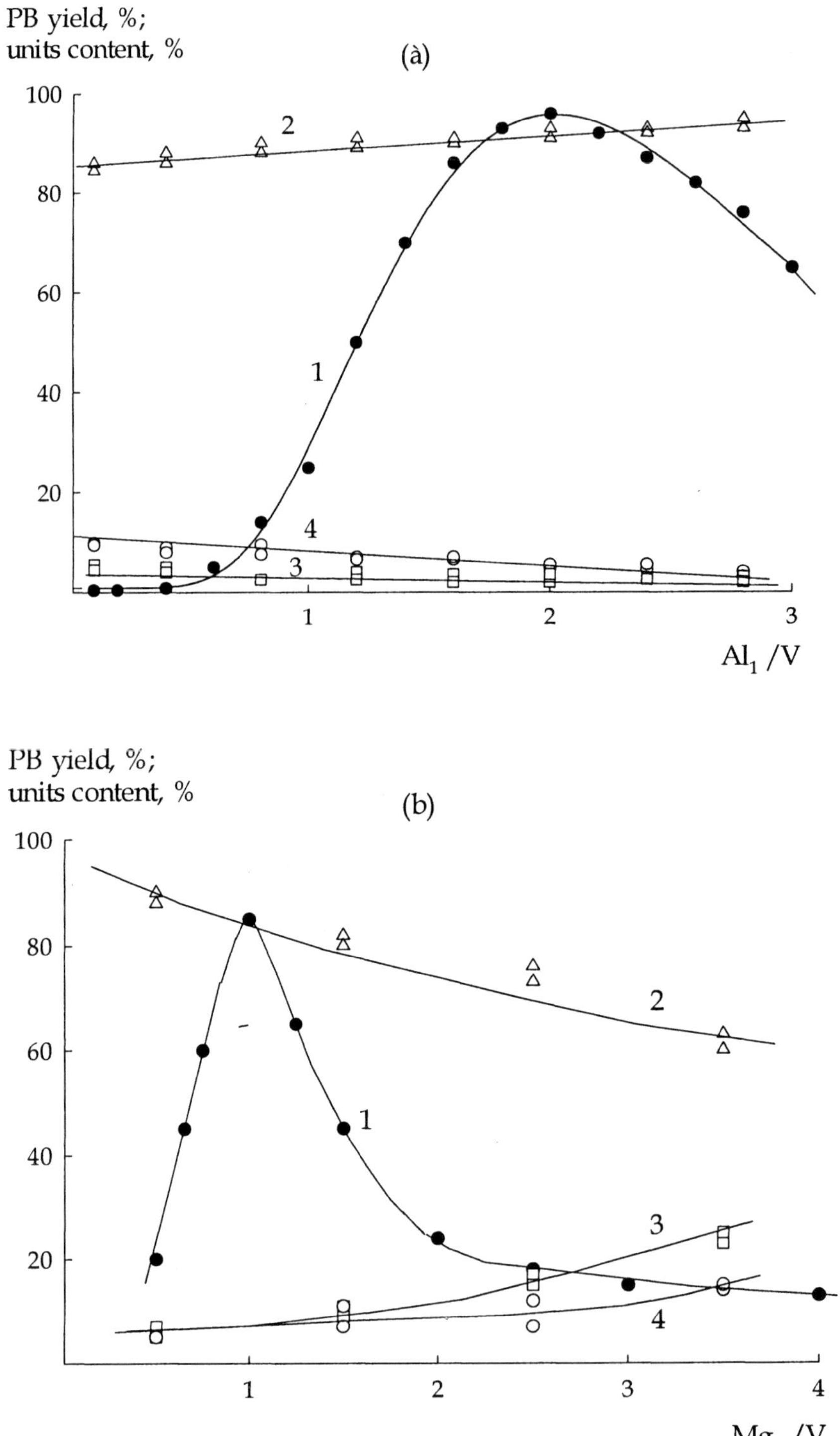

Figure 3. Variation in the (1) PB yield and (2-4) microstructure of polymer with the molar ratios Al_1/V (a) and Mg_2/V (b) in system [$VOCl_3$–$TiCl_4$–TIBA]–(heating)–MgRR′ (2 – 1,4-*trans*-, 3 – 1,2-, 4 – 1,4-*cis*-units). Conditions: $MgRR'_2/V$=1.0 (a), TIBA/V=2.0 (b); the rest as in Fig.1.

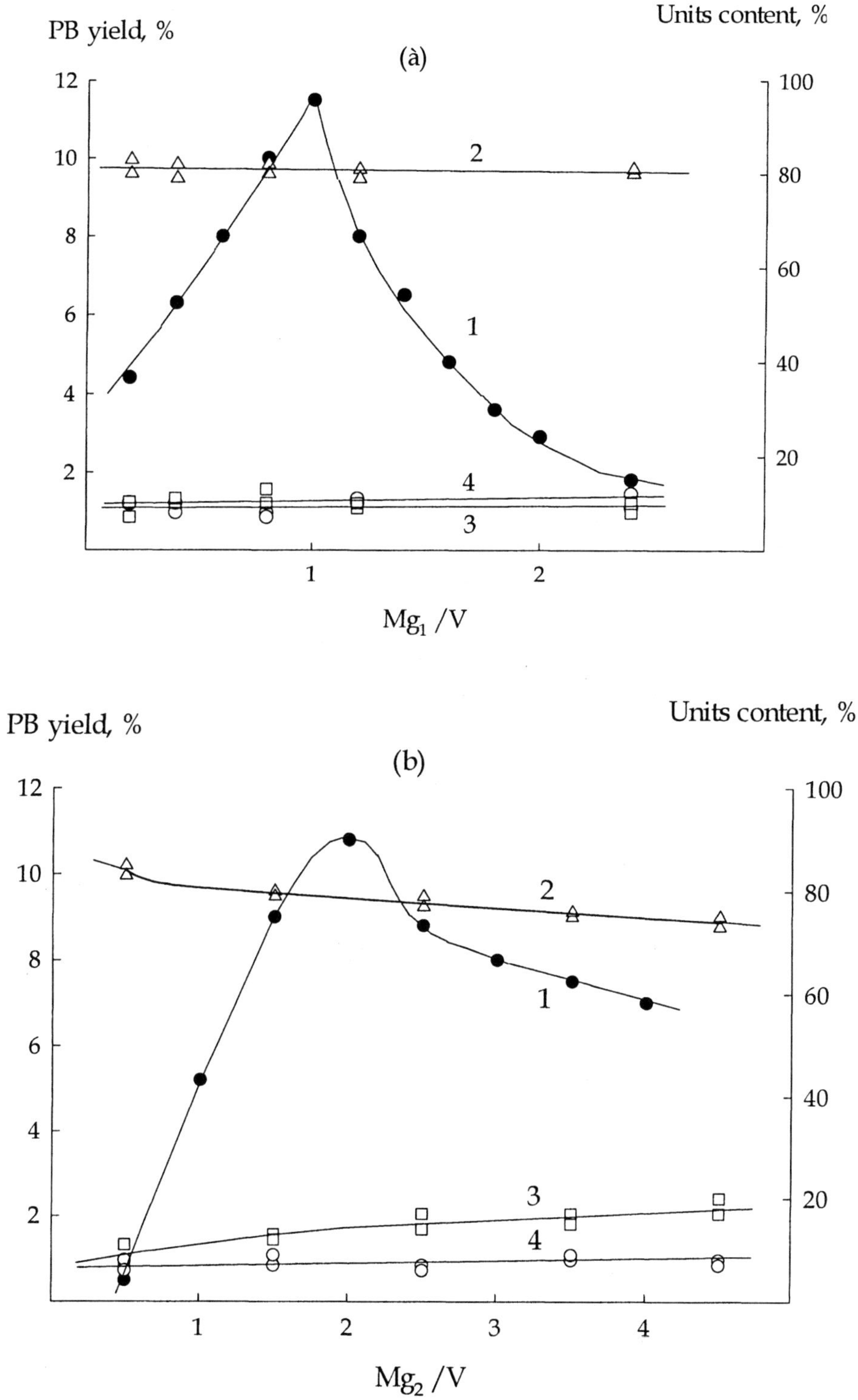

Figure 4. Variation in the (1) PB yield and (2-4) its microstructure with the ratios Mg_1 / V (a) and Mg_2 / V (b) in [$VOCl_3$–$TiCl_4$–MgRR′]–(heating)–MgRR′ (2 – 1,4-*trans*-, 3 – 1,2-, 4 – 1,4-*cis*-units). Conditions: $MgRR'_2$ / V = 2,0 (a), $MgRR'_1$ / V =1,0 (b); the rest as in Fig.1.

The dependence of activity and stereospecificity of action of system III on temperature and duration of its thermal treatment at fixed ratios Ti/V=0.5, Mg_1/V=1 and Mg_2/V=2.0 was investigated. When the time of catalyst aging with the first portion of MgRR' at 70°C increases the polybutadiene yield is raised a little, and at the 90°C it remains practically constant. Preparation of catalyst at 110 or 130°C leads to the decrease of catalyst activity when duration of treatment is increased (Fig. 5a), as in the case of two-component $VOCl_3$–MgRR′ catalyst preparing separately [14]. By this *trans*-stereospecificity of action of system III is increased a little: 1,4-*trans*-units content is increased at the expense of 1,4-*cis*- and 1,2-structures amount decrease (Fig. 5b). In this concrete case conditions of thermal treatment are probably favour to more complete transformation of $TiCl_3$ β-form into *trans*-regulating α-, δ- or γ-modifications that are able to participate in formation of combined crystal lattice with VCl_3 and thus promote the rise of systems *trans*-stereospecificity. Obtained picture of dependence of activity and stereospecificity of action of system III on preparation conditions may be caused by high reduction ability of dialkylmagnesium. At temperatures required for formation of double chlorides (not less than 130°C according to [7, 8]) more significant lowering of V^{3+} and Ti^{3+} content presumably occurs than in the case of OAC use. Earlier for the system IV containing TIBA they showed that in both maximums regions both transition elements existed in trivalent state [6].

Kinetics of butadiene polymerization on catalytic systems I–III was studied. In all cases the kinetic curves do not show the induction periods. Polybutadiene microstructure doesn't change in the course of polymerization from 1 minute up to 3 hours: 90% of 1,4-*trans*-units, 5% of 1,4-*cis*- and 5% of 1,2-structures for systems I and II; 85% of 1,4-*trans*-, 10% of 1,4-*cis* and 5% of 1,2-units when used catalyst III.

In all cases the first reaction order on monomer was observed in concentrations diapason C_M=0,1÷2,4 mole/l. At the same time polymerization reaction order on catalyst deviates from the first and for indicated systems is oscillated from 1.4 to 1.8. The last fact may be consequence of both their heterogeneity and topologic characteristics [15], and complex multicomponent structure. Thus, for example, reaction order on lanthanide catalyst containing several components including two non-transition metal derivatives is 1.7–1.75 [16, 17]. Apparent activation energies E_a of butadiene polymerization on catalysts I–III were calculated in temperature interval 0–60°C (Table 1) and turned out to be differ. The received values are lower than for analogous catalysts including only OAC [8]. Polymer microstructure doesn't depend on temperature of polymerization (in studied interval) for all three catalysts.

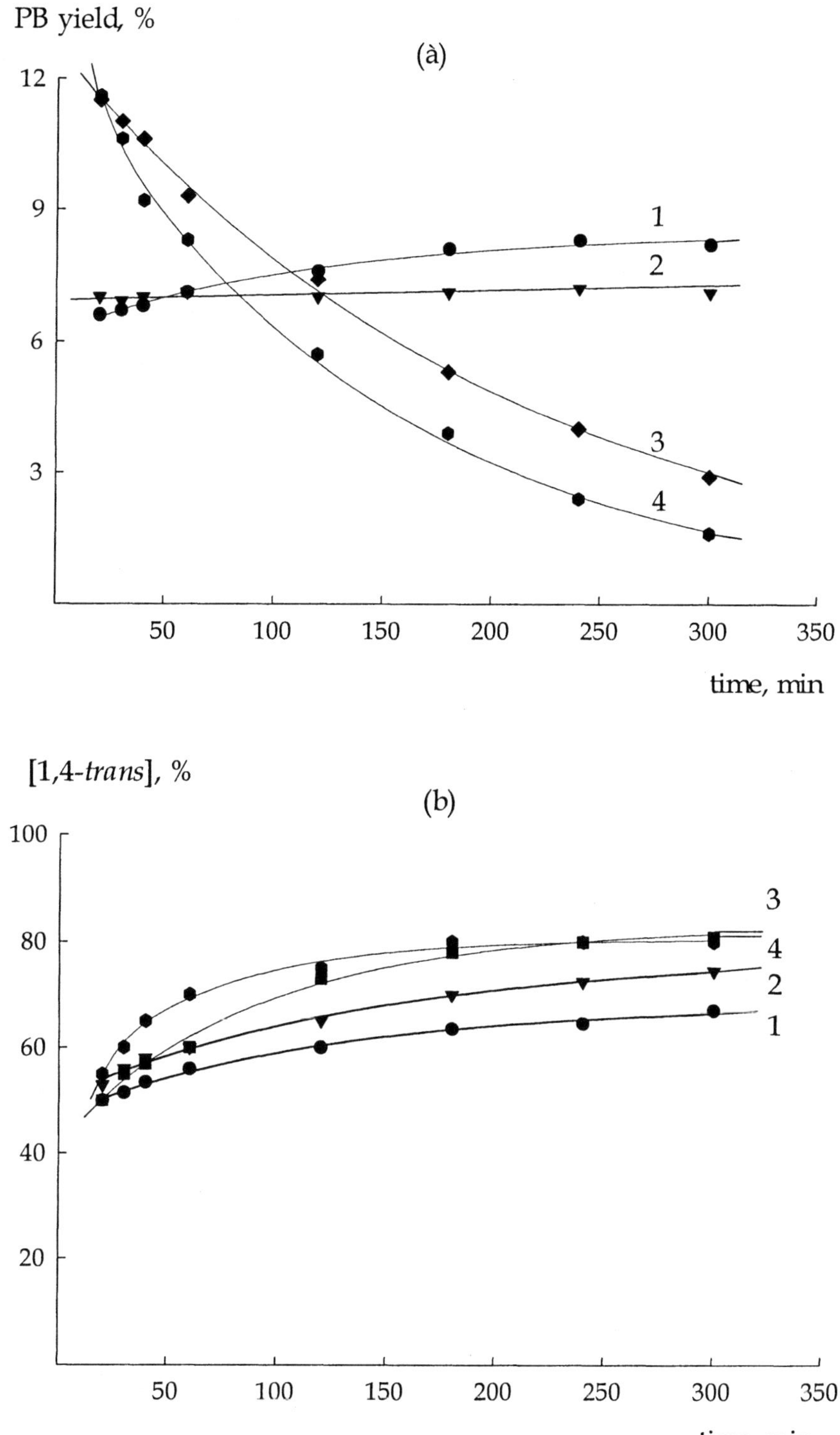

Figure 5. Variation in the (a) PB yield and (b) 1,4-*trans*-units content with the duration and temperature of thermal treatment of system [$VOCl_3$–$TiCl_4$–MgRR′]–(heating)–MgRR′ (1 – 70°C, 2 – 90°C, 3 – 110°C, 4 – 130°C). Conditions: $Mg_1/V=1.0$, $Mg_2/V=2.0$, the rest as in Fig. 1.

Table 1. Kinetic parameters of butadiene polymerization on [$VOCl_3$–$TiCl_4$–OMC_1] –.(heating)-OMC_2 catalytic systems. Conditions as in Fig. 1, C_V=0.3 mole/l.

OMC_1	OMC_2	№№ CS	k_p, l/mole·min	C_a, % from C_v	E_{act}, kDj/mole
MgRR′	TIBA	I	3800	0.4	31.4±1.5
TIBA	MgRR′	II	2400	1.1	27.6±1.8
MgRR′	MgRR′	III	2000	0.4	20.9±1.3
TIBA*	TIBA*	IV	5700	0.46	41.8±3.2

* System IV, the second activity maximum on Al_1/V [8].

Analysis of Table 1 showed that values of k_p for complexes I–III are dozens of time higher than for two-component systems $VOCl_3$–TIBA [11], $VOCl_3$–MgRR′ [14], $TiCl_4$–TIBA and $TiCl_4$–MgRR′ [18] (260, 15, 100 and 40 l/mole·min accordingly under butadiene polymerization under analogous conditions). We proposed that it may be resulted from the formation of transition metal double chlorides in the case of studied systems too. According to Table 1 values of k_p are significantly changed from system I to III. On the one hand, higher propagation reaction rate constant in the case of catalyst I may be probably caused by presence of TIBA in AS structure; on the other hand, lower and closely approximated values of k_p for system II and III indicate that in this case butadiene polymerization presumably occurs on V–Mg sites.

Thus, the nature of non-transition metal organic compound used at both catalyst preparation stages influences on the concentration and reaction ability of AS of butadiene polymerization initiated by systems I–III, and also on molecular characteristics of produced *trans*-polybutadiene

ACKNOWLEDGEMENTS

This work was done with the support of Russian Fund of Fundamental Investigations (grant 02-0333315) and grant 728.2003.3 of project "Leading scientific schools".

REFERENCES

[1] Boor I.J. *Ziegler Natta Catalysis and Polymerization.* New York; San Francisco: Academic Press (1979).

[2] *Pat.* 3347839 USA

[3] *Pat.* 3008945 USA

[4] *Pat.* 6927903 Japan

[5] *Author certificate* 774187 SSSR

[6] Monakov Yu.B., Martzina V.G., Sabirov Z.M., Kozlov V.G., Sigaeva N.N., Rafikov S.R., *Polymer Science Ser. A*, 33: 11 2300-2305 (1991).

[7] Mullagaliev I.R., Kharitonova E.Yu., Monakov Yu.B., *the article in first volume its book.*

[8] Mullagaliev I.R., Kharitonova Ė.Yu., Monakov Yu.B., *the article in second volume its book.*

[9] Krentzel' B.A., Nekhaeva L.A., *Polymer Science, Ser. A*, 36:10 1607 (1994).

[10] Zakharov V.A., Echevskaya L.G.,Bukatov G.D., *Polimery*, 34: 6-7 P.277-281 (1989).

[11] Mullagaliev I.R., Kil'diyarov A.R., Ionova I.A., Danilov V.T., Monakov Yu.B., *Polymer Science, Ser. A*, 42: 6 596-603 (2000).

[12] Chirkov N.M., Matkovskii P.E., D'yachkovskii Ph.S., *Polymerization on complex organometallic catalysts.* Moscow: Khimiya, (1976).

[13] Kozlov V.G., Budtov V.P., Nefed'ev K.V., Monakov Yu.B., and Tolstikov G.A., *Dokl. Akad. Nauk SSSR*, 297: 2 411-414 (1987)

[14] Monakov Yu.B, Mullagaliev I.R., Kharitonova E.Yu., *Polymer Science, Ser. A*, 44: 2 220-225 (2002)

[15] Yu.B.Monakov, G.A.Tolstikov, *Catalytic polymerization of 1,3-dienes*, Moscow: Nauka, (1990).

[16] Monakov Yu.B., Bieshev Ya.Kh., Berg A.A., Rafikov S.R., *Dokl. Akad. Nauk SSSR*, 234: 5 1125-1130 (1977).

[17] Gong Z., Li B., Yang G., Wnag F., *Gaofenxi Tongxun*, 2 116-120 (1983).

[18] Kharitonova E.Yu., *Doctoral dissertation*, Institute of Organic Chemistry, Ufa, Russia, (2002).

INDEX

A

B

C

D

H

I

K

L

M

N

O

P

Q

R

S

T